PELICAN BOOKS

A412

MAN THE PECULIAR ANIMAL

R. J. HARRISON

MAN

THE PECULIAR ANIMAL

R. J. HARRISON

PENGUIN BOOKS

Penguin Books Ltd, Harmondsworth, Middlesex
U.S.A.: Penguin Books Inc., 3300 Clipper Mill Road, Baltimore 11, Md
AUSTRALIA: Penguin Books Pty Ltd, 762 Whitehorse Road,
Mitcham, Victoria

—

First published 1958

—

Made and printed in Great Britain
by The Whitefriars Press Ltd, London and Tonbridge
Gravure plates by Harrison & Sons, Ltd

CONTENTS

LIST OF TEXT FIGURES

LIST OF PLATES

EDITORIAL FOREWORD

ON any definition, man is an animal, although he may well be something much more than an ordinary animal, and as an animal, by any standards and from many points of view, he is certainly a most peculiar animal indeed. But the controversy which Darwin started has died down. It is now generally agreed that man must have evolved in steps from stock common to himself, the anthropoid apes and all the other animals.

With the problem of why and how organic evolution has come about, Professor Harrison is not particularly concerned. Rather, accepting the generally held view that it has occurred, somehow, somewhere, sometime, and that man is a member of the animal kingdom, he proceeds in this fourth volume of the Pelican Medical Series to bring up to date in the light of modern research our concept of man's place in nature and our knowledge and realization of his peculiar characteristics as a member of the animal kingdom. For, not only have we learnt much about the details of his structure since Darwin wrote his famous books and Huxley joined issue with the Church, but also in these days the anatomist is less and less content to think in terms of structure alone. Rather it is now generally accepted to be his business to interpret structure, not only in terms of embryological development and evolutionary history, but also in terms of the function which structure has served or is destined to serve. Indeed it would be as nonsensical for the anatomist to describe the human body without reference to the origin and function of its different organs, as it would be for an engineer to give an account of an engine without reference to the way in which it has been put together and the different purposes of its various parts.

This Pelican book should prove not only of great interest to scientists and laymen, but also of great value to medical students. For it will do much towards breaking down that unfortunate dichotomy which has grown up in our system of medical education between the study of structure, on the one hand, and that of function, on the other. It will help the student to realize that there is no real dividing line between structure and function. Our distinction between anatomy and physiology is entirely for reasons of technical convenience. It will make him see that one merges imperceptibly into the other. For the study of structure is sterile without some understanding of whence it came and of the function which it serves; that of function futile without some understanding of the static or rapidly changing structure on which it is based. From this book he will also learn that anatomists now have new instruments and physical methods to investigate structure and function undreamt of by earlier workers.

Further, Professor Harrison's book will widen the student's outlook which is one of the main objectives of the Pelican Medical Series. It will help him to see how in evolution, as in disease, structure can become adapted to functional demand and how new functions can become associated with old structures within a changing pattern. They will see man more clearly in relation to the animal kingdom: how sometimes his peculiarities have been forced on him by ancestral circumstance; how at other it has paid him 'hand over fist' in the struggle for existence and in his upward progress to become peculiar.

In short, Professor Harrison has made a notable contribution to that much neglected subject in medical education, namely real human biology.

A. E. CLARK-KENNEDY

ACKNOWLEDGEMENTS

GRATEFUL acknowledgement is made to Drs A. T. Hertig and J. Rock, the Carnegie Institute of Embryology and the Wistar Institute for permission to reproduce Figures on Plates VIII and IX; to Professor W. J. Hamilton for Plate VIII.1; to Dr H. Steiner for Plate III; to Professor G. H. Bourne for Plate XXIII.2; to Dr G. Szabo for Plate XXII.3; Dr P. E. Steiner and the Wistar Institute for Plate V; Professor H. Butler for Plate I. Thanks are also due to the Prosectorial Committee of the Zoological Society of London for much valuable material. The other photographs are the work of Mr R. Quinton Cox; Mr R. B. Price prepared the illustrations.

I should like to thank the Editor of the Penguin Medical Series, Dr A. E. Clark-Kennedy, for inviting me to write this volume and for his helpful suggestions. Grateful thanks are due to those who helped prepare the MS and who so kindly read and criticized it at various stages. I am particularly indebted to Professor J. Z. Young and to Dr J. C. Trevor, to my Departmental colleagues Dr J. D. W. Tomlinson and Dr J. W. S. Harris and to my father, Dr G. A. Harrison. I fear I cannot have done justice to their careful scrutinies and much appreciated interest.

Chelsfield,
Kent, 1957

R. J. HARRISON

CHAPTER I

HIS CURIOSITY ABOUT HIS ANATOMY

MAN has attempted to classify animals and to place himself somewhere in the classification since the days of Aristotle (384–322 B.C.). The Greek philosopher did not himself draw up a definite scale of animals, but it is possible to do so from his writings. He made numerous close and acute observations, and carried out limited experiments, but there is little evidence that he ever dissected a human body other than a foetus. He realized that there were simple or 'lower', as opposed to more complex or 'higher' forms of life, with man at the top – his acme of perfection.

Aristotle may be considered the first comparative anatomist, and he may even have thought of a theory of evolution, because he discussed adaptation of animals to their environment and 'evolution' of various organs. Thus he did not call a whale a fish, but placed it correctly among mammals.

The Birth of Anatomy

Anatomical tradition as we know it, like many other branches of rational, scientific thought, originated in ancient Greece. Yet there is no evidence that the most famous of ancient schools of medicine, that founded by Hippocrates (b. 460 B.C.), had any first-hand knowledge of the structure of man. The early Greek physicians did little human dissection, but were accused of performing on living men – charges that were probably malicious and without foundation. Tertullian (born *c.* A.D. 150) accused the Alexandrian Herophilus (fourth–third century B.C.) of having dissected six hundred living people, and called him a butcher of men. Herophilus is said to have been the first to have dissected the human body in public. He discovered the nervous system and maintained that arteries carried blood not air, as had been previously thought (the word artery means 'air-carrier'). Several parts of the brain are still known by the names he gave them.

Galen (*c.* A.D. 129–199), born in Asia Minor, was one of the great physicians of antiquity and for a time attended Marcus Aurelius. He founded a system of medicine, later called the 'Galenical system', which exercised a great but unfortunately stultifying influence throughout the world for thirteen hundred years. Galen, too, probably did not dissect the whole human body, but as a 'consultant' to the gladiatorial arena he presumably saw some crudely dissected parts. He made a number of anatomical observations on man, but committed 'howlers' by ascribing to man structures he found in animals.

His particular contributions to anatomical knowledge concerned the muscles (*musculus* – a little mouse – from the fancied resemblance of the mouse-like movements of muscle beneath skin) and the skeleton; he wrote *On Bones for Beginners.* It is known that he once had a complete human skeleton to study. Most of his work on muscles was on a species of Macaque monkey – the Barbary 'ape' – and although he introduced many names (for example *masseter,* a powerful chewing muscle that clenches the jaws) there is much confusion from lack of established nomenclature. His statements about other parts of the body are more inaccurate, although he made good observations on veins of the brain. We still refer to the *great cerebral vein of Galen* that drains the inside of the cerebral hemispheres. His opinion of man's position in nature, or what he thought a man was, is difficult to assess. Many of his writings are lost, but probably he adopted the attitude of a high priest as in his *Uses of the Parts of the Body*. In this he finds that the anatomy of man is perfect, and that all his organs and their functions are in absolute harmony, all being created by an Omniscient Being on a determined plan. That Galen's work was important cannot be too greatly emphasized, for after his death anatomical inquiry and observation practically ceased. Galen's word became law, and even as late as the sixteenth century his words were quoted as cogent arguments for undertaking particular procedures. Even in 1945 a certain Professor of Greek consulted Galen's text when advised that his daughter should have her tonsils removed. Galen remarked that the operation was particularly bloody (it still can be) – and the daughter kept her tonsils.

The Middle Ages

The next stage in the history of anatomy, after the downfall of the Roman Empire, is associated with transference of intellectualism to the East, to Syria, Persia, and Arabia. Many of the important Greek medical texts were translated into Arabic. Later, in the monasteries of Italy, the Arabic was changed into Latin. Thus the writings of Galen became available in the new universities of Italy and Western Europe. Monks responsible for the Latin versions included Constantine of Monte Cassino, Stephen of Antioch, and Gerard of Cremona. Gerard made an important translation of the works of Avicenna of Bokhara (980–1037), a brilliant Arabic physician whose *Canon of Medicine* became the textbook of the Middle Ages. It was a restatement of Galen's writings with added descriptions of blood-letting from veins. Some of the names we use for veins, such as *saphenous* for the long vein on the inside of the leg that so frequently becomes varicose, are derived from Arabic words (saphenous means apparent or visible).

The thirteenth century saw the origin and development of universities and a rise of scholasticism, but, as Charles Singer has written, 'scholasticism, however it may sharpen the wits, does nothing to develop the senses'. Re-appearance of the texts of Galen did not advance anatomy, and at first no dissection was carried out in medical schools of the new universities. After all, everything was described in Avicenna's book, and that was founded on the omniscient Galen, so dissection would merely confirm what was already known – or believed.

Dissection is said to have been resumed in the Medical School (founded in 1156) of the University of Bologna, perhaps to obtain evidence for legal purposes – hence it could be called forensic anatomy. Bologna University was famous as a seat of Law, and its Law School seems to have had control over the Medical Faculty. The legal dissections, or extended post-mortems, added little to anatomical knowledge, but were an important beginning of serious dissection. They became more important when Mondino de' Luzzi (1270–1326) became virtually the first Professor of Anatomy; he earned himself the title of 'Restorer of Anatomy'. Although Mondino is said to have dissected in person, a professor usually sat high above the scene in his professorial chair, shaped like a pulpit, and read or lectured while his demonstrator carried out rapid dissection of a corpse, usually a criminal's, and students listened and watched. This method is not without its faults, and it has been described best by the famous Vesalius (see later) as 'A detestable ceremony in which certain persons ... perform a dissection of the human body, while others narrate the history of the parts; these latter from a lofty pulpit and with egregious arrogance sing like magpies of things they have no experience of, but rather commit to memory from the books of others.'

Dissection had to be done quickly in fourteenth-century Italy; there were no preservatives, and the climate being warm, the bodies soon started to decompose. Corpses were difficult to obtain, and, belonging to criminals, could not be ordered for a particular date. Public opinion was prejudiced; there was a superstition that dead bodies should not be mutilated and added to this heads of religion opposed dissection. It became clearer, however, that medicine could not advance without adequate anatomical knowledge, and gradually civic authorities permitted limited public dissection, first in Bologna, and then more widely. Despite this, advance was slow.

Art and Law

The first illustrated textbook of anatomy appeared in 1521, to be followed by many famous successors, most of them destined to run into numerous editions. The aim was to substitute sketches or drawings for distasteful and arduous tasks of dissection. Berengarius of Carpi (1470–1530) produced the first of these anatomical 'visual aids', and he, too, was professor at Bologna. He was eventually dismissed from his chair, accused of dissecting living people, indecent language, and profligate habits. It is interesting that Benvenuto Cellini was one of his patients. The anatomical accuracy of neither professor nor patient can, however, withstand criticism.

More lasting and illustrious was the contribution to anatomy of Leonardo da Vinci (1452–1519), who spent his life between Rome, Milan, and Florence. Not only did Leonardo emphasize the way in which art could assist anatomy, but he made many profound anatomical observations. His purely anatomical drawings, many of which were not published till long after his death, were chiefly of muscles and their action on bones to form a system of levers. Structures he was the first to delineate accurately include the paranasal air sinuses of the skull, the ventricles of the brain, the shapes of the different vertebrae, the diaphragm, and the intraventricular bundle of tissue known as the moderator band of the heart. It has been said that Leonardo's artistic skill was an important factor in the success of the greatest anatomist after the Middle Ages, Andreas Vesalius, who outshone all except John Hunter. Born of an English mother and a Belgian apothecary in Brussels on 31 December 1514, Vesalius studied at Louvain, Montpellier, and Paris. He obtained bodies by devious means and dissected avidly, even taking parts home to his rooms. His dissections of 'that true Bible as we count it, the human body and the nature of man' soon showed him that Galen's teaching was often wrong. In 1543 Vesalius published his famous *De humani corporis fabrica*, which roused a storm of protest. He was attacked even by those who had given him instruction. He was so incensed and disgusted that he destroyed much unpublished work and abandoned his dissections. In 1563 he made a pilgrimage to Jerusalem, perhaps to atone for carrying out post-mortems, though he may have been condemned by the Inquisition to encourage more orthodox behaviour. He came back from Jerusalem the next year, hoping to return to academic life, but was shipwrecked, or taken ill, on the coast of Zante, an island off Greece. He died there on 2 October 1564.

Vesalius was the founder of modern human topographical studies and we still approach the structure of the body in the Vesalian manner in surgical operations. As experimentalist he was not as outstanding as William Harvey, but he made original experiments on neuromuscular relationships and nerve conduction. His demonstration that the pleural cavity in a living dog can be opened to the air if the lungs are rhythmically aerated with bellows is a principle adopted in present-day thoracic surgery. Educated humanist though he was, Vesalius was no philosopher and did not consider deeply the nature of man. He seems to have accepted Galen's teleological approach and the then current consideration of man as a work of art. His drawings, or those of Jan Stephen van Calcar under his guidance, did justice to the subject; if the drawing was not as superbly lucid as Leonardo's, it possessed an expressive vitality not surpassed in the multi-coloured blocks of the modern artist with his ink-spraying technique.

Structure has a Function

There next followed a golden age of human anatomical discovery and modern topography still eponymously remembers the names of many sixteenth- and seventeenth-century anatomists. At the end of the sixteenth century England became the chief centre of anatomical research. The barber-surgeon Thomas Vicary (died 1561) had published the first textbook of anatomy in English (*The Englishman's Treasure or the Anatomie of the Bodie of Man*), and though not original, it was widely used.

John Caius (1510–73) was mainly responsible for introducing thorough dissection of the human body in England, first in London and then at Gonville Hall, later renamed Gonville and Caius College, Cambridge. Caius had spent five years in Italy and visited universities and medical schools. Though he shared a house with Vesalius, he remained an ardent Galenist and contributed little to anatomy. Caius College, however, was the alma mater of William Harvey (1578–1657), who altered completely ideas about the structure of man and founded an experimental basis for functional anatomy. He, too, visited Italian universities, in particular Padua, where he was influenced by Fabricius, a pupil of Vesalius. A few years later, 1615–16, Harvey delivered anatomical lectures at the Royal College of Physicians, in which he outlined briefly his ideas of the circulation of blood by the heart. Twelve years later, in 1628, he published in Frankfurt his great, but brief, work *Exercitatio anatomica de motu cordis et sanguinis in animalibus*, giving results of observations on living man and animals. Harvey's great contribution demonstrated that purely anatomical description, without consideration of the physiological or functional aspects, was of small value and that hypothesis should be tested by experiment. Although his work was revolutionary and caused adoption of new names for blood vessels, Harvey was strangely conservative and much influenced by Galenism. He was responsible for several wrong ideas, particularly of the part played by the male in formation of the mammalian embryo. Unfortunately, much of his work on comparative anatomy was lost in the Civil War;

this must have been a great blow, for it is said that he dissected nearly a hundred species. He was also one of the first to introduce apparatus into biological experiments; to him a pump must have been of tremendous importance. Harvey in his lifetime did not have disciples; his reputation suffered after publication of his book, his practice dwindled, and not a few thought him slightly mad.

Harvey's work revealed a wide field for experiment and for research in comparative anatomy (and still does). Yet advances were slow before the days of two brothers, John and William Hunter, in the eighteenth century. However, in intervening years two significant methods of anatomical investigation were developed. The first, the invention of compound microscopes, opened a new world to anatomists, and was one of the earliest of many valuable gifts that investigators of the physical world were to give to biologists. The second involved critical assembly of morphological facts relating to each species of animal so that all could be comprehensively classified.

Microscopy produced the conception of a cell, the simplest unit of structure of multicellular animals, and enabled investigation of all types of cells and their components. So histology, or the study of tissues, was born and thus later enabled investigation of growing, dividing, and developing cells and tissues. Magnification of fine structures in the fabric of man by means of physical instruments is still not perfected. The excitement of deciphering the revelations of the most recent microscope – the electron microscope – equals that experienced by Malpighi (1628–94), Leeuwenhoek (1632–1723), and Swammerdam (1637–80) with their primitive light microscopes.

Except for certain spectacular discoveries, such as the existence of spermatozoa, progress was slow. This was due mainly to the gradual evolution of methods of preparing cells and tissues for examination with eyepieces, objectives, and condensers of Huyghens, Ramsden, and Abbé. Fixation, dehydration, embedding, sectioning, and staining became established only in the nineteenth century. In 1838 T. Schwann and M. J. Schleiden founded the cell theory and provided a great stimulus to histology. Even then many maintained, with not a little justification, that one was only examining under the microscope chemical artifacts displayed in dead tissue. The anatomist has been strangely reticent in fully exploring what microscopes can show. Most of the nineteenth- and some twentieth-century anatomists altogether ignored the instrument, or used only objectives of the lowest power, and preferred the Vesalian method of gross dissection long after the time when it could be considered to have given its best results.

The Stairway of Animals

The most famous classifier was a Swedish naturalist Carl Linnaeus (or von Linné), 1707–78, and it was he who first placed man, *Homo sapiens*, within the order of Mammals known as Primates. Linnaeus invented the term Primates to define the first, or highest, Order of the Class Mammalia. He included in this order all apes, monkeys, and marmosets, and also the lemurs. The latter were included because he considered them to be so like monkeys; they are now put in a sub-order Lemuroidea because of their lower organization and inferior brain development. Linnaeus incorporated in his definition of the Primates the criterion that they had hands on the anterior, or upper extremities. Nearly a century earlier the Dutch anatomist Nicholas Tulp (figured in Rembrandt's painting *The Anatomy Lesson*) had described a chimpanzee, and Edward Tyson had dissected another and recorded his observations in 1699. The latter maintained that his young specimen resembled in its anatomy that of man 'more closely than any of the ape kind, or any other animal in the world, that I know of.' Linnaeus never saw an ape, live or dead, but he was aware of Tyson's work and concluded that apes and man could well be placed together at the head of the Order Primates. He also included the bats within the order, but for good reasons we now do not.

Other zoologists, however, thought that only man really possessed true hands and argued that the human hand was such an evident characteristic of his anatomy that he could be placed by himself in a separate Order *Bimana* (J. F. Blumenbach, 1779, the founder of physical anthropology; Baron Cuvier, also, in his *Règne Animal* of 1817). All other primates were grouped in an Order *Quadrumana*, the implication being that all apes, monkeys, and their lower relatives were four-handed. The anatomy of the human hand and foot will be commented on in a later chapter; it is enough to note here that the apparently striking differences in the human foot, when compared with the human hand and hands and feet of other primates, are not now thought to be as significant as has been maintained.

Man has also been placed in a separate Order *Erecta* (J. K. W. Illiger, 1811) under an impression that erect posture and bipedal gait were unique human characteristics; these claims also will be discussed in a later chapter.

Arranging animals in trees of kinship may seem a somewhat sterile pastime, often leading to great difficulty in nomenclature or in deciding the exact limits of a particular genus or species. Yet in these attempts to marshal all known creatures into a 'stairway of animals' or *échelle des êtres*, an occupation for many years of French anatomists about the time of the Revolution, one can see preliminaries for emergence of the great biological concept of the nineteenth century – *evolution.* The preliminary essays in serial classification tried to demonstrate that there existed a common plan, found best in a basal type, with infinitely subtle modifications and variations developing on this plan. This idea developed into what was known as Transcendental Anatomy, there being, philosophically, 'only a single animal', and subsequently the great search for the 'archetype' began. Arguments concerning the nature of the archetype, attempts to explain the entire skull as being derived from multiple vertebrae, and so on, became 'nothing short of a nightmare'; and it was Charles Darwin who later provided the awakening from the nightmare with his *Origin of Species.* The stairway or scale of animals ceased to be a series of static forms and became a row of ancestors with descendants being modified on their evolution. Such modifications as are exemplified in successive generations of *adult* animals formed a series of stages known as a *phylogenetic* series.

Inevitably embryology became involved in each new theory. Even before announcement of the concept of evolution the German embryologist Karl von Baer had noticed a remarkable similarity between early embryos of different animals. Omitting to label two early embryos, he was unable to say to what animal they belonged any more precisely than that they were early embryos of some vertebrate or vertebrates. Such observations had been made previously by a number of anatomists and had led to a series of pronouncements. It was realized, as soon as von Baer had convincingly demonstrated the existence of the mammalian egg in 1828, that mammals gradually passed through a successive series of stages in development from unicellular egg until adult form and shape were reached. Such a series became known as an *ontogenetic* series. It then seemed obvious to attempt to link the phylogeny of an animal with its ontogeny – or to say, as did Serres and many others, that man only became a man after passing through transient stages resembling those of fish, reptiles, birds, and mammals. Thus came the 'Laws' of von Baer, and the theory of recapitulation of phylogeny in ontogeny of Haeckel; the latter to enjoy a prestige that 'has had a great and, while it lasted, regrettable influence on the progress of embryology' (de Beer). It must be remarked here that John Hunter held views somewhat similar to those of the recapitulationists. He did not, however, indulge in much theorizing, and dismissed the difficulty of explaining anatomical variations by saying the whole thing was quite obvious!

We must now return to the somewhat earlier period of John Hunter, because, in a way, he was the originator of the modern approach to anatomy. Born in Lanarkshire in 1728, he came to London at the age of twenty and studied anatomy at St Bartholomew's Hospital. After some early adventures as a naval surgeon and with the army in Portugal, he returned to London and started to amass his famous collection of dissections, specimens, and pathological curios. He was said to have had a pond in his garden ornamented with skulls.

Hunter's approach to anatomy was essentially practical and experimental; his ambition was to epitomize in his museum the structure and function of animal and human organs. His reputation must ultimately rest on the grand conception of the Hunterian museum, but as experimentalist the dictum 'Don't think, try it' has often been quoted as his. It is remarkable how many research papers today begin with a reference to his work. Unconsciously, perhaps, he preached and practised an approach that would have saved much of the effort expended by his contemporaries and successors on theoretical and philosophical aspects of anatomy. It could have led them more rapidly to study causes and modifications in ontogeny and morphogenetic forces that underlie evolution. Hunter's museum may have been enclosed in static glass jars (many of which were destroyed in the blitz on London in 1940), but his ideas and vital approach are now more than ever an encouragement to anatomical research.

Evolution

It was Charles Robert Darwin (1809–82) who finally exploded the medieval view of the place of man in Nature and gave biological studies a stimulus that can still be felt. In July 1958 the Fifteenth International Congress of Zoology is being held in London and will duly acknowledge that one hundred years earlier Wallace and Darwin read their joint paper to the Linnean Society 'On the Tendency of Species to form Varieties; and on the Perpetuation of Varieties and Species by Natural Means of Selection.' In 1859 appeared the first edition of *The Origin of Species by Means of Natural Selection.* At once there followed a storm of disapproval and emotional objection now difficult to appreciate. The book was really an abridged version of a vast projected work and it was only under pressure from friends that a shortened form was published; Darwin wanted to carry out further research and think longer before announcing his theory of evolution.

The term evolution is generally defined as stating that 'living organisms are all related to each other and have arisen from a unified and simple ancestry by a long sequence of divergence, differentiation and complication of descendent lines from that ancestry' (G. G. Simpson). It is the antithesis of the doctrine of special creation of each species of animal or plant, but not antithetical to the view that evolutionary process may be the divine method of creation. As is now well known, natural selection, according to the Darwinian theory, is an important factor causing evolution, and it became in the view of neo-Darwinists supporting Weismann (1834–1914) probably the only important factor. This is not the place to discuss in detail the views of Lamarck (1744–1829), who argued that acquired effects of habit are inherited, nor of the neo-Lamarckists who considered natural selection to have only a secondary part to play in evolution by eliminating unsuitable forms. There is no space to discuss the theory of Vitalism, to which Aristotle could be considered an adherent, with its idea of a vital force (*élan vital* of Bergson). As Simpson writes 'nothing is achieved by saying that evolution is the result of an innate force or tendency'. These and other theories can be read about in some of the books mentioned at the end of the chapter. Modern evolutionary theory is occasionally described as

Synthesism, in that it arises from a synthesis of the neo-Darwinian school and that of de Vries (1848–1935) which considered that new sorts of organisms arise suddenly, at random, as the result of mutations. A mutation is the inception of an inheritable variation due to a change in one of the genes that control characters or in one of the chromosomes that carry the genes. Mutation does not alone govern the course of evolution; mutations are seldom advantageous because, being random, they only rarely fit into, or improve on, the complex workings in any organism.

The immediate impact of Darwinism was forcefully brought home by Bishop Wilberforce at the meeting at Oxford in 1860 of the British Association for the Advancement of Science. He demanded of Thomas Henry Huxley, then thirty-five years of age, 'was it through his grandfather or his grandmother that he claimed his descent from a monkey?' Huxley retorted that if he had to have an ape for grandfather, or a man highly endowed by nature yet who employed these faculties for the 'purpose of introducing ridicule in grave scientific discussion' then he unhesitatingly preferred the ape. Huxley rapidly assumed the self-chosen office of Darwin's advocate, became his 'bulldog' and dealt summarily with certain ill-chosen criticisms. Richard Owen unfortunately chose to do battle against evolutionary theory on the matter of whether or not apes and monkeys possessed parts of the brain called 'the third lobe, the posterior horn of the lateral ventricle and the hippocampus minor' which he claimed were parts peculiar to *Homo*. Huxley retorted to the effect that anyone who couldn't see the posterior lobe in an ape's brain was not likely to have much of an opinion on other matters. 'If a man cannot see a church, it is preposterous to take his opinion about its altar-piece or painted window.' At the height of this famous controversy *Punch* summed the matter up thus:

Am I satyr or man?
Pray tell me who can,
And settle my place in the scale;
A man in ape's shape,
An anthropoid ape,
Or a monkey deprived of a tail?

Huxley maintained that man's reverence for the nobility of manhood should not be lessened by the fact that he is 'in substance and structure, one with the brutes'; for man possessed the endowment of rational speech and had been able to accumulate and organize experience, and that his grosser nature could reflect, here and there, 'a ray from the infinite source of truth'.

T. H. Huxley died in 1895 and since his time the theory of organic evolution has been accepted as part of biological orthodoxy. Gradually, but with increasing momentum, anatomists have turned their attentions from arguments about the hippocampus minor, and matters that really only meant discussions about names. They began to use apparatus more complicated than the scalpel, that sharp-edged fact finder with two thousand years of service, to determine man's peculiarities.

It must not be thought, however, that the days of dissection of the human body are quite gone, and that no more can thus be learnt of man's peculiarities. Had there been no bodies for dissection little of this chapter and practically none of the subsequent ones could have been written. Body-snatchers, sack-'em-up men or Resurrectionists are no longer in existence. The activities of Burke and Hare in Edinburgh during the early nineteenth century resulted in a Bill, 'An Act for Regulating Schools of Anatomy,' which received the royal assent on 1 August 1832. Medical science was thereby entitled to receive a legal supply of dead bodies for the purpose of dissection, advancement of knowledge and study of surgery.*

Modern Anatomical Research

Anatomists have only recently realized that it was no longer necessary to attempt to stamp parts of man's anatomy with hallmarks of uniqueness. The problems to solve are concerned with how

*There is no property in a legal sense in a dead body, and on the death of an individual the body belongs to the State. It is possible for the authorities to direct that the body of an individual who dies without kith or kin should be sent to a Medical School. An individual may also bequeath his body for purposes of medical research in a will. In both instances, after appropriate examination, the body is buried or cremated with due rites. These matters are carried out under the direction of H.M. Inspector of Anatomy at the Home Office.

man's anatomy and form became different from those of other animals, by how much do they differ and by what processes is the nicely calculated less or more controlled. No method that could possibly interpret structure can be ignored, and full use is being made of the techniques and instruments hitherto used only by mathematicians, chemists, and physicists for examination of the world of matter and inanimate things. The subsequent chapters will consider many of the methods that are being used and will discuss some of the results that shed light on human structural peculiarities. Advances in physiology and biochemistry, discovery of hormones, statistical treatment of measurements, experimental embryology, tissue culture, histochemistry, micro-radiography, electron microscopy, and the use of radio-active isotopes have all encouraged a breaking down of barriers between various disciplines engaged in studying man. The series of brief reviews that follows must necessarily be compressed and must be select, and since the writer's interests are mainly in certain fields of comparative anatomy and embryology, these are unashamedly allowed to contaminate the text. Invasions into fields other than those in which the writer has personally worked will assuredly and inevitably be subject to the deficiencies and dangers of such presumption, quite apart from his inability to do justice to the absorbing interest of his own fields. Virtually all topographical anatomy has been omitted, the main endeavour being to introduce man as a biological entity. Many anatomists will quarrel with the topics selected and would wish others in their place, or will maintain too much has been omitted. A list of books for further reading is given at the end of each chapter and should at least guide the more inquiring.

FOR FURTHER READING

(These volumes and those given after subsequent chapters are selected guides to the literature.)

Evidence as to Man's Place in Nature. T. H. Huxley. London, 1863
The Descent of Man. C. R. Darwin. Murray, 1871
The Evolution of Anatomy. C. Singer. Kegan Paul, 1925
The Rise of Embryology. A. W. Meyer. Stanford University Press, 1939
A History of Embryology. J. Needham. Cambridge, 1934

HIS CURIOSITY ABOUT HIS ANATOMY

A History of Comparative Anatomy. E. J. Cole. Macmillan & Co., 1944

The Meaning of Evolution. G. G. Simpson. Oxford University Press, 1950

Evolution; the Modern Synthesis. J. S. Huxley. Allen and Unwin, 1944

CHAPTER 2

HIS PLACE IN NATURE

After all, if he is an ape he is the only ape
that is debating what kind of ape he is.
G. W. CORNER

'MY vanity will not suffer me to rank mankind with *Apes, Monkeys, Maucaucos* (Lemurs) ...' wrote the English zoologist Pennant in 1781, but his and many other people's vanity has had to suffer. We now classify man in the way that G. G. Simpson does in the classic vol. 85 of the *Bulletin of the American Museum of Natural History* (1945);

SUB-PHYLUM – Vertebrata
CLASS – Mammalia
ORDER – Primates
SUB-ORDER – Anthropoidea
FAMILY – Hominidae
GENUS – *Homo*
SPECIES – *Homo sapiens*

The first two statements are easily understood and simply indicate that man is an animal with a backbone or vertebral column (*vertebra* is derived from a Latin word meaning to turn, since the individual bones, or vertebrae, of the column can rotate upon each other to varying degrees). Man is a mammal since he shares with them features of warm-bloodedness, a hairy skin, mammary glands to suckle the newborn, an embryonic existence within a maternal womb or uterus, and an afterbirth or placenta. Certain characteristics of his teeth, jaws, and respiratory system are typically mammalian: these features will be discussed in later chapters. Numerous variations and adaptations of basic structure are found in representatives of the different orders of which the Class Mammalia is composed.

LIVING MAMMALS

Linnaeus first used the term Mammalia in a strict classificatory sense, and he intended it to include all those animals that are viviparous (give birth to young rather than to eggs). Until 1884 the interesting Australian animal known as the Duckbill or Platypus, or *Ornithorhynchus*, of the Order Monotremata was considered viviparous and thus included in the Mammalia. On 2 September 1884, at the meeting of the British Association for the Advancement of Science, a telegram from W. H. Caldwell was read out: 'Monotremes oviparous, ovum meroblastic.' This indicated that the animal laid eggs and that the early stages of division of the active substance of the egg occurred in a manner similar to that of birds and reptiles. But it did not mean, as is sometimes erroneously maintained, that *Ornithorhynchus* was a link between the reptiles and mammals. The egg-laying habit is a primitive feature inherited from the ancestral reptilian forms, whilst the possession of true hair, a form of mammary gland, a diaphragm, and many other anatomical features make it certainly a mammal. The so-called duckbill is like soft leather in the living animal and the webbed feet it possesses are somewhat larger than, but not very different in structure from the web between two human fingers. The animal is therefore one of the surviving representatives (others are the Spiny Anteater (*Tachyglossus*) and the Long-billed Anteater) of an otherwise extinct Sub-class that branched off the evolutionary tree well over a hundred million years ago. The Sub-class is called the *Prototheria*, meaning 'the primitive animals'.

Another group of surviving primitive mammals is the *Marsupialia*; opossums, wombats, and kangaroos are members of this Order. These animals all have mammalian characteristics, but with several interesting modifications in their method of reproduction. The period of intra-uterine gestation is short (12–20 days) and only a simple form of connexion with uterine maternal tissues is established as a placenta. The young are born in a markedly undeveloped state and crawl into a special pouch within a ridge or fold of skin on the abdominal wall of the mother. Within the pouch embryos become attached to nipples and they are forcibly fed until the sucking mechanism is

TABLE I

LIVING MAMMALS

Class Mammalia

Sub-class PROTOTHERIA	
Order Monotremata	Spiny 'anteater', duckbills or platypuses.
Sub-class THERIA	
Infra-class METATHERIA	
Order Marsupialia	Opossums, kangaroos.
Infra-class EUTHERIA	
Order Insectivora	Hedgehogs, moles, shrews.
Order Dermoptera	Colugos.
Order Chiroptera	Bats.
Order Primates	(See Table II).
Order Edentata	Sloths, armadillos.
Order Pholidota	Pangolins.
Order Lagomorpha	Rabbits.
Order Rodentia	Squirrels, rats, mice, hamsters, guinea pigs.
Order Cetacea	Whales.
Order Carnivora	Dogs, bears, cats, seals, walruses.
Order Tubulidentata	Aardvark.
Order Proboscidea	Elephants.
Order Hyracoidea	Hyrax, coney, dassie.
Order Sirenia	Dugong, manatees.
Order Perissodactyla	Horses.
Order Artiodactyla	Pigs, camels, deer, cattle, sheep.

sufficiently established. These peculiarities of reproduction place the marsupials in an Infra-class of the Mammals called the *Metatheria.*

The other Infra-class of the Mammals is called the *Eutheria* ('good' animals or true mammals) and is characterized by the possession of a longer intra-uterine period of gestation, a well developed placenta, and large mammary glands. The Infra-class is divided into a number of Orders – some with only fossil representatives. Some sixteen extant Orders are recognized (see Table I) and man naturally belongs, by reason of his anatomy, to the Order Primates.

THE PRIMATES

There is no common, inclusive, distinguishing feature to be found in all Primates and it is not easy to give a precise definition. No clearly graded succession of types occurs within the order and the situation only becomes more complicated when the fossil Primates are considered. Such a state of affairs delights the controversially-minded anatomist and not a few have made good use of the opportunity it affords.

Primates are curiously distinguished by preservation of generalized anatomical features. There is a relative lack of the particularly developed or specialized features found in other Orders. Some members of the Order, particularly man, carry forward into adult life features characteristic of foetal life. On the other hand, large apes, particularly gorillas, show an opposite tendency in that they develop adult characteristics early. There is a much closer likeness between early developmental stages of man, apes, and monkeys than there is between the adult forms. It has been argued that all Primates evolved from a single precursor; some retaining certain ancestral features, others developing and specializing the originally primitive characteristics as they evolved. Yet others, and perhaps we could include man in this category, preserved some primitive or ancestral features and at the same time showed tendencies towards specialization. It has been argued that anatomically adult man is more like a foetal chimpanzee than any adult ape or monkey, allowing of course for difference in size.

This does not imply that man necessarily evolved from some primitive type of chimpanzee, but that certain features found in foetal apes are retained in adult man. This foetalization theory is associated with the name of a Dutch anatomist, L. Bolk. There is also evidence of a differential degree of foetalization not only in apes, but also in different races and families of living and even of ancient man. American slang grasped the anatomical point more quickly than the academic world when it referred to a female acquaintance as 'babe'. It is in the human female, most markedly in the western white, that retention of foetal and early infantile characteristics is best displayed. The beautiful film star with her smooth round-cheeked face, high forehead, linear arched eyebrows, large blue eyes, long eyelashes, rather broad, squat, but retroussé nose, pouting full lips, soft blonde hair and a dimple on her chin, a well-covered figure with rounded buttocks and not too long in the leg – is an eloquent testimony of foetalization.

Primate Characteristics

It is possible to attempt a definition of a primate, provided that evolutionary trends and differential tendencies described above are kept in mind, and perhaps more important if we consider the generalized characteristics of man and do not get over-enthusiastic in looking for minute bony or other specializations. Anatomists have been a little too keen in labelling the differences in the minutiae of man's structure as 'hallmarks', indicating his elevation to the primate peerage, or stamping him as if made of 'real silver'.

Primates show a tendency to preserve a generalized arrangement in the anatomy of their limbs, displaying mobility, particularly of the toes and fingers. This freedom of the digits is most marked in the big toes and the thumbs, and at least one pair is opposable. The term opposition means that a digit, say the thumb, can be rotated or turned round on its axis so that the palmar surface is brought against the palmar surface of any of the other digits. This movement is, of course, essential in grasping, but this involves other movements besides that of opposition. The true movement of opposition is shown to varying degrees in the Primates, but not all human beings can truly oppose the thumb. The movement is one of great antiquity among Mammals and is suggested as evidence of an arboreal existence. Certain marsupials can oppose their digits, and they too, are arboreal. It is thus often argued that the Primates have retained this characteristic during their long residence in the trees.

Associated with a free opposable digit is the broadened, flat thumb nail, but this is no more characteristic of Primates than is the possession of nails. The nails are certainly flattened, and not claw-like, but in fact a large number of mammals other than Primates bear nails at the tips of their digits. A few Primates have one or more digits bearing a claw.

Possession of a well-strutted attachment of upper limbs to trunk by a collar bone or clavicle is a distinct advantage when swinging on boughs by the arms. The very word 'clavicle' means a little key (cf. the word clavichord – a stringed instrument struck with keys) and implies that the arm is keyed to the trunk by the clavicle. Swift-running, four-legged animals would not find a clavicle advantageous, and it has almost disappeared during evolution of cats and dogs, deer and horses. Thus retention of a clavicle is not only associated with arboreal life, but is yet another of the more generalized and primitive of our anatomical possessions. When man's upright posture evolved, the clavicle assumed additional importance in that it provided a strut which allowed man to manipulate his upper limb in space, and together the two clavicles provided him with a ready-made bony yoke to help in carrying. The importance of the clavicle is clearly shown when it is fractured; the individual has to support his now useless arm, which hangs dependent by his side, by making use of his intact clavicle and associated shoulder muscles of the opposite arm.

Living in trees requires a well-developed ability to grasp and also mobility and strength in limbs and limb girdles. We find marked development in Primates of certain muscles in the shoulder region and also in the trunk. Animals that embark on a terrestrial life tend to lose the grasping power and all that is associated with it, and their limbs become adapted for running. Deer run on the tips of two fingers in each forelimb and on the tips of two toes in each hind limb. Horses walk or gallop on the tip of one much modified digit in each limb.

Arboreal life not only involves modifications in limbs and musculature, but makes available additions to the diet that are unobtainable on the ground. We are so used to man eating meat that we forget that Primates in general live on young shoots, leaves, fruits, and occasional insects. Thus their dentition has not become specialized by development of grinding molars for pulping grass, carnassial teeth for shearing through bones and tough meat, sharp tusks for digging up roots, or sabre-like canines for ripping open a victim. Primates retain the more generalized dentition of early mammals in that they have small cutting teeth or incisors, holding teeth or canines, moderately developed premolar and molar teeth that can grind and crush. Some specialization or modification of this fundamental plan does occur in various Primates, and will be mentioned later.

Other characteristics of Primates are seen in the special senses. They are associated with arboreal life and result in a facility for catching insects in a crepuscular light. Primates all show a reduction in their powers of smell and corresponding regression in those parts of the nervous system concerned with olfaction. Mammals are referred to as *macrosmatic* when the sense of smell is markedly developed, as in carnivorous mammals, *anosmatic* when the sense is apparently completely lost, as in whales, and as *microsmatic* when the sense is appreciably reduced, as in Primates. The microsmatic condition is often associated with a shortening of the muzzle or snout, there no longer being any need to smell or 'nose out' food in odd places. Freedom of the upper limbs and presence of a grasping pentadactyl or five-digited limb relieves Primates of using their jaws for carrying and grasping; a large, elongated snout would be an embarrassment. Life in trees may be quite successful despite a reduced sense of smell, but without keen eyesight many a Primate might well hurtle to the ground having missed its grasp, or having failed to observe a dead bough, particularly as night falls. Thus Primates tend to display more elaborate visual powers and an enlargement of that part of the brain concerned with the reception and interpretation of visual images.

Primates show their greatest and most important characteristic in their possession of large and well developed brains. The enlargement of the size of the brain relative to the size of the body is most marked in man, but it is also seen in other Primates. It is mainly due to an increase in the part of the brain known as the cerebral cortex. We cannot, however, be absolutely convinced that Sir Arthur Keith was correct when he stated that the difference between the brains of man and the apes was only quantitative, although he did add a rider that the importance of the difference could not be exaggerated. Nevertheless, Primates owe their success to this increase in quantity and complexity of the brain. Professor Sir Wilfrid Le Gros Clark sums up the situation: 'The wile and cunning of the earlier Primates have become the intelligence of the higher Primates, and Man himself has surpassed all other members of the animal kingdom in his capacity for mental activities of the most elaborate kind'. The same writer points out that it is difficult to explain why this precocious expansion of the brain 'began earlier, occurred more rapidly, and proceeded further than in any mammalian Order'. It may indeed have been favoured and encouraged by arboreal life, but this cannot be ascribed as the cause. The problem will be discussed again later in connexion with man's intra-uterine existence and his manner of birth.

Primates, then, are characterized by possession of numerous generalized and almost primitive mammalian features, but no *single* particular feature, either general or special, distinguishes them from other mammalian Orders. Rather it is by the possession of all of these generalized features and by an expanding brain capable of giving added importance and functional skill to these features, that we recognize the Primates.

Subdividing the Primates

We can now proceed further in describing man's position in nature by considering if he falls into any subdivision of the Primates. As already stated, it has been a great joy to anatomists to play the game of subdividing the Primates. We follow here the American palaeontologist G. G. Simpson (but see Hill, 1953, p. 24) and consider Primates as divisible into Prosimii and Anthropoidea. The former comprise an intriguing group of animals including tarsiers, lemurs, and tree-shrews. The latter are found in south-east Asia and are the lowliest members of the Primates. They are so primitive that until recently they were more humbly placed in the Order Insectivora. Close examination, however, reveals many features that show distinct tendencies towards, or strong suggestions of primate type. The fossil record provides additional evidence of primate relationship and we must consider them primitive members of that Order. There is further evidence that strongly suggests that fossil tree-shrews, or creatures like them, were the fore-runners of all the Primates. It is almost certain that there was at one time a transformation of a tree-shrew ancestor into animals very like lemurs. Lemur-like primates were fairly widely distributed about fifty million years ago, but true lemurs (Lemuriformes) are now only found in Madagascar. A second group, the lorisoids (Lorisiformes) include galagos, pottos, and lorises, and are found on the African mainland and in Asia. Lemurs have primate characteristics, but they are not very apparent at first sight. They also possess some anatomical features found in mammals that are not primates. Such features are their moist muzzle, projecting snout, midline cleft in the upper lip, and large, mobile ears. They are often referred to as 'Halbaffen' or half-monkeys for these reasons. It is probable that soon after their appearance lemurs became segregated from an evolutionary point of

TABLE II

THE PRIMATES

Order PRIMATES	
1. *Sub-order* PROSIMII	
Infra-order LEMURIFORMES	
(a) Tupaioidea	Tree shrews.
(b) Lemuroidea	Lemurs.
(c) Daubentonioidea	Aye-aye.
Infra-order LORISIFORMES	
(d) Lorisidae	Lorises.
Infra-order TARSIIFORMES	
(e) Tarsiidae	Tarsiers.
2. *Sub-order* ANTHROPOIDEA	
(f) Ceboidea (Platyrrhini)	New World Monkeys.
(g) Cercopithecoidea (Catarrhini)	Old World Monkeys.
(h) Hominoidea	
i. †Parapithecidae	†*Parapithecus*.
ii. Pongidae	†*Pliopithecus*, gibbons. †*Proconsul*, †*Dryopithecus*. orang-utan, chimpanzee, gorilla. †*Australopithecus*.
iii. Hominidae	†*Pithecanthropus*, Neandertal man, all prehistoric and living races of man.

NOTE: † means extinct.

view, and we need discuss them no further, since most authorities do not consider them or their fossil predecessors to lie on the direct line leading to higher Primates.

Much has been written about the third division of the Prosimii – the Tarsiers. There were many of these curious and intriguing animals in the world of fifty million years ago and they existed in many different forms. Only one genus, however, survives today, and that is a little animal, hardly larger than a small rat, called *Tarsius spectrum*. It possesses certain anatomical features of a specialized nature, such as its large eyes, its hind limbs that enable it to jump more than ten times its own body-length, its large, constantly twitching ears, and the remarkable way it can rotate its head to look right round behind itself. In other characteristics the animal displays features that are distinctly monkey-like, such as in the anatomy of the nose, the reproductive organs, and in the brain. At least one anatomist has suggested that fossil tarsioids, or creatures very like them, were directly ancestral to higher forms of Primates and even to man. Despite their generalized characteristics and the possibility that they may indeed be showing us something of the anatomy of early ancestral Primates, it is usually held that tarsioids left the main line of descent to man some time in the Eocene (Eocene means the 'dawn of the recent' and is a term used for the geological epoch extending from about 45 to 50 million years ago).

TABLE III

GEOLOGICAL PERIODS OF QUATERNARY AND TERTIARY ERAS

Geological Periods	*Started*
Holocene (wholly recent)	10,000 years ago.
Pleistocene (most recent)	1 million years ago.
Pliocene (more recent)	15 million years ago.
Miocene (less recent)	35 million years ago.
Oligocene (few recent)	45 million years ago.
Eocene (dawn of recent)	50 million years ago.
Palaeocene (old of recent)	70 million years ago.

We may therefore conclude that the Prosimii are 'primitive' Primates in that they show certain features found in Insectivores. We know that three main stocks have arisen, the lemurs, lorises, and tarsiers, and we feel that the tree-shrews can be placed either in the Insectivora or in Primates without great anxiety. Finally, we consider that the anthropoid stock most probably arose from some form ancestral to the tarsioids.

The Anthropoidea

The Sub-order Anthropoidea is the name of the group in which monkeys, apes, and man are placed, and we shall have to examine the reasons for so placing them. Fossil anthropoids first made their appearance in the geological epoch called the Oligocene (meaning the 'few of the recent' and extending for some ten million years after the Eocene). They seem to have been successful from the first, and although many genera have become extinct, some thirty-six are still flourishing. Anthropoids are active, adventurous, and inquisitive; their facial expression reflects their emotions and give them every semblance of being 'alive'. The very word monkey is a diminutive of the word *homunculus* – a little man, and the word for them in at least one language means when translated 'little man of the trees'. (*Homunculus* is in fact the generic name for an extinct form of New World monkey.) Most monkeys are accustomed to live in trees but many can live at ground level. Some exist wholly on the ground and are thus easy to keep in zoological gardens. The idea of 'a little man' living in the trees gives a wrong impression of their method of locomotion, for both in trees and on the ground monkeys run four-footed (pronograde) fashion, occasionally leaping from one rock or bough to another. Yet they can sit on their haunches with their knees bent up and the soles of their feet flat on the ground. Their heads are so set on the vertebral column that they can look straight ahead with ease. This posture is the characteristic one adopted when examining a neighbour for pieces of dried skin. It represents one of the stages through which an animal might have to pass before adopting an upright stance. A human baby does not squat in quite the same way, but one of the indications that it is going to stand up is its preliminary ability to sit unaided and hold its head up. Monkeys can pull themselves upright and will often walk round a cage on two legs, holding on to the bars, particularly if offered food at a high level.

There is a clear indication in monkeys of the relative enlargement of the brain that is found progressively through the Primate series. Although the sense of smell is much reduced (microsmatic) the visual capacity is greatly increased. Certain anatomical features in the eyes give a monkey binocular, stereoscopic vision. There is sometimes a marked appreciation of colour. A pet sooty mangabey was particularly fascinated by the coloured wrappings of toffees and liked to collect coloured pencils, which it cracked open and ate with relish. Increase in visual perception is clearly associated with partial freeing of the hand. From being purely a structure for locomotion, it is used in grasping, exploring, touching, and feeling interesting objects. A monkey also uses 'older' methods of acquiring information on the nature of objects. It very often carries them to its mouth and bites on them, much in the way a dog will mouth and bite on something thrown to it. Thus it appears that information coming from the eyes and hands cannot be completely utilized by the brain, or that the perception patterns reaching the monkey's brain cannot be fully 'associated' with past events or experiences. Certain animals are characteristically found in *packs*, such as wolves, in *herds*, such as deer, in *troops*, such as baboons, in *schools*, such as whales, or in *colonies*, such as seals. The advantages of hunting together, feeding together, or merely sharing the same sandbank are obvious. There is probably always a leader that carries out particular duties until old age causes retirement. Living together is carried a little further in monkeys and to even greater advantage. Quite elaborate forms of integrated social activity develop. There are many examples of this, but perhaps the best stories are about baboons. Dr Anwyl of Hargeisa has given an account of what happened when a troop of baboons was pursued by a leopard. Five of the troop lagged behind as the rest travelled through the trees and at an appropriate moment four dropped on the leopard and held its four paws while the fifth tore out its intestines. Baboons can be ferocious and not unintelligent opponents.

Full advantage of a social existence is obtained only if it is possible to communicate in some way with the other members of the group. The social species of insects, such as bees and ants, have methods of informing each other by special signals or by performing dance patterns on the comb. The patterns exhibited indicate the direction of food and the flying-time, or distance, from the hive. Communication between animals is now being studied extensively. Work has already been done on monkeys, but there is no evidence that they can communicate by articulate speech. They express their moods by means of howls, grunts, or shrieks variously modulated. Even so a remarkable variety of signals can be communicated, though perhaps not to the level that Rudyard Kipling's *Bandarlog* enjoyed.

New and Old World Monkeys

The Anthropoidea have been classically divided into the *Platyrrhini* (Ceboidea) or New World monkeys of Central and South America and the *Catarrhini* or Old World monkeys (Cercopithecoidea), Apes, and Man. These two words of Greek etymology are derived from the fact, not always clearly shown, that in platyrrhines the two nostrils are separated by a relatively broad septum and they appear flatter-nosed than catarrhines with their narrow central septum. This may seem rather a restricted criterion upon which to differentiate the two main groups, but there are other features of the New World Monkeys (presence of three premolar teeth, large bulla, and prehensile tail, absence of a drawn-out, tube-like tympanic bone in the ear, etc.) which distinguish them from the Old World family.

The Platyrrhini are now found only in South America, and they comprise two families, the more primitive marmosets (*Callithrix*) and the Cebidae, of which the howler monkey (*Alouatta*), the capuchin (*Cebus*), the spider monkey (*Ateles*), and the squirrel monkey (*Saimiri*) are examples. It is generally believed that the platyrrhines are an offshoot from the main evolutionary line of descent and that they have evolved independently in relative isolation in the South American land mass. Many of them share certain specializations, such as a prehensile tail, and occasionally possess features of their own. The large howler monkey possesses a curiously resonant voice which is due to enlargement and hollowing out of the hyoid, a bone in the upper part of the neck beneath the tongue. Other characteristics of these animals will be mentioned in subsequent sections.

Many anatomists would agree that there is considerable sense in Simpson's division of the Catarrhini into Old World monkeys (Cercopithecidae), apes (Pongidae), and the extinct and living forms of man (Hominidae). The relationship and common ancestry of these families and the time when they diverged are by no means settled. There is evidence, but only from a single yet informative fossilized lower jaw, of the existence of an animal now called

Parapithecus that lived in Egypt in the Lower Oligocene (45 or so million years ago). The anatomy of its teeth and jaw suggest that it might well have evolved from some form of Eocene tarsioid. It must be considered seriously, at any rate until more palaeontological evidence appears, as a candidate for the common ancestor of the diverging evolutionary lines that survive today in the Old World monkeys, the apes, and men. Some authorities consider that the catarrhine monkeys soon separated from the other forms and that evolution of the ape stock and the hominid stock ran more or less parallel. In fact, one often reads, and students are frequently required to comment on, the statement that man shows a closer resemblance in his anatomy, or in the preponderance of his features, to the living anthropomorphous apes than he does to any other mammalian group. Unfortunately such academic pronouncements have sometimes resulted in the idea that man ... 'descended from a creature almost precisely like those apes of today. But this is a gross misconception for which there has never been the slightest foundation'. This quotation from Professor Sir Wilfrid Le Gros Clark continues ... 'when we compare anatomically man and the anthropoid apes of today, we are comparing the terminal products of two separate (and in many ways contrasting) lines of evolution which presumably diverged from each other at quite a remote geological period. Failure to recognize this rather obvious point has certainly led to a certain amount of confusion in discussions on human origins.' In a footnote from the same paper (*The Advancement of Science*, No. 43, December 1954) this author emphasizes that a clear distinction should be drawn between the biological species *Homo sapiens*, that is, anatomical and physiological man, and the wider, philosophical concept of *Man*. These chapters are concerned purely with the former aspect; fortunately, perhaps, anatomists are seldom asked, or required, to write on the latter.

The Old World monkeys are represented by the one family already mentioned, the Cercopithecidae. Its members are found mainly in Asia and Africa (and even in Gibraltar). The family includes among others the macaques (Rhesus monkey, *Macaca*), mangabeys (*Cercocebus*), mandrills (*Mandrillus*), baboons (*Papio*), and the langurs (*Presbytis*). The last has been suggested as a possible manufacturer of the tracks in the Himalayan snow ascribed to the Abominable Snowman.

In general these monkeys are somewhat like New World monkeys, but they do not have a prehensile tail and are not all so well adapted for arboreal life – in fact mandrills and baboons have almost abandoned the trees. They all have only two premolar teeth, a tubular tympanic bone, and also possess hardened areas of skin on their backsides called ischial callosities (ischium is the name for the lower part of the hip bone which has tuberosities on which the reader may well be sitting). In relation to these callosities is an area of skin devoid of hair and often highly coloured at certain times during reproductive life. Reproductive characteristics closely resemble those in the apes and man and are described in a later chapter. Several of the Old World monkeys show anatomical specializations, in the teeth and other parts of the body, which are brought forward as evidence to suggest that the group deviated early from the ancestral stock.

The Great Apes

The Catarrhini also include the Pongidae – the gibbons and great apes. Together with the Parapithecidae and the Hominidae they comprise Simpson's super-family Hominoidea (see Table II). The living genera are the gibbons (*Hylobates*) and the related siamang, the orang-utan or 'man of the woods' (*Pongo*), the chimpanzee (*Pan*), and the gorilla (*Gorilla*). The gibbons are the most numerous and successful but are the smallest apes. They seldom weigh more than 10 kg. (21 lbs) and their brain often weighs less than 100 gm. Cerebral development of gibbons is less than that in some monkeys. Gibbons received their name from the French naturalist Buffon (1707–88), who was not himself an anatomist but was assisted in this aspect by Daubenton (1716–99). They are found today in Malaya and other parts of south-east Asia. The relatively great length of their arms enables them to swing through the trees; they are veritable jungle trapeze artists. This method of progression, so fascinating to watch in a zoo, has been called brachiation by Sir Arthur Keith (*brachium* – the Latin for an arm) and, as will be seen later, many authorities have considered that brachiation could have been involved in the evolution of the upright posture. Gibbons are the only apes that can maintain erect posture and run upright on their hind limbs for some distance, although they prefer to live in trees.

They are also the most vociferous of apes, being very noisy. The noise is, of course, increased by their group living habits.

The name 'chimpanse', which was the old name of the ape we now call a chimpanzee, was apparently a native word from Angola in West Africa. There is an interesting history of the confusion about the generic names of apes. Thomas Henry Huxley, in his famous book *Man's Place in Nature and other Essays*, refers to the first edition of an amusing book, *Purchas, His Pilgrimage*, published in 1613. Purchas, refers to an old friend of his, Andrew Battell or Battle, who had visited Angola, and also lived in the Congo for several years. Purchas says that an old soldier told Battell of 'a kinde of great apes, if they might so bee termed, of the height of a man with twice as bigge feature of their limmes, the strength proportional, hairy all over, otherwise exactly like men and women in their whole bodily shape.' In a marginal note it is stated that these great apes are called *Pongos*. Huxley points out that the old soldier friend of Purchas was probably confusing the pongo with the gorilla. The name 'gorilla' is alleged to be an African word for a wild or hairy woman. One is said to have been found in the Greek account of a voyage made by the Carthaginian sailor Hanno in the fourth century B.C. The name gorilla was finally adopted as the specific name for the ape *Troglodytes gorilla* by the missionary Dr Savage in 1847; but in fact the specimen might have been a chimpanzee. Only in the last century has the confusing situation been clarified. It is now realized that the chimpanzees and gorillas come from the tropical forests of Africa and that the orang-utan comes from Borneo and Sumatra. The gorilla is the heaviest, a full grown male weighing up to 600 lb; the orang is the next largest, weighing up to 170 lb, and the average weight of an adult chimpanzee is about 110 lb. (A full-grown man of 12 stones would weigh 168 lb.) These three great apes are not as at home in the trees as are the gibbons. Chimpanzees and the gorillas progress more easily than orangs, but all of them use a particular technique in that they walk with their forefeet not palm downwards on the ground but on their knuckles. It has been suggested that gorillas, chimpanzees, and orangs have taken to the ground secondarily because with their great increase in weight they could only be supported in trees by particularly thick branches. In their general anatomy the great apes lack certain specializations found in monkeys. They have no sitting-pads or callosities in the ischial region nor an external tail. Reproductive processes in apes are closely similar to those in the human female. Young apes are well developed at birth but there is a longer period of infancy and adolescence than in the monkeys. The newborn ape is carefully tended by its mother for many months. Puberty is generally reached between eight and ten years.

The most remarkable anatomical change in the great apes is a marked increase in bulk of the brain. This increase can, of course, be partly accounted for by the increase in the size of the body. Brain weight varies from about 300 gm. in the female chimpanzee to up to 600 gm. in a full-grown male gorilla. There is a considerable difference in temperament between the chimpanzee and the gorilla. The former is capable of being tamed more easily and has been the subject of a number of behavioural studies. Sensory perception in the chimpanzee is keen, and is said to be equivalent to that of man, but development of brain activity seldom progresses beyond that observed in early childhood in man. More details about the differences of the brain and the behaviour of apes will be discussed later.

Apes possess a vermiform appendix; in this they are like man, but are unlike the catarrhine monkeys. They have large canine teeth which they use for attack and defence, but are mainly vegetarians and only eat flesh if they are unable to find their preferred diet. The American P. E. Steiner finds as a result of his recent investigations that in general the organs and tissues of the gorilla can be considered under four headings. There are those that by present methods of investigation are indistinguishable from the same organs in man. Then there are those that are *qualitatively* distinguishable, for example, the large laryngeal air-sacs present in the gorilla. There are also those organs that are distinguishable because of differences in proportion or size, and lastly those that can be differentiated because of certain quantitative differences in particular situations.

We can now consider the fourth family that Simpson placed in the Catarrhini. This is the family Hominidae, which includes the extinct and living races of man. It has always been regretted by the anatomists who have studied the ancestry of man that when ancient apes or men died, their soft parts have never been preserved, and one can only study prehistoric man or ancestral forms of ape-like men by their skeletal structure. The evidence available from the study of fossils is unfortunately very incomplete, yet what has been discovered must be very seriously considered. It is not the purpose of this particular volume to describe the fossil remains that are believed to be those of early types of men, and the reader is referred to the book by Dr J. C. Trevor, *Man and His Kind*, for a fuller description of this interesting subject.

Fossil remains

It will probably surprise the reader to learn that fossil remains of undoubted human type are not as ancient as might be expected. There are many fossil apes from Miocene and Pliocene times, but no evidence has yet been presented of the existence of man until the beginning of the Pleistocene, less than a million years ago.

At least ten genera of fossil apes of the Miocene and Pliocene have been described from sites in Africa, Asia, and Europe. Most are known only from their teeth and jaws. Space prohibits description of these interesting remains of *Propliopithecus* and *Pliopithecus* to whom all apes are probably related. The latter was very similar to the gibbon and lived in woods in Europe. *Dryopithecus* (tree ape) and *Proconsul*, named because of the resemblance of its teeth and jaws to those of 'Consul', a chimpanzee in the London Zoo, are both noteworthy. It has been concluded that members of the group *Dryopithecus* gave rise at different times to the three great apes, and man. Most authorities assume that *Proconsul* could not be directly ancestral to man because it possessed so few unequivocally human features. The human stock probably diverged from that of apes in early Miocene times before the brachiating habit developed fully (J. Z. Young). Our interest in *Proconsul* is increased when it is realized that, in the remote times in which it lived, those features we consider distinctly human had probably not begun to be differentiated from those of primitive apes.

Ancestry of Man

Study of these and other fossil apes suggests that the stock that gave rise to man originated in Africa. It has long been known that in the higher terraces in Uganda and in parts of Tanganyika there lived primitive men who were able to chip pebbles crudely, and such cultures have been referred to as 'the pebble cultures' of Africa. Examples of chipped pebbles have now been found in many other parts of Africa and from their geological setting they appear to belong to the early Pleistocene of over half a million years ago. The primitive men that made these pebble tools lived at about the time small man-like Primates called the Australopithecinae inhabited caves in the Transvaal. These 'Southern apes' have now been intensively studied in various countries, and it is nearly certain that they stood upright. The Australopithecinae were relatively small, probably less than four feet high, weighing between 40 and 50 lb. Their brain and brain case were also relatively small, and that somewhat puzzled anatomists during early stages of investigation. In some features, for example the teeth, they have a closer resemblance to man than to modern great apes. It may be asked whether the Australopithecinae were the makers of the chipped pebbles, but so far there is no definite evidence of stone implements found in association with remains of the bones. It is clear that there were two main groups of hominids living in Africa; they are called *Australopithecus* and *Paranthropus*. The latter, which probably lived later, is closer in its anatomical characteristics to the gorilla, or rather to the great apes, and it is notable for a large bony crest running along the back of the skull, a feature also found in gorillas. Though it is not possible to use modern methods of dating the bones – methods such as those used to disprove the authenticity of the Piltdown skull – other evidence can help us date the material. The Australopithecines lived at too late a date in time to have been man's actual ancestors, but it is certain that their predecessors would have been alive in the Pliocene and might well have been candidates for this role.

It must not be thought that Africa is the only continent in which remains of primitive man have been found. In 1891 the Dutch anthropologist E. Dubois discovered portions of a skeleton in Central Java which was given the name *Pithecanthropus*. From 1936 to 1939 further remains of *Pithecanthropus* were discovered. In 1927 in China, some 40 miles south-west of Peking, Dr Davidson Black found a single tooth, apparently from a primitive human skull. Working on this single tooth he thought it justifiable to state that it must have belonged to a very early type of man, 'Peking man', known as *Sinanthropus.* Later, other discoveries were made that showed conclusively that the original suggestions were correct. However, a number of authorities consider that these two creatures belonged to the same genus. Their cranial capacity, however, and the size of their brain was much more than that of any known ape. In 1954 Professor C. Arambourg discovered three human lower jaws in a site near Ternifine in Algeria. These bones were associated with a hand-axe industry. Other material was also discovered and has been used as a basis for describing a new genus – *Atlanthropus.* This form has not yet been fully investigated, but it is apparent that it is similar in some respects to Peking man and shows several characteristics found in *Pithecanthropus.*

Pithecanthropus walked upright and in many ways must have been very like modern man. Indeed, there is some evidence that *Pithecanthropus* may have been as advanced as some of the less civilized races which inhabit the world today.

The secondary evolutionary level usually recognized in the family Hominidae is that of the Neandertal. The name is derived from the fact that the remains of the specimen, a skull-cap, a few ribs and limb bones, were found in a cave in the Neander valley near Düsseldorf. Perhaps the earliest of the fossils placed in this group is that of the lower jaw of Mauer man discovered in a sandpit near Heidelberg in 1907. It is older than Neandertal man proper and is probably, at the moment, the most ancient human relic from Europe. Heidelberg man was probably larger than typical Neandertal man, judging of course only from the jaw, and in certain characteristics was definitely ape-like. There are, however, abundant remains of Neandertaloid man and of Neandertal man proper; they have been found in many parts of Europe and in the Middle East. Neandertal man had a long, low braincase particularly prominent behind, and also large brow ridges. The face was rather prognathous and there was little or no chin. The skull was definitely stouter than that of modern man. There is also some doubt as to whether Neandertal man did walk fully upright, more likely he progressed with a slouching gait. Although probably many features in the anatomy of Neandertal man are shared by *Pithecanthropus*, in brain size Neandertal man reached that found in modern man and sometimes even surpassed it.

Neandertal man might seem to have been a particularly coarse individual, but there were two main types existing at the same time. They are called the progressive and conservative types; the second being the later and the more coarsely built. The progressive type is exemplified by the Steinheim skull found in a valley of a tributary of the river Neckar, and also by the Ehringsdorf skulls. We can consider the progressive type as being generalized in structure not only because it lacks some of the specializations of the conservative form, but also because it approaches or indicates some characteristics of modern man. It is generally felt that Neandertal man was not a direct predecessor of modern man – at any rate in Europe – but that he was replaced by a wave of invaders that probably came from Central Asia.

We must now consider the stage of modern man, or, as he is sometimes called, Neanthropic man. It is difficult to define modern man, apart perhaps from stating that we would expect to see in him absence of features characteristic of Neandertal man and presence of a number of specific characters that we can say are truly those of modern man. The progressive form of Neandertal man displayed some features that can be compared with those of modern man, but it is clear that there were in existence men very like ourselves *before* the emergence of Neandertal man. A fuller treatment of this fascinating problem will be presented in Dr J. C. Trevor's book in this series.

FOR FURTHER READING

Man's Place in Nature. T. H. Huxley. London, 1863
Man's Place among the Mammals. F. Wood Jones. Longmans, 1929
Up from the Ape. E. A. Hooton. New York, 1947
Mankind So Far. W. Howells. London, 1947
The Life of Vertebrates. J. Z. Young. Oxford University Press, 1950
Evolution Emerging. W. K. Gregory. Macmillan, 1951
Man's Ancestry. W. C. Osman Hill. Heinemann, 1954
History of the Primates. Sir Wilfrid Le Gros Clark. British Museum, 4th ed., 1954
The Fossil Evidence for Human Evolution. Sir Wilfrid Le Gros Clark. University of Chicago Press, 1955

Primates. Comparative Anatomy and Taxonomy. A monograph. W. C. Osman Hill. Edinburgh University Press, 1953–57.
Dating the Past. F. E. Zeuner. Methuen, 1946
'Taxonomy and Human Evolution'. S. Zuckerman. 1950. *Biol. Rev*. 25, 435.

CHAPTER 3

HIS MANY KINDS

It is generally agreed that all human beings alive today fall into a single but polymorphic species, *Homo sapiens*. Most anatomists and anthropologists would also agree that all human beings that have lived on this earth during at least the past 10,000 years can be included in this one species. There has been little unity or agreement, however, as to how the species should be subdivided.

Man has been aware from the time of Herodotus (480–425 B.C.) that different groups of men display certain physical differences and he has used certain of these features for purposes of discrimination. Each system of classification has, however, been nearly always bedevilled by difficulties in nomenclature. Furthermore, anthropologists have always had to resist the determination of politicians and others to segregate mankind into arbitrary groups of nationalist or imperialist expediency. The word 'race' is too deeply absorbed into our language for it to be avoided in any classification of mankind. Unfortunately its use in a zoological sense meaning 'sub-species' or 'variety' has been confused with its use in a national sense. It would be a brave man who attempted an anatomical differentiation of a 'Dutch' race from an 'English' race. Thus it is necessary to define the meaning of race in terms as precise as possible.

A race, as used in a classificatory sense, is a group of people characterized by possession of *certain inherited physical* features. This may sound quite reasonable, but at once many difficulties arise. What features are to be selected, and are all features of equal value? If, as is obviously so, there are differences in relative importance of various features, who or what is to decide their hierarchical order and weighting?

Linnaeus (p. 22) classified mankind into four main continental varieties, basing his decision on *colour* of skin, hair, and eyes. His divisions were *Americanus rufus*, *Europaeus albus*, *Asiaticus luridus*, and *Afer niger*; there was a fifth to include several, to him, abnormal forms. Blumenbach (p. 22) pointed out, however, that there were so many intermediate gradations in colour, appearance, and height tha all men must be related and differences were only those of degree. He recognized five main divisions, basing his discriminating criteria on *shape* of head, face, and nose, *form* of hair, and *colour* of skin and hair. His varieties were the Caucasian, the Mongolian, the Ethiopian, the American Indian, and the Malay. We now realize that Blumenbach laid too much emphasis on very variable features of the facial skeleton, but at least his concern with anatomy of the skull allows us to consider him the founder of scientific study of that structure – craniology.

More and more anatomical – or physical – features were subsequently employed in efforts to sub-divide mankind. Seldom, though, was there any realization of the nature of the forces causing the differences that were so ardently observed and measured. The degree of projection of the jaws ('snoutiness' or 'prognathism'), the curliness and alleged differences in origin of hair from the scalp, the cephalic index (maximum breadth of skull × 100, divided be maximum length), facial breadth and height, slope of the nose and characteristics of the bony nasal apertures all had their protagonists as essential discriminatory criteria. It is to W. L. H. Duckworth (1870–1956), a Cambridge anatomist, that we perhaps owe the first attempt to evaluate seriously the relative importance of the various features. His classification (1904) used cephalic index, prognathism, and cranial capacity as primary criteria; facial, nasal, orbital, and epidermal features being of secondary importance. Duckworth's criteria were widely adopted and are still quoted in textbooks.

Cephalic Index

Dolichocephalic Index below 75; (long-headed)	Australian aborigines, Kaffirs, Zulus, Eskimos, Fijians.
Mesaticephalic Index 75 to 80; (medium-headed)	Europeans, Chinese, Polynesians.
Brachycephalic Index over 80; (broad-headed)	Malays, Burmese, American Indians.

Subsequent classifications, such as those of J. Deniker (1926) and A. C. Haddon (1929), used characteristics of hair as primary criteria.

Deniker recognized six main divisions: woolly hair, with a broad nose; curly or wavy hair; wavy brown or black hair, dark eyes; fair, wavy, or straight hair, light eyes; straight or wavy black hair, dark eyes; straight hair. Shape of skull, facial differences, and other physical features enabled numerous sub-divisions to be defined. Haddon used the terms *Ulotrichi*, spiral or woolly hair, *Cymotrichi*, curly hair, and *Leiotrichi*, straight hair, to denote his main groups, and cephalic index and skin colour to determine sub-divisions.

Most modern anthropologists are somewhat hesitant to make a definite formal arrangement of types of mankind for reasons to be mentioned later. New methods have recently produced results that could easily make nonsense of a classification based purely on physical features; with guidance from Dr J. C. Trevor, however, the following classification is given. Dr Trevor will be considerably enlarging this aspect of the study of man in a forthcoming volume in this series. Five main races will be described together with some of the accepted sub-divisions of each, the adult male being the standard of comparison.

1. *Europiforms.* These people occupy the whole of Europe (exclusive of those who have migrated to set up colonies, dominions, etc.), north and north-east Africa, and parts of Asia. Colloquially known as 'white', the word is not descriptively accurate (p. 72). There is much variation in skin colour, and it is better described as 'not black'. The hair is wavy, curls, and is abundant. There is no prognathism and the nose is narrow and tends to be pointed. No comment is possible about head form and stature because almost all grades are present. Sub-divisions include Nordics from round the North Sea, the Baltics, the Samians or Lapps, and the Uralics from the district between the Ural mountains and the Ob basin in Russia. Also included are Alpines or Rhetians from the central European massif, Dinarics or Illyrians of the Balkans, the Taurics ('Armenoids') of the Caucasus and Asia Minor. A large group comprises the Mediterraneans from countries surrounding that sea. The Europiforms are completed by Erythriotes or 'Eastern Hamites' (including Somalis and Abyssinians), Chersiotes from India and Ceylon, Aralians from southern Russia, and the people who appear to have been the aboriginal inhabitants of Japan – the Ainu. It is not possible to consider here

the numerous differences in physical appearance of all these peoples, or to discuss arguments for placing them in this and not another group. England is inhabited by people almost exclusively derived from Nordic, but some from Mediterranean and Alpine stock.

2. *Mongoliforms.* They represent in general the 'aboriginal' inhabitants of Asia, the Americas, and certain parts of Europe and Oceania. They are the most numerous peoples on earth today and are recognized by their broad, flat faces, prominent cheek bones, scanty, straight, black hair, and medium or short stature. Skin colour varies from a light yellow to reddish brown. Two curious features are also often observable; a grey or blue *sacral spot* or spots which appear on young children just above the cleft on the back between the buttocks, and an *internal epicanthic fold* of skin that leaves the upper eyelid and passes to the side of the bridge of the nose and hides the inner angle (canthus) of the eye. The Mongolians form a large group of this subdivision and are widely distributed from Siberia to Astrakhan and from north China, Japan, and Korea to the East Indies. The eastern or 'true' Mongols are still nomadic and are good horsemen. The Huns were also a Mongoliform people, who lived 'rivetted to their horses'.

Other subdivisions of the Mongoliforms are the Nesiotes of Indo-China and Indonesia, the Polynesians, and the Arctics, who include the Eskimos. There has been much controversy as to the position of the Polynesians. Some authorities maintain that they are better placed in the Europiforms. It has also been suggested that Eskimos should be considered a race in their own right. American Indians have been placed in a separate category in a number of classifications, but the evidence is not clear-cut and they are best considered as Mongoliforms. At least eight divisions have been recognized, one of which includes the 'redskins of the plains', the Sioux, Crow, and Blackfeet.

3. *Negriforms.* This group was confined to that part of Africa south of the Sahara and to parts of Asia; the slave trade has, however, resulted in their establishment in the New World. They are characterized by a dark, 'black' skin, hair in tight coils or spirals, a broad nose, a prognathous face, and thick turned-out lips. The African

Negriforms contain the Negroes, who are sub-divided into five sub-races. In the north are the tall Sudanians from grasslands south of the Sahara, the even taller Nilotes from the Sudan; the Guineans and Congolians from Central and South-West Africa, the former including the Yoruba from Nigeria; and the Zingians from south of the equator who comprise the greater part of the Bantu-speakers. A curious group, accorded separate racial status, are the Negrillos or pygmies of the equatorial forests. They are the smallest human beings known, except for pituitary dwarfs (p. 248); the men are seldom over 4 feet 8 inches tall and the women are usually some 3 inches shorter. The term pygmy is derived from a Greek word meaning a cubit. Pygmies are usually sub-divided into three sub-races, according to their western, central, and eastern habitats in the belt between 5° N. and 5° S. The three sub-races are anatomically similar; most noteworthy is their abundant rust-coloured hair on scalp, axillae and pubes; hair on their backs is like yellow down. The Negritos and the Oceanic pygmies are both small peoples like African pygmies, but their hair is black. The former are found in Malaya, the Andaman Islands, and the Philippines; the latter live now in Dutch New Guinea, although they were once more widely distributed. The Negriforms are completed by the Papuans of New Guinea, the Melanesians from New Guinea and Fiji, and the extinct Tasmanians who are believed to have been descendants of Asiatic Negritos. The last full-blood aboriginal Tasmanian died in 1876.

4. *Khoisaniforms.* This group is represented by the Bushmen and the Hottentots; they have commonly been included in the Negriforms, but modern authorities maintain that they display traits sufficiently differentiated and stable to allow them group distinction. The word Khoisaniform is derived from the two words by which Hottentots describe themselves and the Bushmen. Their skin is wrinkled and yellow-brown. Their hair is spiralled and of the peppercorn type in tufts. The head is tall, with a bulging forehead, the cheek bones of the small face are prominent, but there is no marked prognathism. Their external genitalia display characteristic features and in females there is an excessive protrusion of the buttocks due to large deposits of fat (steatopygia). These features and their short stature, delicate build, relative shortness of limbs, and overall child-

like or infantile appearance have often been referred to as examples of persistence into adulthood of foetal characteristics (p. 33).

5. *Australiforms*. The word is derived from *austral*, meaning southern, and the group includes people found in India, Ceylon, and Australia. The skin is yellowish to dark brown, the hair black and wavy. The head is high in relation to its length and there are prominent ridges at the eyebrows (supraorbital ridges). Veddians of India and Ceylon and Australian aborigines comprise the two main subdivisions. The latter are of particular interest as they are often called the most 'primitive' people alive today. They have, however, a highly specialized culture which unfortunately has not been adaptable to the impact of European civilization; their numbers are now reckoned at only 50,000. Current Australian usage refers to them as 'blacks' or 'blackfellows', but their dark chocolate skin differentiates them from the Negriforms, as do their less everted lips, hairy bodies, and hair form. A low, retreating forehead and an almost keel-like top to the skull add to their primitive physical appearance. It is not known for how many thousands of years they may have inhabited Australia.

Disadvantages of Classifying by Physical Features

However carefully they are measured those physical features mentioned in the brief classification given above suffer from certain disadvantages as accurate discriminatory criteria. Physical characters, with a few exceptions, are not inherited in a simple manner and in many instances their manifestations are controlled by several independent genes. A single physical feature may also be the resultant of effects of several factors, each of which may again be controlled by more than one gene. Skin colour results from the presence of at least five pigments (p. 72). Stature is obtained because of the length of the lower limb bones, depth of part of the pelvis, thickness of vertebrae, height of skull *and* because of the thickness of articular cartilages, intra-articular discs, and other soft tissues. It varies according to the position of the body in which it is measured, and everyone is slightly taller in the morning. Physical features also vary with age, sex, nutrition, and climate. Classification of mankind thus becomes something of a struggle despite the most careful mathematical treatment of measurements, institution of statistical devices such as the *co-efficient of racial likeness*, and analysis of intercorrelations of groups of characters. Recent research has also shown that certain modifications and deficiencies in maternal diet during early pregnancy can exert remarkable effects on the form of the foetus (p. 143) in experimental animals.

Non-Physical Traits

It could therefore be of immense value if there were characters that were genetically determined at fertilization, fixed for life, sharply differentiated, and which would not be subject to controversy over accuracy because of personal error in observation and measurement. Fortunately there are a number of such characters that have anthropological value (more will certainly be discovered). As yet methods of detecting these characters have not been applied to sufficient numbers of men for their fullest value or final interpretation to have been obtained. They are not anatomical or physical in the gross sense but are detectable by biochemical or serological methods. A brief review only is given here of such methods; the books quoted at the end of the chapter will give access to the literature.

About 8 per cent of males in Europe are *colour blind*, whereas the percentage is lower in Mongoliforms. It is also lower in females because colour-blindness is a sex-linked recessive condition. The gene is carried on the X-chromosome (p. 108) and when present on the one X-chromosome of the male it causes colour-blindness. A gene has to be present on each of the two X-chromosomes to cause the condition in females. Certain rarer types of colour-blindness are not sex linked.

The majority of North American Indians can *taste* the intensely bitter substance *phenylthiocarbamide* (P.T.C.) because they and other tasters possess the single dominant gene T. There are fewer tasters than non-tasters among most Europiforms, but more in Lapps and Egyptians. It is not yet certain that tasting the substance, and other chemically related compounds, is genetically determined, nor is there an explanation of why more females can taste it. The inability to *smell hydrocyanic acid* is probably a sex linked recessive characteristic;

the somewhat dangerous tests have not been used widely enough to be of great value.

Two recognizable abnormalities of blood are in each case due to the presence of single genes that can cause manifestations in both homozygotes and heterozygotes. One is called *Thalassaemia* (from a Greek word meaning great sea), or Mediterranean anaemia, in which the pigment of red cells, haemoglobin, is of the foetal type. The condition is regionally so prevalent in Italy that there has been much discussion as to how its frequency is maintained. The condition is generally fatal during childhood in homozygotes; so it is probable that medical attention has resulted in survival of increased numbers of heterozygotes. The second abnormality is called '*sickling*' or the *sickle-cell* trait and expresses itself in distortion in shape of red corpuscles and in abnormal properties of haemoglobin. The trait is particularly common among Negroes, some African groups showing a frequency of up to 40 per cent: the relation of anaemia and lethality with the trait are much disputed. The method of maintenance of the high frequency is again difficult to understand. Recent work has suggested strongly that heterozygotes possess a compensatory resistence to malaria, and thus distribution of the gene takes on additional interest. Other genetically determined blood abnormalities are known, such as acholuric jaundice, and although rare they may be of anthropological value.

BLOOD GROUPS

Whether or not blood could be removed from one individual and transfused into the circulation of another might well have been a question asked by physicians of antiquity. Apart from some early records of blood drinking as an attempted therapeutic measure it was not until 1664 (J. Denys in France) and 1666 (Richard Lower in England) that the experiment was actually tried. Lamb's blood was the first to be introduced into a man's circulation, though Pepys records a payment of one pound to an early human blood donor. Transfusion of animal blood into a man's circulation must have had serious results because animal and human blood are not compatible. Blood quickly clots after withdrawal and so until this and other difficulties had been overcome blood transfusion was thought impracticable.

The discovery during the early years of the twentieth century that individuals could be grouped into four main classes because of characteristics of their blood was of vital importance in making transfusion safe. Transfusion must be carried out with blood from individuals in the same group as the recipient or with blood from the single group known as 'universal donor'. If carried out with blood from any other groups incompatibility results in serious and even fatal consequences. The difficulty of blood clotting was overcome by employing anti-coagulants such as sodium citrate. Soon other blood groups, some very rare, were discovered. It was not long before it was realized that blood groups could provide another means of classifying mankind. It might even be possible to detect racial affinities and evidence of group migrations if sufficient persons were examined. Animals also were shown to possess blood groups; man's place in nature could be examined from yet another point of view. More recently anthropologists have wondered if any evidence of blood groups were locked away within remains of ancient man.

The blood groups of the *ABO* system were discovered in 1900–2 by K. Landsteiner. He found that human blood could be divided into four classes according to the way that their red cells agglutinated with normal human sera. The reaction depends on the presence of one, or both, or neither of what are probably complex polysaccharide substances called *A* and *B* on the cell surfaces. The substances are present in about 80 per cent of persons in saliva, gastric juice, and other secretions. Such persons are called 'secretors' and *A* and *B* substances can be prepared from such fluids in a fairly pure state.

The behaviour of red cells depends on a set of three allelic genes *A*, *B*, and O. Their presence and arrangement on the chromosomes ordains that there may be genotypes *AA* or *AO* (Group *A*), *BB* or *BO* (Group *B*), *OO* (Group O, universal donor), and *AB* (Group *AB*). The percentage frequency of the groups in the United Kingdom is O: 47 per cent, *A*: 42 per cent, *B*: 9 per cent, and *AB*: 3 per cent. The situation is much more complicated by the facts that Group *A* can be sub-divided into A_1 and A_2, that there are also rare groups A_3 and A_4, and that there exist certain sera (anti-*H* and anti-O) that react strongly with Group O cells. Three individuals at least have been found in Bombay whose cells and sera behave in a way such that they may possess yet another allelic gene of the *ABO* system.

Determination of *ABO* blood groups has now been carried out in a large number of countries and many millions of individuals have been tested. Distribution of the groups and the more important gene frequencies throughout the world are thus moderately well known. Highest group *A* frequencies are found in tribes of North American Indians; high frequencies also occur in the Australian aborigines, western Asia, the central mountain chains of Europe, and in Scandinavia. Maximal frequencies of *B* occur in central Asia and northern India, also in Egypt and central Africa. It is generally low in Europe, very low in the Basques, and absent in most of the American Indians and Australian aborigines. The Indians of South and Central America are almost entirely group *O*. Populations with a high group *O* frequency tend to have peripheral distribution in Europe and Africa, in places where isolation is caused by geographical conditions. Those interested in distribution of blood groups should consult one of the books quoted at the end of this chapter.

The *Rhesus* or *Rh* factor was detected by K. Landsteiner and A. S. Wiener in 1940 by means of serum that had been immunized with red cells from the Rhesus monkey, *Macaca mulatta*. It is a complicated system, probably consisting of four adjacent loci on each of a pair of chromosomes, and cannot be considered here. The mere fact that genes called D, d, D^u, C, c, C^w, C^u, C^v; and E, e, E^u and F, f are detectable will give an idea of the complexity of the group. It will not be surprising to learn that there is considerable polymorphism in many populations. Of more than medical interest is the fact that *Rh* groups are involved in the production of haemolytic disease of the newborn (p. 154). In marriages where the mother is *Rh*-negative (*dd*), the father *Rh*-positive (*DD* or *Dd*), the foetus will be always *Dd* in the first instance and half of the foetuses will be *Dd* in the second. No ill effect will result in the majority of such pregnancies, but in some the mother's serum becomes immunized to the *D* antigen of the foetus. The anti-*D* antibody in the maternal circulation crosses the placenta (p. 154) into the foetal circulation and causes damage to foetal red cells. Damage may be such that it results only in slight anaemia, but in a number of such babies death from severe red cell destruction occurs unless appropriate treatment is given by blood transfusion. A most interesting discovery with considerable anthropological meaning is that the Basques have the highest *Rh*-negative (*d*) frequency of all known populations (Mourant). It can be suggested from this and other blood group determinations that the pattern of *Rh* frequencies in Europe is the result of mixing of two strains, one *Rh*-positive, the other *Rh*-negative, and that this occurred a mere few thousand years ago. Mongoliforms appear to be *Rh*-positive and it is evidence such as this that allies Australian aborigines to Mongoliforms rather than Negriforms (p. 56).

Yet another system of blood groups, *MN*, was discovered by Landsteiner and Levine in 1927; their sub-groups *Ss* were found twenty years later. They have been much used for anthropological and classificatory purposes: fortunately they do not complicate transfusion because there are no natural anti-agglutinins in human sera. High *M* frequencies are found in American Indians and Eskimos; high *N* values are found in New Guinea and in Lapps. *S* is almost completely absent from Australian aborigines.

In the course of work that defined the *MN* system Landsteiner and Levine also discovered the *P* blood group, but variations in the reactions mean that many results may not be reliable. Many other blood factors have been described, several being very rare; examples are those known as the Lewis (Le^a, Le^b), Kell (*K*, *k*), Lutheran (Lu^a), Duffy (Fy^a, Fy^b), and Jay (Tj^a) systems. Several of these systems are so difficult to test and sera so insufficient in quantity that only some will be of certain anthropological value.

The immense value of blood group determination could be illustrated in many ways, but the information is now so vast that only books of reference can cover it all. As an indication of what can be done the percentage frequencies of various blood groups for samples from the population of Scotland are given in Table IV together with frequencies of blood group genes. The latter are necessary information because heterozygotes mask the frequency of certain genes.

Comparison of these figures with those from neighbouring populations shows that the proportion of group *A* diminishes while that of group *O* increases as one passes from south England to north Scotland. The hypothesis that the population of north Scotland has a large proportion of Scandinavian ancestors is not obviously supported by blood group analysis: modern Scandinavians have an even higher group *A* frequency than southern English. But it has been

TABLE IV

FREQUENCY OF BLOOD GROUPS AND BLOOD GROUP GENES IN SAMPLES OF POPULATION OF SCOTLAND

Groups per cent — *Genes per cent*

ABO Groups

O	*A*	*B*	*AB*	*O*	*A*	*B*
59·32	30·68	7·95	2·05	76·90	17·97	5·13

MNS Groups

MMS	*MsMs*	*MNS*	*MsNs*	*NNS*	*NsNs*	*MS*	*Ms*	*NS*	*Ns*
19·92	7·02	26·38	27·51	4·17	14·99	24·65	29·24	4·98	41·13

P Groups

P^+	P^-	*P*	*p*
75·52	24·48	50·52	49·48

Rh Groups

Rh^+	Rh^-	*D*	*d*
82·81	17·19	58·54	41·46

Lutheran Groups

Lu(a+)	*Lu(a−)*	Lu^a	Lu^b
5·50	94·50	2·79	97·21

Kell Groups

KK	*Kk*	*kk*	*K*	*k*
0·00	8.92	91·08	4·56	95·44

Lewis Groups

Le(a+b−)	*Le(a−b+)*	*Le(a−b−)*	*Le(a+b+)*
28·46	67·74	3·80	0·00

Duffy Groups

Fy(a+)	*Fy(−)*	Fy^a	Fy^b
66·79	33·21	42·37	57·63

This information is from the work of Kirkpatrick (1952), Ikin *et al.* (1952), Allan (1949); see also Mourant, A. E. (1954) at the end of the chapter.

suggested on the basis of *A*, *O* frequencies that both Iceland and north Scotland were originally colonized by an ancient Scandinavian stock. The populations of northern Scotland and Iceland have probably remained relatively isolated and retained unmixed blood groups, whereas Scandinavia has received emigrants from central Europe. The blood group frequencies of the Scandinavian population therefore exhibit results of mixture with new blood groups.

Blood Groups of Animals

Substances very like human *A* and *B* substances are present throughout the animal kingdom and blood groups have been found in certain birds and many species of mammals. So far, however, only in a few mammals has a system been discovered as complex as that in man.

Blood groups in Primates have been much studied; those of chimpanzees most closely resemble those of man. All chimpanzees are either group *A* or *O* (11 per cent), possess *M* and *N* and appear to be *Rh*-negative, but there are varying differences between some of their antigens and those of man. Gorillas are either group *A* or *B* and orangs and gibbons are *A*, *B*, or *AB*. Old World monkeys lack *A* and *B* antigens on their red cells, New World monkeys have a *B*-like antigen: saliva of monkeys may, however, contain antigens that cannot be detected on their red cells. It would seem undeniable that *ABO* groups are common to animal life and thus inherited by man in his place in the pattern. Part at least of the *MN* and *Rh* systems appear to have been inherited from ancestral primate stock.

Blood Groups of Skeletal Remains

Determination of *ABO* groups of bones long dead, blood group archaeology, is not easy and requires special techniques; thus few reliable observations are available. Apparent blood groups have been determined in Egyptian and American mummies: in general most prehistoric and early Egyptians were of groups *A* and *B*, most American Indians group O. The obvious need to extend such techniques and apply them to other skeletal material should not require any emphasis.

BODY HABITUS AND SOMATOTYPING

We must finally consider yet another way of sorting out kinds of men, that is by considering their *constitution.* This can be defined as the sum total of structural, functional, and psychological traits of individuals. It is an approach to man that has fascinated thinkers in numerous fields. Essentially it suggests that there is some relationship between the shape of a man and his parts (body habitus) and his character and temperament. Hippocrates wrote on the matter and his ideas were passed on by Galen to be accepted by subsequent generations until the seventeenth century. Hippocrates maintained that there were in the body four 'humours' or liquids–blood, black bile, yellow bile, and phlegm. An excess of any one of these affected the temperament, an individual's anatomy already having certain characteristics to bring about that particular excess. The majority of men were therefore classifiable as sanguine, melancholic, choleric, or phlegmatic, though blends of the various humours were allowed. Shakespeare was, perhaps, a little extreme in his views:

> *Let me have men about me that are fat:*
> *Sleek-headed men and such as sleep o'nights;*
> *Yond' Cassius has a lean and hungry look;*
> *He thinks too much: such men are dangerous.*

John Hunter also considered what might be meant by constitution, and its importance to medicine was clearly recognized by Jonathan Hutchinson (1828–1913), a surgeon to The London Hospital. Early attempts at analysing constitution failed because they only considered extremes, dealt with individuals as wholes rather than as composites of numerous parts, and did not realize that many factors cause variations. The nomenclature of a German psychiatrist, Ernst Kretschmer (1921), embraced three main types, all individuals tending in their build towards one of them. A stocky, compact and rotund individual was called *pyknosomatic* or *pyknic*; a tall, lean man was *leptosomatic* or *asthenic*; and a big, broad Carnera-like man was *ath eticosomatic.* It was further suggested that one type was more likely to exhibit particular mental disorders and was more liable to certain diseases than another. Despite its popularity the scheme suffers too many defects to have survived. Its worst failing is the absence of any basis for measurement.

Another attempt was made by W. H. Sheldon (1940) who used three 7-point scales to assess the amount any individual showed of three components, *endomorphy*, *mesomorphy*, and *ectomorphy*. An individual high in endomorphy would scale 7:1:1, would be spherical in caricature, with roundness of head and abdomen, penguin-like limbs – an epitome of the adjective 'runcible' of Edward Lear. Predominance of mesomorphy, 1:7:1 on the scale, implied a muscular athlete with cubical head, muscular neck, and rippling chest. The ectomorphic, 1:1:7, is a rake of a man, with lowest mass and thus relatively greater skin area, thin-faced with high forehead, receding chin and spindly limbs. Naturally these extremes are rare in any group, and the majority of individuals have ratings of 3:4:4, 3:5:2, and so on. The respective rating was called the *somatotype* (soma λ = body). Sheldon also introduced a further component, called *gynandromorphy*, by which he hoped to show the degree, on another 7-point scale, to which a male body resembled a female and vice versa. Characters in the male of large hips in relation to shoulder breadth, much fat over the symphysis pubis and in the mammary region, and overlap of the thighs with the feet placed together, would be those of gynandromorphy.

Even though Sheldon placed somatotypes on an anthropometric basis by compiling tables of 17 standard diameters, the valid criticism remains that the original classification is a subjective one. Little is known about such scales, the scale itself only allows limited jumps in rating and the components are correlated. What is needed therefore is a form of factor analysis that can present comprehensively large numbers of measurements, taken at the same time, of several variables. Again and again we are faced with such a problem in any endeavour to compare biological materials by measurement. The technique of such analysis cannot be discussed here and reference should be made to textbooks quoted at the end of the chapter, particularly to that by M. S. Bartlett. Applications of such methods to anthropometry will be found in the work of C. Burt, J. M. Tanner, B. Škerlj, and others.

Sheldon has also endeavoured to relate by measurement physique with temperament, an even more difficult problem. Any attempt to find a relationship of body and mind is of more than just academic interest and must be considered seriously. Sheldon and his collaborator Stevens suggest that temperament could be assessed as the result of 60 traits correlated in three groups of 20. The first group or component is called *viscerotonia*, and embraces traits of love of comfort, relaxation, sociability, gluttony, conviviality, and need of contact with people when troubled. The *somatotonic* of the second group is vigorous, assertive, noisy, courageous, indifferent to pain, and in need of expressive action when troubled. The third group is composed of the *cerebrotonics*, who look youthful and show restraint, inhibition, love of privacy, secretiveness, sensitivity, fear of pain, and need of solitude when troubled. A scoring system is used, an extreme viscerotonic rates 7:1:1, and the results of observations on individuals over the period of a year are used in comparison with the somatotyping scales. It will be obvious that various criticisms can be levelled at the definitions and what is included in the traits; most authorities would agree that the system represents only an exploratory or experimental stage. Others, perhaps a little too harshly, condemn it as a complete failure. For the doctor, at least, there is much evidence that susceptibility to certain diseases is correlated with a particular constitution, and it is significant that it has been psychologists, rather than anatomists, who have made efforts to define constitution.

FOR FURTHER READING

The Distribution of the Human Blood Groups. A. E. Mourant. Blackwell, Oxford, 1954

Genetics and the Races of Man. W. C. Boyd. Little, Brown & Co., Boston: Blackwell, Oxford, 1954

Principles of Human Genetics. C. Stern. W. H. Freeman & Co., San Francisco, 1950

Mankind so far. W. Howells. Sigma Books, London, 1947

Blood Groups in Man. R. R. Race and R. Sanger. Blackwell, Oxford, 1950

The Varieties of Human Physique. W. H. Sheldon. Harper, New York, 1940

The Varieties of Human Temperament. W. H. Sheldon. Harper, New York, 1942

Human Constitution in Clinical Medicine. G. Draper, C. W. Dupertuis, and J. L. Caughey. Hoeber, New York, 1944

An Introduction to Physical Anthropology. M. F. Ashley Montagu. C. C. Thomas, Springfield, 1951

An Introduction to Stochastic Processes. M. S. Bartlett. Cambridge, 1955

CHAPTER 4

HIS PECULIAR FEATURES

> Man hath all that Nature hath, but more,
> And in that more lie all his hopes of good.
>
> ARNOLD

A CERTAIN eminent embryologist, now deceased, used to amuse himself by considering what might be the anatomical and other changes that could characterize the next species of man, *Homo sapientior*, as he called the squat, broad-hipped, large-headed, imaginary successor to ourselves. It was, perhaps, a somewhat academic exercise, but it served to draw attention in an intriguing way to certain peculiarities in man's structure. We shall therefore consider in this chapter some of the gross and obvious features of man's anatomical arrangement, perhaps as they might strike a visiting anatomist from another planet who had never before seen a man.

We shall allow the visitor to have dissected enough animals to have become acquainted with the general structure of vertebrates, to have realized their common patterns of arrangement. He will also, perhaps, have come to similar conclusions as to how man might be classified and how he was related to other animals. He might even have attempted a definition of a man along the following lines:

Man, *Homo sapiens*, is a vertebrate animal of the Class Mammalia and belongs to the Order Primates. He is placed in a Sub-order (Anthropoidea) of monkeys, apes, and himself and because of his similarity in so many respects to apes he is classed with them as Hominoidea. Superficially he appears to be a relatively primitive and apparently hairless ape with a large brain: certain foetal characteristics seem to have persisted in his adult anatomy.

He is bipedal, walking upright or *orthograde*, with the sole of the foot placed downward on the ground in a *plantigrade* fashion. This method of locomotion is associated with numerous adaptations in the skeleton, from the foot to the skull. The freeing of the upper limb from assisting in locomotion enables it to be used for prehension, particularly as the arm is strutted to the body by a collar-bone or clavicle. The forearm is long and can be rotated with the arm by the side so that the palm faces forwards or backwards. The thumb is well developed and can be placed against the other fingers to grasp. The pelvis is expanded and helps to support the viscera, its cavity is capacious and associated with the birth of a large-headed foetus. The legs are long and greatly strengthened, the hip in the upright position is extended, as is the knee joint; certain muscles concerned with walking are enlarged. The great toe is large and the bones of the feet are arranged in an arch. The skull possesses a large cranial cavity, the face is orientated forwards in the upright position, and the head is poised above the vertebral column. The jaws are not massive and the teeth are small, but there is a prominent chin.

He is a social, gregarious, and political animal: the majority display a complex way of life, or culture, and have an aesthetic sense. Man shows varying degrees of freedom from conduct enforced by primitively predetermined responses in behaviour. He is educable and can develop a complex intelligence. He can communicate in various ways, mainly based on articulate speech, and he shows a marked capacity for symbolizing his speech and thoughts.

Man is increasing in number rapidly; yet the number of young is one, twins occur once in every eighty-five births. The gestation period varies between 250–285 days. Puberty is reached in both sexes at 10–15 years, when in the female, a twenty-eight day reproductive cycle commences that is repeated for some 40 years. The cycle has external manifestations in the phenomenon of a 3–5 day period of menstruation. Reproductive activity ceases in the female at a menopause about the age of 50. There is no definite sexual cycle, nor determinable point of cessation of sexual activity in the male. Man is probably the longest lived of all mammals.

Man's Nakedness

We can be sure that one of the first things about the outward appearances of a human body that would impress our visitor, particularly after he had dissected his way through most of the residents of a zoo, would be man's apparent hairlessness. The *apparent* absence of hair in man has been a subject of much comment by comparative anatomists, but it must be realized that man is really quite hairy. Hair is entirely absent from palms and soles and from certain other areas, such as the rosy part of the lips, but the numbers of hairs per unit area, both on the head and elsewhere, are greater than in apes and nearly as great as in a Rhesus monkey. Over most of man's body hair is rudimentary in nature, although hair follicles are present almost everywhere. Strong hair appears at puberty in the armpit or axilla, on the face in males, and with a varying distribution over the pubic region in both sexes. There is considerable variation in the degree of hairiness in man at any given age, also in its texture, colour, and degree of curling. There is much difference in hair character (p. 54) in the main races of man.

It is also a characteristic of adult man that he possesses no tactile whiskers or vibrissae. Even so it has often been maintained that hairs of eyebrows and moustache are homologous with the tactile vibrissae of non-primate animals. Microscopic examination of the nerve supply of eyebrow and moustache hairs of man, and also of their developmental stages, shows nothing that suggests that they differ from hair elsewhere. There are embryonic hairs, possibly of vibrissal type, to be found transitorily on the back of the wrist and perhaps elsewhere in the human foetus, but they apparently retrogress before birth. There are many other interesting matters to discuss relating to hair; we may observe here that man's apparent, but not actual, hairlessness exposes the surface of his skin for inspection.

Man's skin envelops his whole body and is continuous at the openings on its surface with the linings of the passages of alimentary, respiratory, and urogenital systems. It is modified somewhat in several regions, such as on the external surface of the eye, conjunctiva, and on the outer surface of the eardrum, tympanic membrane. It varies in thickness and in its composition; it possesses numerous derivatives in the form of nails, hair, and several kinds of glands. It must be considered as a diffuse, important, and highly active organ that is capable of continually replacing its superficial layers. If you skin a man you will have removed about 16 per cent of his total body weight and you will have some 2,800 square inches of skin. When you look at a man, or at yourself in a mirror, you are looking at a dead rind or mask, because the superficial cells of skin are dead. Every time anyone washes his hands some of this dead superficial layer is rubbed off and is lost. If a man gets sunburnt even more of the dead surface cells flake off and occasionally leave a raw, painful area exposed. The remarkable features of human skin deserve a chapter to themselves; here we shall only consider some of its appearance.

The colour of human skin varies considerably and even dramatically owing to variations in pigmentation, genetic or racial in origin, to excessive exposure to light or heat, and to certain pathological conditions such as anaemia and jaundice. Man can be divided into at least three main groups because of his skin colour (but see p. 57); white-skinned or *Leukoderms*, yellow-skinned or *Xanthoderms*, and black-skinned or *Melanoderms*. Normal variation in skin colour in 'white' races is due partly to inherited pigment content of skin and partly to the degree of activity of pigment-containing cells exposed to light. It also varies in colour with thickness of the horny superficial layers of the skin and because of the amount and proportions of reduced haemoglobin and oxyhaemoglobin prevailing in blood circulating in thin-walled vessels immediately beneath the skin. Thus we can account for the olive, tanned skin of Mediterraneans and the apparently whitish palms of the Negro.

Human skin varies in texture, a feature better observed in living persons because it is to a great extent controlled by activity of glands associated with skin. The thickness and nature of the superficial horny layer, the structure of the subjacent tissue, whether of bone or of muscle, and the profuseness of blood supply all modify skin texture. The quantity of sweat and sebaceous glands and their degree of activity in different regions influence it equally profoundly. At least two of these factors are under a controlling influence from their nerve supply, and thus skin texture can reflect its owner's temperament and temperature. At different times the same area of skin can be bluish-white, cold and almost inert, or else it can be warm, red, and dry, or even cold and clammy.

Skin Creases and Finger-prints

Skin may be smooth (ignoring degrees of hairiness) or it may be roughened or marked by flexure lines, creases, folds, ridges, and furrows. The fixed creases or joint flexure lines are congenital and are lines where skin is more tightly bound down by anchoring fibres; they are well shown on the palmar surfaces of fingers and palms. There is no scientific evidence that their configuration can foretell the future, but there is much about an individual's past that can be learnt from a careful examination of his hands. One is reminded of the surprised agreement of a patient on being told by a certain observant physician who had just examined the former's hands that he rowed. 'Furthermore, you row at four.' Guesswork? – perhaps; but read of a similar skill possessed by Dr Joseph Bell on whom Conan Doyle based his immortal Sherlock Holmes. It needs only slight skill to detect a seamstress, a typist, a writer, a gardener, a road-driller, or a golfer (particularly 'rabbits') by examining their hands, but read the fascinating book *Occupational Marks and other Physical Signs* by F. Ronchese and J. G. Downing.

Other creases and cleavage lines, not always so marked or so deep as joint flexure lines, are present from birth. They may be seen where skin is particularly mobile and liable to be creased by movements; look for example at skin on the back of the wrist or about the neck. Many of these creases become more deeply etched and new ones appear as a result of certain occupations or as an individual grows older. Some creases become so deeply indented that they gain attachment and become anchored to underlying tissue; even when the skin is relaxed such creases are still visible. These changes can occur at the outer angles of the eyelids to form tell-tale crow's feet.

Another, finer type of furrowing is that found on the skin of the hands and feet and is clearly seen on the finger tips. Patterns are made by numerous minute ridges and grooves that run in parallel rows, or in concentric whorls or loops. The pattern is fixed from birth and cannot be altered. It is entirely individual to each person; even like twins have patterns that can be told apart. So marked is the individuality of the patterns, or *dermatoglyphics*, that they are used throughout the world for identification purposes; impressions of the dermatoglyphics produce finger prints. When the water has evaporated from a fingerprint enough organic and inorganic components are left for it to be visualized by one of several chemical methods.

Fingerprint patterns are not limited to man. If an ape or a monkey were to indulge in safe-breaking its dermatoglyphics would leave characteristic prints. Comparison with dermatoglyphics of other Primates brings to light a certain primitiveness in the human pattern. There is some evidence of divergent specialization in the dermatoglyphics of great apes and man, but because of a similarity in basic plan to that of Old World monkeys, Midlo and Cummins incline to the view that 'man stemmed from an ancestral stock more primitive than any recent ape, having dermatoglyphic traits more closely allied to those of the monkeys.'

There are two specialized modifications of skin which are found in certain Primates, but not in man. Anyone visiting a zoo must have noticed the naked sitting pads or *ischial callosities* in the region of the lower buttocks of Old World monkeys. They are probably developed, as are other callosities, by firm contact with hard surfaces, and it has been suggested that they have a sensory function comparable to that of sole and palm. Highly developed callosities are found in all Catarrhine monkeys and in gibbons, but are less marked in chimpanzees and only occasionally occur in other apes. They are not found in Prosimii, Platyrrhine monkeys, or in man. It has been suggested that they are specialized adaptations and were acquired after the Primates owning them had begun their separate evolutionary trend. This statement at least gets us out of the muddle we should be in if we were to consider ischial callosities as important as certain other features when considering man's relationship to other primates.

Ischial tuberosities and an area of skin fiomt he root of the tail to a line joining the junction of the abdomen with the front of the thighs, an area known as the perineum, become secondarily modified in Old World monkeys as *sexual skin*. It is variously pigmented and passes through periods of rest, turgescence, and deturgescence, and also exhibits alterations in intensity of colour during each female sexual cycle. These observable changes in perineal skin, and even of that in other parts of the body in certain monkeys, must be considered those of secondary sexual adornment. The appearances are not identical in various genera of Old World monkeys but are marked in apes: there is no trace of sexual skin of any kind in human females. Unless something very strange occurred when man evolved we must support Sir Solly Zuckerman's view that man was derived from animals lacking this structure.

Man's Shape

Man's external form displays relatively smooth curves and contours because of the moulding effect of subcutaneous fat, an effect most noticeable in babies and women. This blanket of fat not only helps to preserve body temperature, but insulates man to some extent from changes in external temperature and protects him from minor injuries. Subcutaneous fat is absent from eyelids and scrotal skin. The layer is particularly thick in mammals such as seals and whales that spend much or all of their lives in the sea; in them it is called 'blubber'. Its increase in thickness in these animals indicates clearly its protective function; it provides a useful source of reserve foodstuffs that can be called on when weather is inclement or when the female is lactating.

Man's head, the flower at the top of the human plant as it impressed the German poet and anatomist Goethe, is that part of man where least tissue intervenes between bone and skin. Look at a shaven or bald head and you look at a scantily covered skull. Yet attempt to reconstruct physiognomy from a skull and the results will be hopelessly inaccurate. Professor Wood Jones wrote: 'It was my lot for seven years to share my room with the skeleton of Professor Collimore. As I worked at my desk his skull looked directly towards me, and at the end of seven years I fancied that I knew very well what manner of face he had, and how his features were formed. It was only then that I managed to obtain a photograph of the living man, and it was at once apparent that the face was utterly different from the one I had reconstructed.' Recently a work has been published that claims remarkable and even recognizable likenesses as the result of rebuilding artificial soft tissue onto a given skull following average estimates of regional soft tissue thicknesses determined from a large number of measurements on cadavers (M. M. Gerasimov, 1955).

Attempts have also been made to confirm identity by superimposing an accurately enlarged photograph of the head on one of the skull at similar magnification. The method has been used to attempt to confirm identity of skulls of famous persons long dead, and also in forensic matters (Ruxton case). Yet there are numerous snags for the unwary and the method is perhaps only really of value in demonstrating that a certain skull could *not* belong to a particular individual.

The human head is composed of two main parts; the larger part contains the brain. It is supported on the vertebral column by the strong skull base and is surrounded on sides and top by the thinner bony vault or *calvaria* covered by the scalp. The smaller part, the face, is given its prominent features by the underlying skeleton of jaws and facial bones, nasal cartilages and facial muscles. The brain-case, even long before birth, is the larger, rounder, and more imposing component.

She saw her brother Peterkin
Roll something large and round,
Which he beside the rivulet
In playing there had found:
She came to ask what he had found
That was so large and smooth and round.

SOUTHEY

The human skull is 'so large' in that the cranial capacity of the more highly civilized races of man (megacephalic) is about 1,500

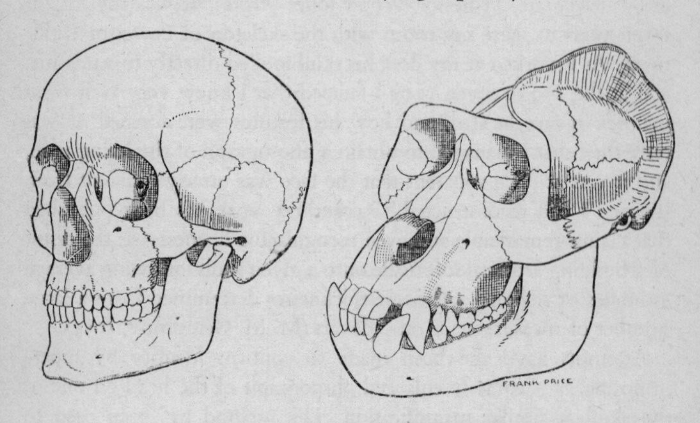

FIG. 1. Human skull (left) and the skull of an adult gorilla.

cubic centimetres. The largest cranial capacity in a great ape is 650 cubic centimetres and is that of an adult male gorilla. Human micro-cephalic idiots have lived with brains only a little larger than those of apes, but they are abnormal and examples of developmental arrest. Female Australian aborigines may have cranial capacities as low as 900 cubic centimetres; those of pygmies vary between 1,100 and 1,350 cubic centimetres. Sir Arthur Keith suggested that there was a dividing line in cranial capacities at about 750 cubic centimetres. Anything below this indicated apehood, anything above might well indicate manhood.

Man's skull is 'smooth and round' in that it lacks the great overhanging forehead ridges and the large sagittal bony crests on the crown and also on the occiput which characterize skulls of great apes. This buttressing of the simian skull is associated with the powerful jaw musculature and that needed to hold the heavy skull upright. A rounded skull also implies that its contents are encased with greatest economy in surrounding material.

Man's Face

At birth the human jaws and face are very small in comparison with the size of the braincase. They grow much larger as adulthood is reached, but man does not possess a heavy, projecting face like apes. There has been a recession of his jaws and a flattening of his face so that modern man is referred to as *orthognathous* rather than *prognathous* (p. 53). Great apes, fossil men to a lesser extent, and primitive living men still less, all show varying degrees of jaw prominence. Jaw recession has occurred, however, without much reduction in number of teeth. In common with Old World monkeys and apes man has ten deciduous teeth and sixteen permanent teeth in each jaw, but his teeth are all relatively small and delicately moulded. There is evidence of overcrowding of teeth in man's jaws. Teeth may overlap or erupt abnormally; some may not erupt at all. His jaws do not seem large enough to accommodate all his teeth; many people argue that man is 'losing' some of his teeth. His 'vanishing' teeth will be considered in Chapter 15.

Man's high forehead, his noble brow, indicate to anatomists a marked development of the frontal lobes of his brain; the transversely creased skin of his forehead delineates his ability to express emotion. This enlargement of the forehead, it will be recalled, is considered one of the foetal characteristics that are carried forward into adult life. It is made even more marked in the adult because from the age of ten certain *air sinuses* develop in the underlying frontal bone. There are a number of these air-containing spaces in the skull bones and they contribute considerably towards the shape of man's face. They start to grow out just before birth as hollow evaginations of mucous membrane from the nasal cavities. They soon invade, or are enclosed by, the developing bones of the young skull. Maxilla, sphenoid, ethmoid, palatine, and frontal bones of each side are invaded and the spaces formed become the para-nasal air sinuses. They are all poorly developed at birth; most grow slowly until about the age of four and then more rapidly during the period of eruption of the permanent teeth. Growth slows again after full eruption and

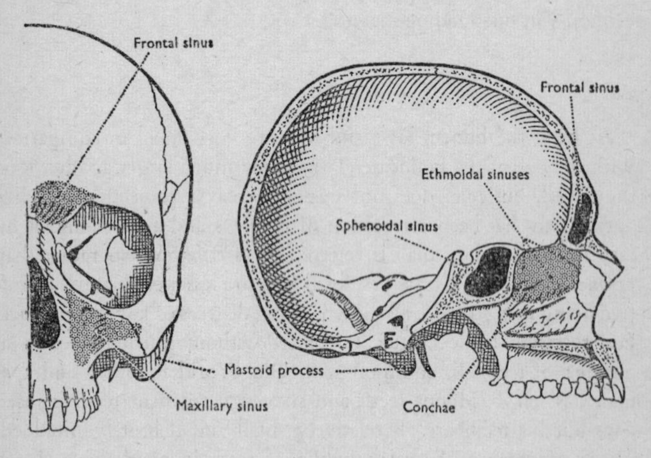

FIG. 2. Positions of the para-nasal air sinuses, the conchae, and the foramen magnum (F) in a human skull.

ceases at about 21–25 years of age; they may enlarge again in old age because of absorption of bone surrounding them. Sinuses play an important part in hollowing out, in modelling, and in lightening the weight of facial bones. They act as resonating chambers and being relatively larger in men than women they are responsible for some of the differences between the voices of the two sexes. They communicate by small apertures with the nasal cavities and thus disease of the nose can spread to them. Inflammation can be the cause of headache in the forehead region, aches between or behind the eyes or in the cheek, depending on which sinuses are involved.

Other mammals are by no means devoid of sinuses; in some they are large and well developed, and in mammals that walk on four legs the sinuses drain more freely into the nose. It is one of man's disadvantages from having an upright posture that some sinuses, such as the maxillary, do not drain into the nose from their most dependent part; mucus and pus can therefore accumulate in them.

The *nose* of mammals is associated with breathing and with olfactory reception. The external opening is usually paired, even in sharks which have no internal opening into the mouth. The evolution of a palate has resulted in long nasal cavities, or air passages, opening into the back of the mouth (choanae). Coiled scrolls of bone, covered with epithelium, subdivide the air passages in mammals, filtering, warming, and moistening incoming air. Olfactory reception occurs at the top and back of the airway and in mammals with a keen sense of smell the bony scrolls, *turbinals*, reach their highest complexity. Man possesses only three scrolls on the lateral wall of each nasal cavity. His external nose shows some racial differences, but in general it is taller than it is broad. A skeleton of cartilage beyond that of bone at the bridge ensures some mobility; the skin is tightly adherent to the cartilages and inflammation of one of the many skin glands can be unduly painful. The downward directed opening is guarded by stiff hairs from inside the nose and by those of the moustache. The nose may be much modified in mammals, into a proboscis such as the elephant's trunk, a most delicate muscular specialization, or into a single (or double) blowhole on the highest point of the head in whales. Man can move his nostrils only slightly; marine mammals can close them tightly by means of muscles or complicated pocket valves.

The hairless, rosy *lips* of man are freely moveable, so much so that the word 'labile' arises from this attribute. The human lips are used in speech, in eating and sucking, and in the Bushman's gesture language. De Beer has suggested that 'their present function of kissing may have been of considerable importance in the sexual selection which has undoubtedly accompanied the evolution of man.' Differentiation of the muscles of facial expression, the mimetic muscles that also move the lips, gives man an unmistakable sign of intellectual development and in their functional perfection man far surpasses the great apes. Dissection of foetuses and adults of different races suggests that evolution of facial musculature is still continuing and that it has progressed furthest in Europiforms (Duckworth). Lips of Europiforms are thin, similar to those of apes, whereas the Negro has lips that are much thicker and more protruded.

The *tongue* of man is a relatively short organ that cannot be protruded for great distances as can that of ant-eating mammals. There is no true tongue in earliest vertebrates, but certain fish have teeth-bearing bars in the floor of the mouth that bite against palatal teeth. Life on land means that there is no water that can help manipulate food and ease its passage through the mouth. Salivary glands become important to animals that have often to eat dry food and the tongue becomes an essential manipulator of food now moistened by saliva. The tongue also guides food between the teeth and takes part in swallowing movements after chewing. In all mammals the tongue acts as a sensory organ detecting objects in the food dangerous to swallow or that would damage teeth; it can also appreciate temperature of food. It possesses special 'taste buds' that react to the presence in food of sweet, salt, acid, and bitter substances and can report their presence to the nervous system. Many naturally occurring poisons are bitter or acid to taste and it would seem an admirable mutation that enabled land vertebrates to survive by selection and retention of this gustatory attribute. Man also uses his tongue to produce articulate speech; its muscles make it moveable and mouldable and it can help make many different kinds of sound. It plays its part in the language of gesture, such as biting the tongue in uncertainty or anguish, licking the lips in anticipation and protruding it in rudeness. The tongue cleans the teeth and ensures by its movements that conditions in the mouth return rapidly to normal after meals. The shape of the tongue shows some variation with an individual's build; it is long and pointed in tall, thin people.

Man possesses a *chin*, apes lack one, as do most fossil men. The human lower jaw shows some anterior convergence; grip it between thumb and forefinger and their tips come closer together as the chin is approached. The rami of the simian mandible are less convergent because the posterior teeth are arranged in parallel rows. An ape's mandible is, however, reinforced at the inside of the chin region by a shelf of bone, a simian shelf, that is absent in man.

The external *ear* with its pinna is developed by fusion and subsequent moulding of six embryonic hillocks that arise about the outside of the ear passage, or external auditory meatus. It is subject to great variation in shape and size and is composed of a corrugated plate of cartilage to which skin is closely adherent. The plate can be moved slightly by some people with certain rudimentary muscles. These are highly developed in many mammals so that the pinna can be brought into an erect position and rotated. Many Primates have large mobile ears, but those of most apes resemble man's. Monkeys can also move their scalps, men seldom can, though Darwin records a family who could pitch several heavy books from their heads by movement of the scalp alone. It was to Darwin that a sculptor, Thomas Woolner, showed 'one little peculiarity in the external ear', a little blunt point that he had noticed on the inwardly folded margin of the rim of the pinna whilst working on a figure of Puck. Darwin thought such points 'the vestiges of the tips of formerly erect and pointed ears'. The bony external ear passage in man is short; its configuration and that of the neighbouring jaw joint show several features that differ from those in other Primates. The inner ear will be considered in later chapters.

The human *neck* is slender, only twice the circumference of the ankle; a well-balanced head does not require thick, broad muscles to keep it in position. The mid-line prominence in the front, more marked in adult males, is the Adam's apple and is produced by the thyroid cartilage of the larynx (p. 212).

Man's Limbs

As might be expected the striking features in the anatomy of man's legs are associated with his ability to walk on two legs. Man's method of progression will be discussed more fully in Chapter 9; only a few peculiarities will be introduced here. At birth a baby's legs are almost as long as his arms; by the time man is adult his legs are longer than his arms. This greater length of the lower limb may be considered a primitive feature; apes show the reverse, the upper limb is the longer, being so elongated in brachiating gibbons that the hand lies below the knee in the erect attitude. The pelvis, vertebral column, bones of thigh and leg (femur, tibia, and fibula) are all adapted in many ways that increase ease of walking. The human foot is, however, one of man's distinct peculiarities. Without any anatomical training Robinson Crusoe knew it was a human footprint that he saw in the sand. The large big toe, unable to touch the tips of other toes (not opposable), reduction of the other toes, the very small little toe, the enlarged ball of the foot, its arched form and broad heel are characteristically human. Most anatomists would agree that it is only in the long mid-foot segment and in the leg and foot musculature that the human foot displays generalized or primitive features.

Despite freeing of the forelimbs from weight bearing and locomotion there are few specializations in their anatomy. The relative shortness of the limb, a stout, powerful, gripping thumb capable of being opposed against the other fingers, the arm and hand musculature, all show generalized structure. Presence of a collar-bone or clavicle, an outward deviation of the forearm on the arm (palm turned upwards) to provide a 'carrying angle', and the ability to rotate the forearm so that the palm can face upwards or downwards with a bent elbow (supine and prone) are features shared with many mammals besides Primates. It is as if the special adaptations in his lower limbs for upright posture and bipedal gait freed his more primitive, mobile upper limbs and thus allowed their generalized structure to be expressive tools of his most highly developed brain.

... let us review some of the ordinary actions of the hand ... Consider the swiftness of its movements in following a speaker with a pen; their variety in loosening a tangled knot; their nicety and precision in passing a thread through the eye of a needle. How steadily it guides the edge of the scalpel in a critical operation of surgery; with what singular truth it shapes the course of the schoolboy's marble, or adjusts his arrow to its mark! ... Trained to the juggler's sleight, its joints become nimbler and more pliant. Its evolutions, in the practice of several mechanical arts, are swifter than the eye can follow, of unerring regularity, independent of the guidance of vision, and productive of the most surprising results. In the musician, the statuary, the painter, it becomes the minister of more subtle volitions, and a higher instinct; in them accordingly, it acquires still greater freedom and fluency of motion, a yet more exquisite refinement and fidelity of touch. In the orator it assumes a new character, and functions of an entirely different order. For him, it is a powerful organ of expression, an indispensable auxiliary to speech. ...

F. O. WARD. *Outline of Human Osteology*. 1858.

Man's Trunk

The human trunk is divided into two great compartments, the thoracic (Latin for chest) and abdominal (Latin – concealed) cavities, separated by a muscular partition or *diaphragm*. Such a partition is seen in crocodiles, in which it is not muscular but can be stretched by a muscle attached to the sternum. The mammalian diaphragm is a more complex structure, tendinous in the centre and with muscle at its periphery. It is innervated by the phrenic nerve, and the origin of this nerve in the neck suggests that the diaphragm must have an interesting history. Embryologically its origin is not completely clear, although it is mainly derived from tissue called the septum transversum. This originates in the head region of an embryo (p. 134) and then migrates below the heart, taking its nerve supply with it. It is tempting to assume that the muscle of the diaphragm was originally in the neck in early vertebrates and that later it became associated with descent of the lungs into the thorax. The diaphragm is not thick in man, and except in trained singers and athletes it seldom contracts forcibly in everyday adult life. Only a small percentage of adults are even capable of active diaphragmatic breathing. Aquatic mammals have a thick, muscular diaphragm placed very obliquely. There is in most marine mammals a curious continuation upwards of the diaphragm about the great vein (posterior vena cava), returning blood from the abdomen to the heart in the form of a 'sling' or cuff-like sphincter. This can occlude the vein and prevent blood returning to the heart. This curious structure may be related to the marked slowing of the heart rate that occurs when seals dive. By damming back blood from the abdomen the sphincter can prevent overloading of the right side of the heart.

The thorax has a bony skeleton, a thoracic cage, of vertebrae, ribs, and sternum. In most frogs and toads ribs are almost entirely absent, in snakes there are ribs but the sternum has been lost. In birds the sternum is very large and has a keel (except in some flightless birds) for attachment of muscles. Most mammals have 13, 14, or more ribs on each side, man has 12. The thorax of most mammals is flattened from side to side and is deep and elongated in cursorial tetrapods. Apes show some flattening from front to back, in man flattening is even more marked. This results in the centre of gravity being near man's back and thus facilitates balance when standing and walking. Rate and volume of respiration show more variation in man than in any other mammal. The effect of the will and the emotions is also most marked.

Upright posture means that the abdominal wall does not hang below a horizontal backbone as in four-legged mammals, but that it faces in a more forward direction. Man is elongated between thorax and pelvis, a primitive feature that allows lateral flexure of the trunk. This means a relatively long abdominal cavity made even deeper by a capacious pelvis. Both anterior abdominal wall and pelvic floor are muscular and play important parts in respiration, defaecation, and other functions. Both also have a retentive function, and in Chapter 9 it will be seen that they display points of strength but also of weakness in this respect.

It would now be possible to consider human visceral characteristics, the human heart and lungs, the shape of his stomach, his appendix, and all his other abdominal organs. This might make a long and tedious catalogue; there are many textbooks full of the appropriate details. Few are solely human specializations. Although the shape of many of his organs is characteristically human seldom has it great functional significance. We shall therefore consider some of those features that are peculiarly human both in form and function, and to start at the beginning, we first consider his reproductive pattern.

FOR FURTHER READING

The Vertebrate Body. A. S. Romer. W. B. Saunders, 1949

The Life of Mammals. J. Z. Young. Oxford University Press, 1957

Basic Anatomy. G. A. G. Mitchell and E. L. Patterson. E. & S. Livingstone, 1954

Textbook of Human Anatomy. Edited by W. J. Hamilton. Macmillan, 1956

And any other standard textbook of Anatomy.

CHAPTER 5

HIS PATTERN OF REPRODUCTION

SIR CHARLES DARWIN, a grandson of Charles Darwin, wrote in 1954 that we are living in 'an entirely abnormal period of history', and one of the principal abnormalities that he emphasizes is that the world population is becoming doubled during a century. He has dramatically illustrated one result of the continued doubling of world population each successive century by calculating that by about A.D. 3954 there would be so many people that there would be standing room only for them on the earth's surface. Such a result is impossible, but it is undeniable that the rate at which the world population is *now* increasing only allows this absurd, yet disturbing conclusion.

The threat of increasing world population has already caused concern to many economists, agriculturists, scientists, and to Governments, particularly that of India. Lord Simon has stated that the inescapable conclusion is that every effort should be made to reduce the rate of increase of population, and if possible to stabilize world population as a whole at a reasonably early date. Otherwise the steadily increasing world population will rapidly use up the available material and nutritional resources. The gloomy prognostications of Sir Charles Darwin and Lord Simon had been made earlier by the kindly and much abused Rev. T. R. Malthus, who published his *Essay on the Principle of Population* in 1798. He foresaw the population eventually and inevitably consuming the available food. Many recent writers such as Sir John Russell and Harrison Brown have been more optimistic and point out that man has still to take advantage of the technical possibilities of obtaining food from underdeveloped countries, from the sea, air, and other sources. Yet the implications of Sir Charles Darwin's mathematics are still a cause for reflection.

The problems associated with increasing population not only concern consumption of food and control of disease but also problems of birth control, family size, and old age. It would seem at first somewhat perplexing to find that the contributions of medicine to the problem during the last century are those of increasing the live birth rate and of prolonging the expectation of life of an individual. In general it has been medical progress that has resulted in ensuring the birth of, and prolonging the life of, those members of the population who would have died at birth or lived a shorter life in earlier centuries. It can be argued that this represents a reversal of the law of the survival of the fittest and even the development of a cult of looking after the unfit. However, the advances caused by improving medical attention would be more advantageous for the individual if the population could be stabilized. Medicine has indeed set itself a further problem by making advances in solving immediate ones.

It would seem that by having learnt to combat his natural enemies, pathogenic micro-organisms and parasites, man is doomed to overrun the earth with his multiplying numbers as long as famine and war do not take a significant toll. This seems inevitable as long as man does not interfere with his reproductive processes, control his fecundity, or be influenced by other demographic forces. Many factors control population size (see the *Report of the Royal Commission on Population*, H.M.S.O., 1949); some are biological, some social or economic, and some are the 'vicious practices' condemned by Malthus. Recently C. B. Goodhart has suggested that there may well be factors governing mating or marriage that will tend to stabilize populations by an intrinsic influence. He emphasizes the concept of

TABLE V

ESTIMATES OF WORLD POPULATION AT VARIOUS DATES

Year	*Estimated Total*	*Estimated Increase*
1650	470 millions	
1750	728 millions	55 per cent in 100 years
1800	906 millions	
1850	1,171 millions	62 per cent in 100 years
1900	1,608 millions	
1950	2,377 millions	103 per cent in 100 years
1955	2,528 millions	
2000	3,727 millions	131 per cent in 100 years

varying nubility in women and suggests that the more desirable qualities, that make for success in life, are likely to become genetically associated with lower fecundity.

The figures given in Table v can only be approximate, but they lend emphasis to the argument, and support the contention of the anthropologist A. H. Schultz that the high reproductive rate of man is one of the distinctive characteristics of the species. We must now examine the pattern of human reproduction and then compare it with that of other mammals.

THE EVENTS IN HIS REPRODUCTIVE LIFE

Man reaches *puberty* at the end of childhood, one-sixth to one-seventh of the way through the normally expected life-span. At puberty the female reproductive organs start to pass through a succession of *sexual cycles* each lasting about 28 days, the beginning of each cycle being marked by the phenomenon of *menstruation* (or blood loss); *ovulation* (the shedding of an egg from the ovary) usually occurs near the middle of the cycle. Active changes also occur in the male reproductive organs at puberty and result in the ability to ejaculate *seminal fluid* containing spermatozoa. There is no sexual cycle in the male; the reproductive organs are continuously active. Puberty is followed by *adolescence*, a period of becoming adult or *mature*. During adolescence numerous anatomical changes occur in both sexes (some start even before puberty) and each acquires *secondary sexual characteristics* of proportion, shape, distribution of hair, and quality of voice. The female human has a *menopause*, or cessation of reproductive function (the 'change of life'), at a modal age of 49, and is the only mammal so far known to live long enough to display this phenomenon. There is no change equivalent to a menopause in the male; reproductive ability subsides more or less rapidly as age advances. The gestation period or duration of pregnancy averages 267 days, but is more variable than in any other mammal for which records have been made. The usual *number* of young born at a time is one, *multiple births* occasionally occur, and *lactation* frequently lasts for nine months.

Puberty

The onset of puberty, or menarche, occurs in man between the ages of 13 and 15, and at an average age of 14.5 years. It is frequently maintained that puberty occurs earlier in warm climates. This has not been proved to be due only to temperature, as other factors, such as the level and type of nutrition, are involved. The onset of puberty is gradual in man and in the higher Primates. Hormones called gonadotrophins (experimentally shown to be the cause of the onset of puberty) are produced by the pituitary gland in steadily increasing amounts until they cause ovarian activity sufficient to promote growth of hair and mammary tissue (and sexual skin). Such pituitary activity often starts some years before the first menstruation, or even the first ovulation. The onset of puberty is thus not to be considered as a point in time, although the occurrence of the first menstrual discharge (menarche) is conveniently taken as indicating its onset, but to be a period during which the gonads gradually attain an overtly functional stage, and at which reproduction becomes potentially possible.

TABLE VI

AGE AT REACHING PUBERTY

Mouse	5–7 weeks	Common pipistrelle	2nd year
Rat	6–9 weeks	Sperm whale	15 months–2 yrs
Golden Hamster	7–8 weeks	Bush-baby	20 months
Guinea-pig	8–10 weeks	Blue whale	2 years
Rabbit	5–9 months	Pig-tailed macaque	50 months
Dog	6–8 months	Seal – Common	3–4 years
Sheep	28–35 weeks	Rhesus monkey	3–4½ years
Pig	28–30 weeks	Chacma baboon	4 years
Cow	6–18 months	Brown bear	6 years
Horse	11–12 months	Gibbon	8–10 years
Stoat	1 year	Chimpanzee	8–9 years
Marmoset	14 months	Indian elephant	9–14 years
Cat	15 months	Man	13–15 years

It will be seen from the Table that there is great variation in the time of onset of puberty in different species, but in most mammals there is some correlation between size or weight and the length of time before the onset of puberty. Thus the largest animals tend to enter puberty at or after the second year of age; small mammals reach puberty earlier. There is, however, an absolutely longer period before the onset of puberty in the larger and higher Primates. Man has a longer period of childhood before puberty and a longer period of adolescence between puberty and sexual maturity than all other mammals of his size and of all other primates. In apes body growth ceases about the age of 12 and bone growth ceases by the age of 14; growth in man continues longer and some bones continue growing until the age of 22–25. The other anatomical changes that occur at puberty will be described in Chapter 16.

Adolescence and Sexual Maturity

It must be clearly understood that puberty and sexual maturity are not the same. Gonadal development is gradual; menstruation may at first occur at quite long intervals and ovulation may be delayed until the menstrual cycle is well established. The period of time during which the gonads steadily develop and the secondary sexual characteristics become increasingly more pronounced is known as adolescence. The processes of reproduction and physical development culminate in stages of sexual and physical maturity; the first stage is reached before the second. Sexual maturity implies that the individual has reached a stage when it is best equipped for reproduction. It is reached much later than puberty, although there is considerable racial and individual variation. An animal is sexually mature, therefore, when its reproductive organs have attained a size and degree of activity that indicates full reproductive capacity, both as regards begetting, bearing, and rearing young. Thus many consider that sexual maturity in women also involves the full development of a responsible maternal outlook and a certain mental maturity. A woman may reach her full reproductive capacity from about her 16th to 22nd year; in the male it is a more difficult stage to assess, but in general sexual maturity is reached later than in women.

There is evidence that in most female animals there is a short period of 'adolescent sterility' during which ovulation is irregular or does not occur. Pregnancy during this period is potentially dangerous to both mother and young. Most mammals that usually bear many offspring at a time have fewer when they are younger: thus yearling ewe-lambs usually have only one offspring at their first breeding; as they grow older multiple births are more frequent.

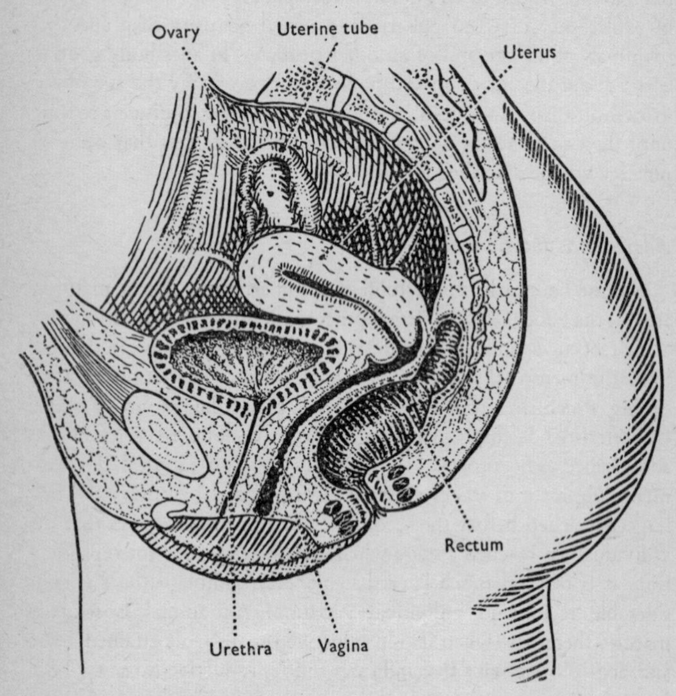

FIG. 3. Shape and position of the human uterus and related structures.

It does not follow that older women are more likely to have twins, but it is an illustration of the gradual attainment of sexual maturity.

Physical maturity assumes that the individual has reached a stage of full adulthood in all anatomical aspects. It coincides with the end of bone growth; it is reached earlier in women (21–24 years) than in men (23–26 years). It will be discussed further in Chapter 16.

Reproduction in the Male

Until puberty is reached the male gonads, the testes, are immature and neither produce germ cells (spermatozoa) nor act as effective endocrine organs. As in the female, there is a gradual development

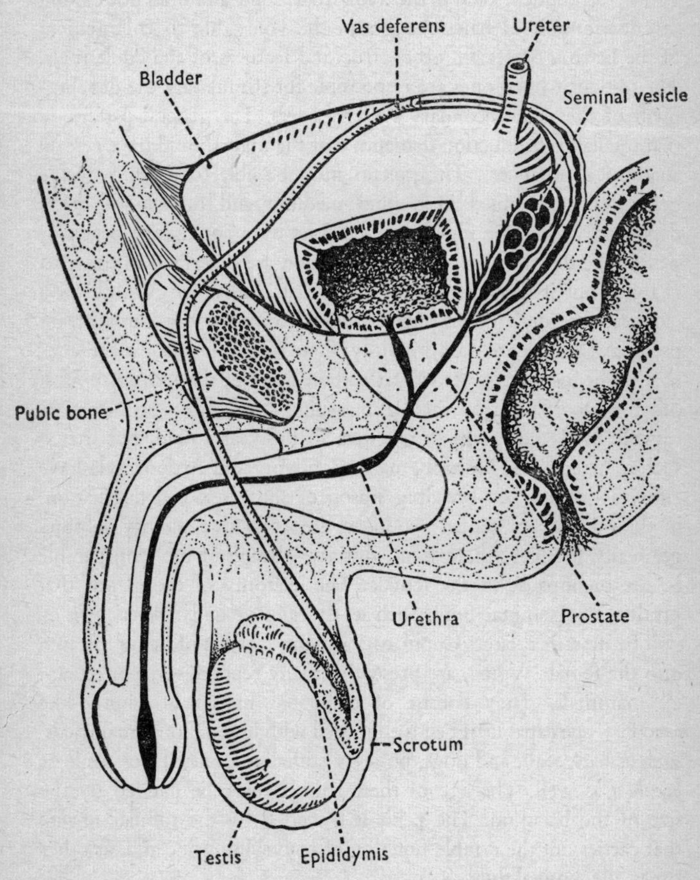

FIG. 4. Arrangement of the male reproductive organs and ducts in man.

of gonadal activity, starting just before puberty and culminating in the ability to ejaculate semen. At the same time the testis is stimulated by the pituitary to secrete increasing quantities of the male sex hormones, *androgens*. It has been known since early times that castration of a boy at puberty prevents the development of the secondary sex characteristics of the adult male. The castrated individual, or eunuch, retains the adolescent build and does not exhibit the distribution of hair, changes in the voice due to enlargement of the larynx, or certain other structural features of the adult male. The testicular hormones are responsible for stimulating the development of the male secondary sex characters. The general pattern of mammalian reproduction demands that the male should have certain anatomical attributes. The gonads must be able to produce fertile germ cells, contained in a fluid medium and capable of being deposited within the female genital tract by a copulatory organ or penis. The details of germ cell production are described in the next chapter, but it should be noted here that man is an example of a 'constant breeder'. From puberty until late in life the human testis produces spermatozoa continuously; there is, however, some evidence of a slight increase in activity at certain times of the year. Amongst other male mammals, rats, guinea-pigs, and most primates are capable of fertile sperm production all the year round, but many, such as hedgehogs, squirrels, many Carnivora and Artiodactyla have either a distinct non-breeding season or show seasonal fluctuations in the quantity of semen produced. Reproductive activity subsides gradually in man; there is no distinct 'change of life' comparable to the menopause in the female. The anatomy of the glands that produce the seminal fluid, such as the *prostate* and *seminal vesicles*, will be described later. Copulatory organs, capable of being inserted into the female vagina, are present in many reptiles, some birds, and all mammals. They consist of elongated masses of sponge-like erectile tissue capable of being engorged with blood. Some mammals, such as bats, seals, and dogs, possess a stiffening bone, the os penis or *baculum* as well. The age of these animals may be gauged by the size of the baculum. The penis is traversed by the tubular *urethra* that carries out the double function of conveying urine and, at other times, the seminal fluid.

The Reproductive Cycle and Menstruation

The first menstrual loss at puberty is followed by a succession of regularly repeated cycles, each cycle involving changes in the ovary and uterus. We may therefore refer to an *ovarian cycle* in the ovary and a *menstrual cycle* in the uterus. The menstrual cycle is under the control of the ovary; when the ovaries are removed menstruation ceases. The ovarian cycle is controlled by the anterior lobe of the pituitary and is initiated only when sufficient gonadotrophic hormones are secreted from the gland: other factors, such as the nutritional state, may have an influence on the time of onset. Once

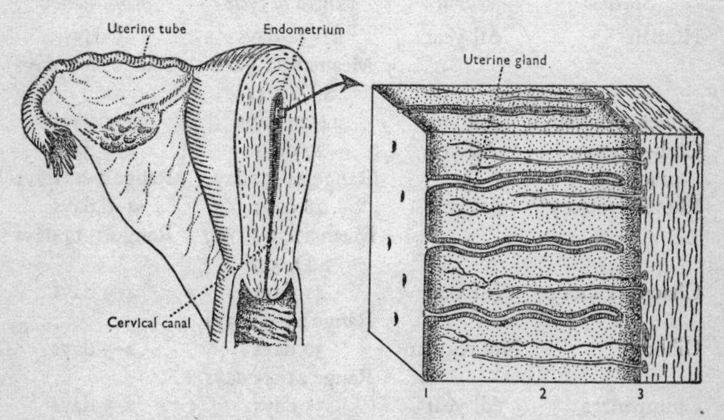

FIG. 5. Uterus (cut through the middle) on the left; to the right an enlargement of a block of endometrium. 1: uterine epithelium with stratum compactum to right; 2: stratum spongiosum; 3: stratum basale.

started the cycle recurs regularly, is controlled by the pituitary, and continues, except when interrupted by pregnancy, until the menopause. Additional factors, such as adrenal secretions, probably also affect the cycle.

The human reproductive cycle is in numerous respects similar to that found in certain other primates. Overt menstruation occurs in the Old World monkeys (Catarrhines) and the Pongidae, but in most New World monkeys (Platyrrhines; *Ateles*, *Alouatta*) the uterine changes are not so dramatic and bleeding slight.

The phenomenon of menstruation in the human female results from the breakdown of most of the inner lining or *endometrium* of the uterus and its loss, together with some blood, from the uterus through the cervix and vagina as the menstrual flow. The first day of the flow occurs 21 to 34 days after the first day of the *last* menstrual period and a similar interval before the first day of the next expected period, as long as pregnancy does not intervene. The average length of one cycle is 28 days, and the average length of

TABLE VII

Species	*Breeding season*	*Length of cycle*	*Length of menstruation*
Human	All year	21–34 days Mean 28·32±0·6 S.D. 5·41	5 days Range 2–8 days
Spider monkey	All year	24–27 days	3–4 days
Crab-eating macaque	All year	27 days Range 24–52 days	2–6 days Range 2–13 days
Rhesus monkey	All year	28 days Mean 27·36±0·17 S.D. 5·7	4–6 days Range 2–11 days
Chacma baboon	All year	41 days Range 29–63 days	4–9 days
Gibbon	Not regular	30 days Range 21–43 days	2–5 days
Chimpanzee	All year	35 days Up to 50 days in young	2–3 days

(See Asdell, 1946.)

menstruation is five days, but only a small percentage of women have a cycle that displays such exactitude repetitively. Considerable variation is shown and is quite normal.

The endometrium is only a few millimetres thick and is composed of numerous glands, blood vessels, and supporting stroma, all of which pass through dramatic changes during each cycle. Three layers can be discerned in the endometrium; the two superficial layers are shed at each menstruation, whilst the basal layer remains and from it each new lining is regenerated. There are no nerves in the endometrium, so the pain that often accompanies menstruation is not due to dissolution of the lining tissue. It is difficult to be precise as to what exactly is the cause of the pain.

After each menstrual period (which lasts two to eight days) there is a stage of repair of the uterine lining followed by a stage of growth, or *proliferation*, succeeded by a stage of *secretory* activity. These stages are successively instigated and brought to fruition by the action of hormones produced by the ovary and possibly from the adrenal gland as well. These hormones are called *oestrogens* – a family of several naturally occurring and powerful hormones that bring about the proliferative phase, and *progestins*, which in their turn and together with the continued action of oestrogens cause the subsequent secretory or luteal phase (Fig. 6). These successive and integrated changes in the uterine lining ensure that it is well developed and active and that its cells possess a chemical composition satisfactory for nutrition of the developing embryo when the latter arrives in the uterus.

Ovulation and Egg Transport

Release of a maturing egg, or oocyte, from the ovary is called ovulation. It occurs at about the 13th–14th day of the human cycle, that is to say about mid-way between two menstrual periods. It coincides with the end of the proliferative phase, but it must be emphasized that there is great variation in the time of ovulation; it may occur as early as the 6th day or as late as the 23rd day of the cycle. The only fixed time interval is that ovulation occurs 13–14 days before the onset of the next menstrual period – for reasons that will be soon apparent.

At the time of ovulation the oocyte is contained in a fluid-filled sphere or follicle in one or other ovary. The follicle ruptures owing to action of pituitary gonadotrophic hormones and the oocyte is ejected into the uterine tube of that side. Each tube is about four inches long in the human female, is sinuously curved and stretches from an outer frilled end near each ovary to an inner end joining the uterus (see Fig. 5). The uterine tube has been referred to for several hundred years as the Fallopian tube in memory of Gabriello Fallopius (1523–63), professor of anatomy at Padua. He was not aware of the function of the tubes as oviducts, but thought of them as tubular chimneys allowing the escape of 'sooty humours' from the uterus.

The oocyte is conveyed towards the uterus by the contraction of the smooth muscle in the tubal wall and by the activity of the fine hair-like cilia projecting from the cells lining the uterine tube. Usually the oocyte soon degenerates; all trace of it is lost in a few days. Should spermatozoa be present the oocyte is penetrated by one of them, undergoes its final maturation process, and the mature egg or ovum is said to have been *fertilized*. Fertilization is the process of fusion of the male and female germ cells to form a *zygote*, and is the start of embryonic development.

The changes that occur in the ovum after fertilization and those that take place simultaneously in the uterine lining are so controlled that by the time the developing ovum has reached the uterus its lining is in a state of full secretory activity. It takes five to six days from the time of fertilization for the developing ovum to reach the uterus. During these early days of its life the ovum develops from a single celled zygote, into a hollow sphere of many cells called a blastocyst.

The Corpus Luteum

After ovulation the spent follicle from which the maturing oocyte was shed undergoes great changes as the result of the influence of gonadotrophic hormones from the anterior pituitary. The rupture point heals over and the wall of the old follicle develops into an endocrine organ, the corpus luteum, that is capable of secreting the progestational hormones. The principal of these, but not for certain the only one, is *progesterone*, and it acts on the proliferating endometrium and causes it to secrete. In a cycle that is not interrupted by pregnancy the corpus luteum persists for only 13–14 days; it then degenerates and menstruation follows almost immediately. Should the egg be fertilized it will reach the uterus when the corpus luteum is fully developed and exerting its maximal influence on the uterine lining. The secretions of the lining are called 'uterine milk' and they provide a nutritious pabulum on which the blastocyst can live. It will thus be clear that the developing egg must be 'delayed' in its arrival in the uterus until the latter is ready to provide it with nutriment. This delay is provided by the length of time (4–10 days in mammals) taken to traverse the uterine tube, and the latter is therefore a truly advantageous structure and not simply a conducting pipe for eggs. It is probable that some eggs do arrive in the uterus too early, and die for want of adequate nutriment; and it is quite certain that some do not reach the uterus until too late. In the latter instance the blastocyst may have got obstructed in the tube, or perhaps passed down it too slowly and entered into its next stage of development before reaching the uterus. Prolonged delay in the uterine tube may result in an ectopic (out of the proper place) pregnancy, and since the uterine tube is not constructed for containing a rapidly growing embryo or invading placental tissue, the embryo soon dies or else the tube ruptures. Ectopic pregnancy occurs in about 0.25 per cent of all pregnancies in man, but is very rare indeed in animals. This is certainly partly because some of the obstructions in the tube are caused by disease processes limited to man, and it may also be due to the possibility that higher brain centres, or other factors, may disturb the efficacy of reproductive functions more in the human female.

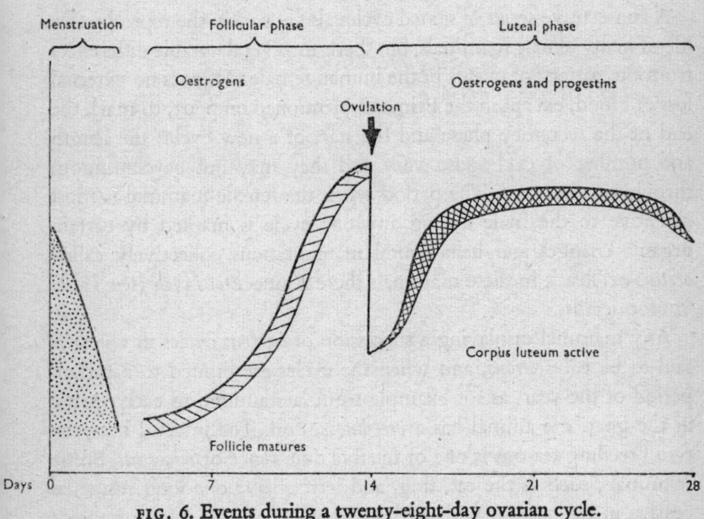

FIG. 6. Events during a twenty-eight-day ovarian cycle.

Implantation

Soon after the human blastocyst has arrived in the uterus it begins to embed into the uterine wall. This is a process known as *implantation*, and it is due partly to the destructive activities of the cells of the blastocyst and partly, perhaps even more so, to the engulfing propensity of the endometrium. Implantation in the human female is called *interstitial* because the blastocyst literally becomes buried amongst the cells of the endometrium. The significance of this type of implantation will be discussed later, but it must be emphasized that the endometrium has obviously been prepared during its secretory phase to play an important part in the process. The blastocyst takes only a few days to become deeply embedded in the endometrium and, by means that we do not clearly understand, sends a hormonal or chemical signal that causes persistence of the corpus luteum and as a result prevents the menstruation that would have followed had the blastocyst not implanted.

Reproductive Patterns in Other Mammals

A consecutive series of sexual cycles also occurs in the reproductive life of many female mammals, but there are several notable differences from the pattern of events in the human female. There is no external loss of blood, except in the Primates mentioned on p. 93, to mark the end of the secretory phase and the start of a new cycle; the length and number of cycles also vary and they may not be continuous throughout the year. The period when the female mammal is most receptive to the male during any one cycle is marked by certain organic changes and behavioural manifestations collectively called *oestrus* or 'heat'; in these mammals there is an *oestrous cycle* (see Table VIII for details).

Any mammal displaying a succession of oestrus cycles in a year is said to be *polyoestrous*, and when the cycles are limited to a certain period of the year, as for example from late autumn to early spring in the goat, the animal has a *breeding* season. The interval between two breeding seasons is one of relative quiescence or *anoestrus*. Some mammals, such as the cat, dog, and ferret, have one long sustained oestrus in the spring, with perhaps another later in the summer or

TABLE VIII

THE CHARACTERISTICS OF REPRODUCTIVE CYCLES IN SOME MAMMALS

Species	*Type of cycle**	*Length of cycle*	*Length of oestrus*	*Time of ovulation*
Hedgehog	Spring and Summer (M)	—	Not known	Spontaneous
Dog	Spring and Autumn (M)	—	7–9 days	Probably spontaneous
Cat	Spring and Autumn (M)	—	4–10 days	Induced
Rabbit	Anoestrus October–March (M)	—	Indefinitely in breeding season	Induced
Rat	All year (P)	4–6 days	20 hours	10 hours after start of heat
Guinea-Pig	All year (P)	16–17 days	6–11 hours	10 hours after start of heat
Pig	All year (P)	20–22 days	2–3 days	End of heat
Cattle	All year (P)	18–22 days	24 hours	Just after heat
Sheep	May have anoestrus in Summer (P)	16–17 days	30–40 hours	24 hours after start of heat
Horse	March–October (P)	20–22 days	6–7 days	End of heat
Rhesus Monkey	All year (P)	27–28 days	Max. receptivity for 2 days	Mid cycle
Chimpanzee	All year (P)	34–35 days	Max. receptivity for about 4 days	Mid cycle
Man	All year	28·32 ± 0·6 days S.D. 5·41	—	Mid cycle

* M = monoestrous; P = polyoestrous.

early autumn, and are referred to as being *monoestrous*. It has been shown that there is a series of cycles in the human female and in a way they are indeed oestrous cycles, except that there are no marked manifestations of heat or oestrus. It is not that changes do not occur in the reproductive organs, indeed they do, but that there is no display or any external signs or any appreciable change in behaviour in women, such as are observable in truly polyoestrous mammals. There is no breeding season in a human female's reproductive life, yet there is some evidence from the study of primitive peoples that there may have been in the past periods of relatively greater sexual activity at certain times of the year. It has been suggested that May Day, with its ceremony of dancing round a phallic symbol – the maypole – may have been associated with seasonal reproductive activity.

The most important event associated with oestrus is ovulation, and in the majority of mammals ovulation occurs spontaneously, under hormonal control, either during or just after oestrus. The length of oestrus varies in different polyoestrous animals from a few hours (at night) in rats and mice to six days or so in the mare. In monoestrous animals ovulation is also under hormonal control, but is so set that it needs to be 'triggered off' by the stimulus of mating and is thus known as *induced* ovulation. It may occur at almost any time during the prolonged heat period of up to several months. Should the mating not be a fertile one there follows a period of false pregnancy (pseudo-pregnancy) during which the reproductive organs enter into a phase of preparation for pregnancy and the animal even behaves as if it were pregnant. Eventually the changes subside and the animal usually enters a period of anoestrus until the next heat. There is some evidence of a condition in the human female which is not unlike pseudo-pregnancy, but it is rare and may well have a strong psychological background.

Biological Significance of Menstruation

Anyone who has kept female pets that are mammals, or who has worked with large female domestic mammals on a farm, will have noticed that there is a blood-stained discharge from their genital openings at certain times. They may well have considered that this loss of blood may be equivalent to menstruation. In fact it is not, but many thought it was until careful studies in reproductive physiology showed that this slight discharge was associated not with the end of one cycle and the beginning of another, but occurred before, or near, the time of ovulation and is often one of the manifestations of oestrus. In the human female there is occasionally a slight discharge associated with ovulation, and even a sensation of pain in the lower abdomen at the same time. These are in no way associated with menstruation but could be considered as occasionally occurring external manifestations of a subdued or masked oestrus.

Although many of the phenomena repeatedly seen in the general mammalian reproduction pattern occur in man, it is in that of menstruation that the species differs from all other animals with the exception of those primates already mentioned (and perhaps as well the little South African Elephant shrew). The phenomenon may play a large part in the culture of primitive races and is the object of various rites, ceremonies, and taboos, as can be realized from even a superficial reading of J. G. Frazer's monumental *Golden Bough* (1890). Many interesting data are reviewed and discussed in another book in the Pelican series, *Sex and the Social Order* by G. H. Seward, and it should be read for a much fuller treatment of the psychological assessment of sexual differences and relationships in man.

It may well be difficult at first to understand the purpose of menstruation; it appears wasteful of tissue and of essential substances such as the iron lost in the blood. The precise cause of the onset of the menstrual flow is not known. It is usually assumed that it results from withdrawal of the action of hormones which built up the endometrium, particularly of progesterone and perhaps indirectly of oestrogen as well. For this and other reasons, it is difficult to find the reason for menstruation in the anatomy or physiology of the uterus. There seems to be no reason why the uterus should need to lose so much of its tissue, nor at first sight why the endometrium could not simply subside in activity at the end of the secretory phase. The degree of secretory transformation is indeed very considerable by the end of this phase in the human uterus. It may be that the degree of coiling of the vessels, the activity of the glands and the great alteration in the stroma result in so drastic a change in its minute structure that the endometrium becomes 'over-ripe'. Subsidence in its activity is not possible without death of the tissue. Theoretically it is possible to maintain that in natural uninhibited relationships all the females in a population of animals should be either pregnant, lactating, ovulating or about to ovulate, anoestrous or abnormal. For example, such a state of affairs almost certainly exists in a large herd of deer such as the one that has been studied for several years at Petworth Park in Sussex. Thus one could imagine a similar state of affairs in a primitive short-lived group of men and women amongst whom intercourse was frequent from adolescence. Menstruation would rarely be seen in such a group and would certainly cause consternation when it did first occur.

Menstruation ceases on the supervention of pregnancy and does not recommence until some months after the birth of the child, depending on the length of lactation. If the child is suckled for a long period this may well suppress the re-establishment of menstruation until that much later, but lactation does not necessarily suppress ovarian function all the time. So it is quite possible for ovulation to occur towards the end of the lactation period, although menstruation has not been re-established. If the child is not suckled menstruation is usually re-established correspondingly earlier.

The Menopause

Menstruation also ceases at the menopause, the latter marking the ending of reproductive life in women. Essentially the menopause must be considered a reflection of a gradual cessation of control by the pituitary over the ovary. Usually the menopause extends over several years and is accompanied by signs and symptoms that can nearly all be referred to the cessation of action of ovarian hormones. In that it also marks the loss of an attribute – that of reproductive power – it is a stage in ageing of the human female organism. At first sight it may seem curiously human to have a menopause – for it is not known in any other mammal in the wild, though it is said to have occurred in certain primates in captivity and occurs in modified form in laboratory rats. It may well have been rare in primitive man with a relatively short expectation of life (see p. 294), but its universal occurrence nowadays indicates that modern woman can outlive her period of reproductive life by many years. The present expectation of life for a newborn female child is about 71 years, and with a menopause occurring at a modal age of 49, this means an average expectation of nearly a quarter of a century as an individual incapable of reproducing, and for that reason as an incomplete individual. This incompleteness does not mean that post-menopausal women are unable to make important and vital contributions to society, but it does raise certain individual problems, perhaps only in that women have a greater expectation of life than their husbands. It is also of interest to wonder what would be the effect in a society in which the mother, as well as the father, goes out to work to provide also for a widowed grandmother who lives with the family and brings up her grandchildren. Could this be a new influence in natural selection?

The Gestation Period

The duration of pregnancy – the gestation period – in the human can be calculated in two ways. The first refers to the *menstrual age* of the newborn child and is calculated from the first day of the last menstrual period. One set of observations gives the duration as $280{\cdot}2 \pm {\cdot}3$ days, standard deviation $= 9{\cdot}2$. This is obviously not helpful in a particular instance, but it provides a practical method of estimating the expected date of arrival of the baby in that it represents ten lunar months. To convert these figures so that they refer to calendar months one goes back three calendar months from the first day of the last menstrual period and then adds on one week. So if the first day of the last menstrual period was 1 April, the child can be expected about 8 January the next year. It will be only approximately at that date, for the length of gestation is so variable in man. The chances are about 21–1 against the child being born on 8 January, and for that matter almost the same against it being born on any given day from 31 December to 17 January. But the chances are steadily higher against the child being born each day earlier or later than the inclusive dates given above, and of all children expected on 8 January two-thirds will be born within the range given above.

The age of the child at birth could also be estimated from the time of fertilization – the fertilization age – but this must rely on the assumption that ovulation occurs about 13–14 days after the first day of the last menstrual period and that fertilization follows within hours of ovulation; thus the figure of 267 days given for the average length of true gestation is somewhat theoretical.

The reasons for the great variation in the length of the gestation period are several. Perhaps foremost they involve the hormonal activities of the maternal endocrine organs and those of the placenta or after-birth. In women and, as far as is known, to some extent in other mammals, the placenta takes over some of the hormonal functions of the ovary. This enables it to act as a timing device in that its hormonal output can vary in quantity and type of hormone, and should they enter the maternal circulation such hormones may affect the maternal endocrine organs and thus the mechanisms controlling the onset of labour. The output of these hormones almost certainly varies in different individuals and the response is equally likely to vary. Other factors influencing the length of gestation involve the size of the child, whether it is the first or subsequent, whether it has a twin, and the state of the uterine muscle; certain psychological factors may precipitate labour earlier.

Number of Young

The term *fecundity* is used to denote the quantitative aspect of the ability to produce young. An animal has high fecundity if it produces many young, it is *fertile* if it is qualitatively able to reproduce. Fertility early in life when also associated with high fecundity tends to persist throughout the reproductive life and in domestic animals these traits are sought after for the purpose of selection.

The usual number of young born at one time to the human mother is one, and that is also the usual number in all the primates except in the lemurs, where two are often born. In one out of every 85 pregnancies in women of western races twins are born, either like or identical twins, or unlike or fraternal twins, the latter being born three times as often as identical twins. Triplets are born in one out of every 85 × 85 pregnancies, and so on to obey what is often called Hellin's law of multiple births. The human uterus is not anatomically intended for more than one foetus, and since twins and other multiple births are so often born prematurely, they tend to suffer a hazardous start in life.

Animals giving birth to more than one young at each labour are called *polytocous*, and *monotocous* animals therefore only become parents of one offspring each time. In polytocous animals the uterus is more often arranged in the form of two long tubes or horns, with the foetuses and their placentae arranged like beans in a pod. In monotocous animals the uterus may be of two-horned or bicornuate type, with the foetus established in one of the two horns, or the uterus may be unicornuate with only one horn, actually compounded of the two fused together. In a later chapter it will be shown that the unicornuate type of uterus may have been a useful evolutionary acquisition essential to the adoption of the upright posture. Again, it is strange that besides the Primates, except Tarsius, only bats have a unicornuate uterus.

Large animals are usually monotocous, although certain whales have been reported to have contained six or more foetuses when killed, and polytocous animals are usually small, except that most bats only have one young at a time. A large animal has to be born in a relatively advanced stage of development to survive; whales and seals can swim at birth and fawns can run so fast seven hours after birth that one cannot catch them on a bicycle. Thus the larger the animal, the better the young should be able to look after themselves at birth. Small mammals do not have such problems and can be born relatively undeveloped, and the immediate post-natal period can be spent wrapped in straw or hay or some form of nest. Bats are an obvious exception; their specialized life demands rapidity in learning to fly so as to leave the mother unencumbered. In the human newborn baby we see the prolongation of a 'foetal' type of life after birth, with its concomitant requirements of mother love and parental care for many months. Therefore in the relatively large human mammal the period of gestation is as long as is anatomically feasible; the young are born in a state far short of being able to fend for themselves, and there is a long period of parental care. This is, of course, associated with the fact that the brain in the adult human is so large that it takes longer to attain full size than in any other mammal. If the human brain were to be more than one quarter of the adult size at birth the foetal skull could never escape from the pelvis. Should the brain be destined to enlarge even more in the next species of man it will have to do so during extra-uterine life, unless changes in the size of the human female pelvis are also destined to evolve at the same time. If the latter were not to occur, the intriguing prospect emerges of man helping the process of evolution by carrying out Caesarian sections to bring his big-headed successors into the world.

FOR FURTHER READING

Ourselves Unborn. G. W. Corner. Yale University Press, New Haven, 1944

The Hormones in Human Reproduction. G. W. Corner, Princeton, 1942

'World Population Growth and its Regulation by Natural Means.' G. B. Goodhart. *Nature.* 1956, 178, 561

Reproduction and Sex. G. I. M. Swyer. Routledge and Kegan Paul, 1954

Mammalian Reproduction. S. T. Asdell. Comstock Pub. Co., 1946

Marshall's Physiology of Reproduction. Third Edition. Vols. I and II. Edited by A. S. Parkes. Longmans, 1956

CHAPTER 6

HIS MINUTE GERM CELLS

FOR reproduction to occur in mammals there must exist individuals of two sexes, males and females. Each must at some time be able to produce germ cells, spermatozoa from testes in males or ova from ovaries in females. Mature germ cells are also known as *gametes*, from a Greek word meaning a wife. A gamete may therefore be either an ovum or a spermatozoon; by their union one with the other at fertilization they produce a fertilized egg or *zygote* (meaning joined or yoked together). A zygote possesses the potentiality to develop, first within the uterus and later independently, into an adult of that particular species. In their turn adults will be endowed with ability to produce germ cells. Sexual reproduction in its fullest sense, therefore, implies possession by an individual of properly differentiated and active primary and secondary sex organs, associated also with exhibition of psychological attributes of that sex. We may consider in turn *determination* of genetic sex at fertilization, *development* of sex in embryo and foetus, *differentiation* of sexual activity, and *behavioural* and psychological manifestations of the sexes.

Determination of Sex

Genetic sex is determined at the time of fertilization of the ovum. Adult cells in a particular mammal each possess a number of chromosomes, the number depending on the species (rabbit, 22; rat, 42; sheep, 54; cow, 60). Whatever the number of chromosomes in the nuclei of cells of adult animals there is half that number in the nucleus of each egg, and also in the head of each spermatozoon. When a spermatozoon fertilizes an egg the original number of chromosomes is restored in the nucleus of the zygote. This reduction by half in gametes of the adult number of chromosomes is essential, otherwise when fertilization occurred there would be a steadily increased number of chromosomes and eventually there would be nothing in the world but chromosomes. It is known that the number of chromosomes in adult human cells is 48*, and that one male chromosome differs considerably from its counterpart in the female. The female chromosome number is composed of 46 (44*) chromosomes or *autosomes* arranged in pairs and two identical sex or X chromosomes. One of the sex chromosomes in male cells is similar to the X chromosome of the female but the second is very much curtailed and is called the Y chromosome. The halving which takes place during formation of germ cells in the female will therefore result in an egg always having 23 + X chromosomes. In the male, however, there will be two kinds of spermatozoon – one possessing 23 + X and the other 23 + Y chromosomes. The genetic sex of an individual will therefore depend on whether an egg (containing 23 + X chromosomes) is fertilized by a spermatozoon containing 23 + X or 23 + Y chromosomes. Should the former occur, then the reconstituted number will be 46 + 2X and the embryo will develop into a female adult. On the other hand, if the spermatozoon fertilizing the ovum contains 23 + Y chromosomes then cells of that embryo will have 46 + X + Y chromosomes and will become male.

It can thus be seen that there is a chromosome difference between the two sexes. This genetic difference ensures that in most mammals the form, shape, and anatomy of males differ considerably from those of females. Technically, therefore, we could say that the human female is true-breeding, and that because of the Y chromosome, the male is a hybrid. The two sexes are obviously well adapted as regards their ability to reproduce, but the genetic difference between the sexes expresses itself in various ways. Not only does it result in sexual dimorphism, but also in certain sexual attributes. The human male, for example, is more variable in his anatomy and is particularly variable in his ability to survive, simply because of his maleness. The death rate of male foetuses is higher than that of female and even after birth the male is more liable to die. It has frequently been remarked during the last 2,000 years that it is males that are more often born deformed or defective. From a genetic, and from other, points of view it is absurd to talk of the two sexes being equal.

* Recent work (Ford and Hamerton, 1956) suggests that there are 46 chromosomes (including X and Y) in human cells.

Gonad Development

According to the nature of the sex chromosomes within the fertilized ovum so will the young embryo develop in a male or female direction. There is, however, no external indication of the sex of a human embryo during the first eight weeks of its life. There is an initial neutral or indifferent stage during which it is only possible to sex an embryo by examining its cells microscopically for sex chromosomes. It has recently become possible to obtain cells of foetal origin during a human pregnancy and so to sex a foetus before birth.

Embryonic gonads also do not at first show clear signs of whether they are going to develop into testes or ovaries; nor do they at first contain any germ cells. Most embryologists agree that germ cells have an origin outside a mammalian embryo, probably in the wall of the yolk sac (p. 131). There is some evidence from a study of early human embryos by histochemical methods that there is a migration or invasion of germ cells along the yolk sac stalk into the embryo and eventually into the gonads. They appear to migrate somewhat indiscriminately into organs other than the gonads and even into nervous tissue. It is only in the gonads that they appear to have any chance of survival.

It will be clear that arriving germ cells will be either male or female (XY or XX) and also that cells of the invaded embryo will have similar genetic make-up. The gonad is induced to become an ovary or a testis as a result of complementary action of its genetic sex and that of the arriving germ cells. The germ cell invasion initiates a progressive divergence in form and type of activity in an embryo towards those of one or other sex. Experiments on embryos of lower vertebrates strongly suggest that removal of the yolk sac early on, and thus of the germ cells, results in failure of sexual differentiation and persistence of a sterile, sexually indifferent stage. Experimental destruction of germ cells in embryos by X-rays also prevents proper differentiation of sexual organs.

Embryonic mammalian testes start to differentiate somewhat earlier than ovaries; a testis is recognizable in a human embryo when it is just seven weeks old. Germ cells steadily increase in number in gonads during foetal life and by the time of birth each human gonad contains over half a million. What happens from then on in the mammalian gonad has been a subject of considerable controversy. Some have maintained that there is continuous formation of germ cells throughout the reproductive period of life, and in the testis this certainly occurs. There is, however, little evidence that there is a similar process in the ovary. A number of histologists have maintained that they have seen changes in adult mammalian ovaries that suggest neo-formation of oocytes. Experiments on ovaries of rats and monkeys and counts of oocytes in ovaries of mammals of different ages have not confirmed that these changes indicate that new oocytes are being formed. Some additional germ cells may be formed during a few months of the immediate post-natal period. Thereafter it seems likely that no further germ cells are formed and that those present at birth are destined to be those that will mature and will be shed during adult life one by one at successive ovulations. It is difficult to find a germ cell in a post-menopausal ovary; thus there must be many that degenerate before reaching maturity.

Sex Ducts and External Genitalia

Not only are gonads indistinguishable during early embryonic life but also external genitalia and those internal duct systems that lead from gonads to the exterior. Embryos of both sexes are initially provided with internal ducts and rudiments of external genitalia which will develop into certain important structures if correctly stimulated. There are four such ducts in any embryo and their fate is of great reproductive significance. Two are intimately related to the developing urinary system and are known as *mesonephric* or Wolffian ducts (K. F. Wolff, 1733–94, Professor of Anatomy at St Petersburg described them in the same year that Wolfe captured Quebec). Two other ducts develop alongside them and are therefore called *paramesonephric* ducts. They are often called the Mullerian ducts after J. P. Muller (1801–58), Professor of Anatomy in Berlin. These ducts differentiate into various derivatives depending on their genetic sex and how they are stimulated by the developing ovary or testis. It has recently been suggested by A. Jost in Paris that gonads can guide sex duct differentiation by production of substances that act as foetal hormones.

The Wolffian duct in male embryos persists on each side to become the *vas deferens* and *epididymis.* The vas extends from the testis through the inguinal canal, where it is contained in the spermatic cord, into the pelvis to join the urethra (p. 92). It conveys spermatozoa. The Mullerian duct of males retrogresses and is of little importance. In females it is the Wolffian duct that degenerates, whereas the Mullerian duct persists. Its upper portion forms the uterine tube of each side; its lower portion fuses with that of the opposite side to a degree depending on the species of mammal. In man, all Primates except Tarsius, and in bats the lower portions unite completely to form a single-chambered (unicornuate) uterus and the upper part of the vagina. In other mammals the middle portions of the two Mullerian ducts remain separated and their uteri each have two horns (bicornuate). The two horns may unite at their lower ends in a small common chamber opening by a single canal (cervix) into the vagina as in cattle, sheep, and goats. They may, however, remain quite separate and each horn opens into the vagina; this is a primitive condition seen in marsupials and many rodents. Occasionally in man the uterus does not develop properly and a type of uterus seen in other mammals may be present. The Dutch obstetrician K. de Snoo has written interestingly on the evolutionary significance of a unicornuate type of uterus and its association with bipedalism. The human foetus lies curled up almost in spherical form within its membranes; a quadruped, on the other hand, has a more elongated foetal form; differing arrangement of uterine muscle is said to be present in the two main types of uterus, each adapted for expelling the differently shaped conceptus.

The duct systems have developed along one line or the other by the third month of pregnancy and the external genitalia of the human embryo have also diverged, though not as rapidly. There is at first an indifferent stage in which the external genitalia are represented only by three small simple protuberances. Only a single common chamber draining urinary, genital, and alimentary systems opens to the exterior between these protuberances. It is called a *cloaca,* a Latin word for sewer. The mammalian cloaca is soon divided up into an opening at the back for the alimentary canal, the anus, and one in front, the *urogenital sinus,* receiving the urinary and genital systems. Subsequent developmental changes in this region are complicated and vary in different mammals. They result in the formation in males of a penis and scrotum into which testes will descend later in most mammals. In females the lower end of the fused Mullerian ducts is incorporated between the developing urethra in front and anal canal behind to form the vagina. The three external protuberances develop into the clitoris, homologous to the penis, and the labia.

Urogenital and alimentary tracts open jointly into a persistent cloaca only in monotremes (*mono* – one, *trema* – a slit); a modified cloaca is present in marsupials and some rodents. The penis is found on the ventral wall of the monotreme cloaca; in marsupials it lies behind the scrotum, but in nearly all mammals it lies in front, along the abdominal wall. It is either completely (bull, seal) or partly (Primates) concealed within an invagination of skin, the preputial sac, from which it emerges on erection. Only man, some bats, and tree shrews have a truly pendulous penis with a short prepuce quite free from the abdominal wall.

Migration of testes to a position outside the abdomen occurs only in mammals but not in all. The testis may not descend at all (whale, elephant) or may descend only into an inguinal or perineal position (seal, rat). It may pass into a scrotum only during the breeding season (bats, some rodents) or, as in most Primates and man, it descends into the scrotum just before birth. Various factors control and guide descent of the testis, but it is still difficult to explain these differences amongst mammals. Evidence has been produced which suggests that in man and many mammals the scrotum has a heat regulating function and that the male germ cells can only mature into spermatozoa at a temperature lower than that in the abdomen.

Maturation of the Ovum

Those cells found in adult mammalian ovaries as a result of the earlier division of germ cells (p. 109) are called primary oocytes. Formed in man before and just after birth, they remain in a state of suspended activity for many years. During this time they are surrounded by an envelope of epithelial-like cells forming a primordial *follicle*. Processes leading to maturation of follicle and oocyte begin just before puberty. Several primordial follicles start enlarging at the

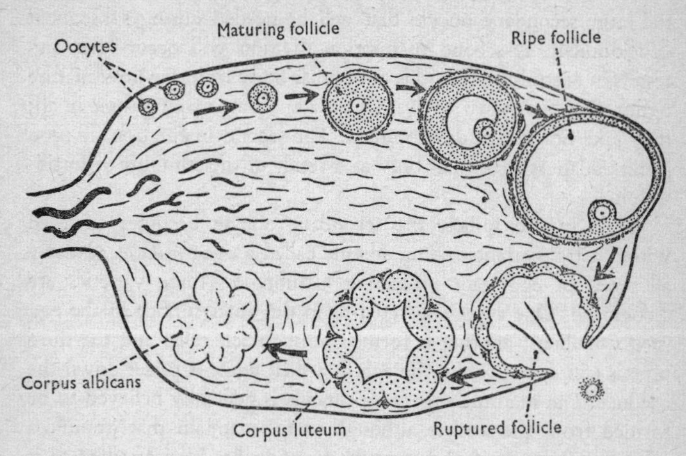

FIG. 7. Successive events in the ovary during one reproductive cycle. See Plate VI.

beginning of each oestrous cycle, but in man only one usually reaches maturity and ruptures to release an oocyte. Those that do not reach this final stage become *atretic* and die.

The single-layered follicle soon becomes surrounded by several layers of two kinds of cell. Closely surrounding the oocyte are *membrana granulosa* cells, outside them lie *theca interna* cells. A split develops amidst the former to give rise to a fluid-filled follicular cavity. The theca interna cells become active and secrete oestrogens. In many mammals the theca interna layer becomes so large that it forms a *thecal gland*. It reaches its highest activity just before oestrus. The follicle enlarges rapidly until it is many times the size of the oocyte. In a human ovary it reaches a diameter of nearly half an inch when mature; it is often known as a Graafian follicle after a Dutch embryologist Regnier de Graaf (1641–73).

About the time the follicle develops its cavity the primary oocyte divides unequally into a large secondary oocyte and one tiny *polar body*. This is the first maturation division and it (and strictly the next division) result in reduction of the somatic (diploid) chromosome number to half (haploid). The excess chromosomes are extruded in the tiny polar body. Inequality of division preserves cytoplasm within the large secondary oocyte that will be needed during subsequent development. A second maturation division will occur later and results in extrusion of another tiny polar body from the now mature ovum. The first polar body may divide again, making three in all; they take no part in development. The second maturation division occurs in most mammals only as a result of the stimulus of fertilization.

While in the follicle the secondary oocyte becomes enclosed within a transparent egg membrane called a *zona pellucida.* Nearly all types of egg gain protective membranes; three varieties are recognized. One type is secreted from the outer surface of the egg itself (vitelline); another is formed from follicle cells; and the third type is laid down round the egg as a shell while it passes down the oviduct. The mammalian zona pellucida is generally believed to be formed from the oocyte although many maintain that granulosa cells contribute to it. A protective function has been ascribed to it but many substances can diffuse through it.

One or more follicles mature during the first part of each reproductive cycle in human females. Maturation may be initiated by adrenal hormones but is mainly brought about by a gonadotrophin (follicle stimulating hormone – F.S.H.) from the anterior pituitary. Usually follicles mature alternately in the two ovaries. The climax of the maturation process is ovulation (p. 98). The follicle ruptures under hormonal control and the secondary oocyte is shed surrounded by a zona pellucida and a covering of loose granulosa cells, the *corona radiata.* Cycles can occur without ovulation and are then called anovular.

The shed oocyte is received into the frilled outer end of the uterine tube. In carnivores the ovary is surrounded in a complete ovarian pouch or bursa of peritoneum from which leads the opening of the tube. In other mammals the egg does not inevitably enter the tube although in some the tube may be attached to the edge of the ovary (ovulation fossa of the mare). The oocyte is transported down the tube by peristaltic movements and by ciliary action that moves mucus in the tube.

Mammalian oocytes and eggs are all remarkably similar in appearance. The eggs are small, 100–150 μ in overall diameter, with little yolk (miolecithal as opposed to the megalecithal bird's egg) and the nucleus is near the centre of the egg as opposed to lying near one pole. Once ovulated their life-span seems to be extraordinarily short. Experiments in laboratory animals suggest that viability and thus ability to be fertilized lasts from 12 to 30 hours, after which time degenerative changes appear in the eggs. It is not exactly known how long human ova remain viable but what evidence there is suggests a period of 24 hours or even less.

Maturation of Spermatozoa

At birth the seminiferous tubules of a mammalian testis contain germ cells, spermatogonia, and 'nurse' or Sertoli cells (Enrico Sertoli (1842–1910) of Milan described '*particolari cellule ramificate dei canalicoli seminiferi*'). The spermatogonia begin to divide just before

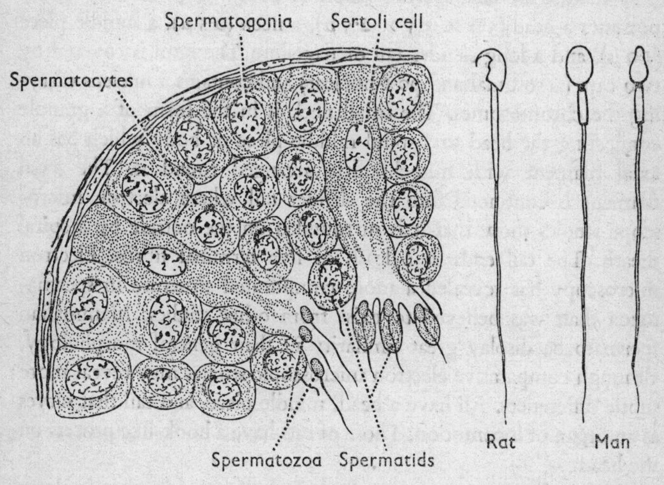

FIG. 8. *Left:* Section of part of one seminiferous tubule of the testis. *Right:* Spermatozoa of rat and man (two views). See also Plate VII.

puberty into primary spermatocytes and these in their turn divide into secondary ones. After puberty the process continues further by the formation of spermatids from secondary spermatocytes and by their maturation into spermatozoa. In contradistinction to affairs in the ovary gametes are actively formed in the testis throughout reproductive life. One primary oocyte gives rise only to one ovum, but one primary spermatocyte can form four spermatozoa. Reduction in chromosome number occurs at the maturation divisions and spermatozoa will contain *either* an X or a Y chromosome as well as autosomes.

Human spermatids are oval cells that do not differ much in appearance from spermatocytes except for certain nuclear details. They soon become attached, however, to the tips of Sertoli cells and metamorphose into spermatozoa. They lose their cytoplasm and become narrow and elongated. Electron microscopy has been of assistance in analysing the complex changes in form and D. W. Fawcett of Harvard University and others have made much use of this powerful instrument to account for abnormalities such as double-headed spermatozoa.

A mature human spermatozoon is about 54 μ in length and possesses a head ($5{\cdot}0 \times 3{\cdot}5 \times 2{\cdot}5\ \mu$), a neck ($0{\cdot}5\ \mu$), a middle piece ($4{\cdot}0\ \mu$), and a long slender tail or flagellum. The head is covered by two caps (acrosomal and post-nuclear) and contains a nucleus carrying the chromosomes. The small neck is in the form of a granule connecting the head to a spiral middle-piece or body which has an axial filament with mitochondria arranged round it. The axial filament is continued into the slender tail where electron microscope studies show that it is surrounded on the outside by a spiral sheath. The tail ends in a leash of five terminal fibrils. Electron microscopy has revealed a more complicated structure in spermatozoa than was believed to exist from other studies. Mammalian spermatozoa display great similarity in their general morphology, although comparative electron microscopic studies may reveal more subtle differences. All have a head, middle piece, and tail that serves as an organ of locomotion. Those of rats have a hook-like process on the head.

The number of spermatozoa in a single human ejaculate is about 210,000,000, but it can vary from 45 million to 730 million.

Seminal Fluid

Spermatozoa are ejected in a seminal fluid that is produced by seminal vesicles and prostate (p. 92). The former are two hollow, sacculated organs, about two inches long, found at the base of the bladder and leading by short ducts to join the tubes conveying spermatozoa from the testes (vasa deferentia) just before they enter the urethra (Fig. 4). Seminal vesicles are not present in Marsupialia or Carnivora, but are particularly large in some Insectivora, such as hedgehogs. The prostate is a glandular organ, one and half inches long, placed at the neck of the bladder around the first part of the urethra. Its secretion is squeezed out by its smooth muscle through a series of ducts into the urethra where it is mixed with secretions of seminal vesicles and with spermatozoa.

The prostate may be of a 'disseminated' type, such as is found in sheep and goats, in which it is represented by a diffuse aggregation of urethral glands. It most other mammals it consists of two or three lobes, but there may be disseminate tissue as well: only in man and dog does the prostate virtually surround the urethra. The gland is absent in Monotremata.

The total volume of fluid in one human ejaculate averages 4·0 ml. (range 1·0–11·0). In those mammals without seminal vesicles the volume of seminal fluid is small, as in dogs; in a boar with large seminal vesicles it is abundant. Functions of the fluid are to permit survival of sperm in a watery medium after they have left the male, to enable them to be motile, and to provide them with nutriment. The fluid contains all substances necessary for these purposes and also, somewhat strangely, the carbohydrate fructose. This is usually found in plants and its presence in the seminal fluid is as curious as it is in the amniotic fluid of certain mammals. Fructose does not seem to be necessary for spermatozoa to live on, but it may give seminal fluid a composition and osmotic pressure that provide sperm with an optimal environment.

Viability and Motility of Spermatozoa

Spermatozoa undergo final maturation in the coiled epididymis and in the vas deferens (sperm withdrawn from a testis are infertile). If not ejaculated they soon lose their potency, degenerate, and may be absorbed. They become motile when mixed with seminal fluid and can remain motile for 48–72 hours within the female genital tract; they may not, however, be fertile for all this time. The tail performs undulatory movements and causes the head to progress forwards with an oscillatory motion along a spiral path. They swim by preference against mucous currents and against gravitational pull. They take about an hour to reach the end of the human uterine tube from the cervix but not many have arrived there by the end of this time. Performance is affected by conditions prevailing in the female genital tract and by the degree of its muscular contractions. Activity of spermatozoa is their basic, defining characteristic; abnormal spermatozoa without tails are incapable of effecting fertilization of a passive ovum.

Metabolism of spermatozoa is of great importance in connexion with artificial insemination. Their longevity can be increased by cooling; sperm of prize bulls may be collected and transported by air to distant countries. Sperm could be preserved by cooling until after death of the donor when by artificial insemination offspring would be obtained that were children of a long dead father (telegenesis). This may be of practical use in improving farm or racehorse stock, but with man it is only for imaginary 'brave new worlds'.

Fertilization

Fertilization may be defined as the series of processes by which a spermatozoon initiates and participates in development. It starts with approach of spermatozoa to an egg and concludes with fusion of the pronucleus of the egg with that of one spermatozoon. Many factors are now recognized as being intimately concerned with the process. Although Leeuwenhoek described spermatozoa in 1679 and von Baer first saw a mammalian ovum in 1827 we still know little about fertilization in man. We do not know if human eggs, as do some eggs, produce substances that increase sperm motility or attract them. We do know, however, that fertilization is an example of a tissue-specific reaction in that sperm will enter only eggs and in that eggs will receive only sperm. In general spermatozoa will not penetrate eggs of other species. It is not therefore surprising that many theories of fertilization are based on analogies with immunological responses.

Extracts of sperm of various species have the property of breaking down egg membranes. Lytic agents in mammalian sperm extracts cause dispersal of follicle cells surrounding unfertilized eggs by dissolving their cementing substances. This property is probably due to presence of an enzyme hyaluronidase, so called because it can break down the mucopolysaccharide hyaluronic acid. Recent research has suggested that in certain mammalian species at least an individual spermatozoon may carry enough enzyme to make a path for itself through follicle cells about an egg. In man spermatozoa probably meet the egg in the outer third of the uterine tube. Several may reach the zona and even penetrate it: only one enters the oocyte (vitellus) and can do so anywhere on its surface. The head immediately swells and becomes the male pronucleus; the middle piece and tail are lost and absorbed.

The oocyte now undergoes its final maturation division (p. 114) and the remaining chromosomes form the female pronucleus. The whole egg cytoplasm or vitellus shrinks within the zona and in some species a 'fertilization membrane' is formed on the surface of the vitellus. Electron microscope studies suggest that this may be a result of re-orientation or even extrusion of fatty materials on the surface of the vitellus. Changes in the zona, or perhaps creation of a fertilization membrane, prevent further spermatozoa penetrating the vitellus. The two pronuclei meet near the centre of the human ovum and a one-cell fertilized egg or zygote has been formed.

Parthenogenesis

When eggs are activated without intervention of spermatozoa the individuals that subsequently develop are said to do so parthenogenetically (*parthenos*, a virgin). The process plays an important part in the life story of many invertebrates and generations produced in this way may alternate with those resulting from normal fertilization. Various types of stimulus can experimentally activate eggs of invertebrates and even lower vertebrates; parthenogenesis has not, however, been convincingly demonstrated in normal mammalian life. Mammalian eggs (rabbit) can be artificially activated to divide through a few cleavage stages, but have to be transplanted into a receptive uterus for further development to occur.

Sex Ratio

The ratio of the number of boys to that of girls born in any period is called the secondary sex ratio. The Registrar-General's *Annual Reports* give the ratio for Great Britain in each year: it is now (1955) 105·6:100. This means that more boys are born than girls, but there is evidence that a still greater proportion of eggs are fertilized by Y-containing sperm. This is the primary sex ratio. It is difficult to determine in man, but in pigs is about 160:100. It is known that the sex ratio of human foetuses that die before birth is high (one set of observations gives a ratio of 150:100). Numerical preponderance of males continues through early age groups; equality is reached by the age group 15–19 years, thereafter a female ascendancy develops until at age 85 there are twice as many females as males. The state of 'maleness' carries with it a certain fragility (p. 108).

Many hypotheses have been put forward to explain the sex ratio and differential viability of the sexes. It has been frequently maintained that those sperm with a small Y chromosome can swim faster, or are more active, than the supposed heavier X-carrying sperm. Y-carrying sperm have been suggested to have a higher metabolic rate, as does the male diploid generation of all species studied. A certain type of environment within the female genital tract may favour one or other type of sperm. Sex-linked, or sex-limited, recessive lethal genes may be responsible for some pre-natal deaths of male heterogametic foetuses. Heterozygous defective genes may accumulate in males because of a less intense selection than in females. The secondary sex ratio may be affected by many factors; they include urbanization, social upheaval, whether first-born, migration, whether illegitimate, social class, and age of mother. Few serious statistical studies have been made on such matters. A thorough study by A. Ciocco in 1938 in the United States found little evidence of much influence on sex ratio by such factors and he condemned speculation on their significance.

Significance of Fertilization and Cleavage

Fertilization marks the origin of a new individual. The diploid number of chromosomes is restored, sex is determined, and cleavage is initiated. The restored chromosome number and related genes determines the characters of the species of embryo (*genotype*). As the embryo develops effects of environment, both pre- and post-natal, will influence the organism so that it appears as a *phenotype*. We are all human beings but we all show phenotypic variation. Human heredity will be the subject of another Pelican book in this Series; suffice it here to state that peculiarities of heredity in man are due to his capacity for out-breeding. Inbreeding is virtually limited to that of race and class; his almost instinctive objection to incest has undoubtedly been to man's immense advantage.

The genetics of sex determination have already been described, but every now and again a child is born in which it is difficult to ascertain sex. Such imperfections in sexual anatomical development are known as 'intersexes'. They suggest that it is not just presence of sex chromosomes, but the quantity of X and its ratio to that of autosomes that finally determines sex. Occasionally an individual thought to be a girl at birth is brought up as a girl but is really a boy with poorly developed male characteristics. Intersexes occurring in man include very rare individuals called hermaphrodites, of whom only some 50 have been described. They possess either one ovary and one testis, or an ovo-testis on one or both sides of the body. There are also a few families in whom the X chromosome of individuals apparently of the XY category is altered by presence of another gene. These individuals ought to be males but they turn into apparent females. Externally their anatomy is female, but they possess no uterus and menstruation occurs only from monthly nose-bleeding. Ovaries have been transformed into poorly developed sterile testes. A *pseudo*-hermaphrodite possesses gonads of one sex and externa genitalia of the other, either wholly or, more likely, partially developed. They are commoner than hermaphrodites and the incidence is about one in every thousand individuals; many authorities believe it is even higher. There are also other categories of intersex in which the body is apparently anatomically normal, but where there is an alteration or variation in expected sexual behaviour.

Cleavage can be defined as a series of rapid divisions in the zygote. In human miolecithal eggs the whole egg divides into two equal-sized parts which again subdivide equally (complete and equal cleavage, as opposed to bird's eggs in which abundant yolk causes cleavage to be partial and incomplete). An increasing number of cells (blastomeres) are produced and, as there is no increase in total cytoplasm during cleavage, there is reduction in cell size to that of somatic cells. Material in the zygote is partitioned among blastomeres; even in mammalian zygotes there is evidence of uneven distribution of certain substances. Cleavage marks the first stage of chemo-differentiation in embryonic cells. It also allows a certain degree of movement of cells within the zona. Groups of cells eventually become arranged in different ways so that there is a change in shape as a result of morphogenetic movements. Histogenetic and morphogenetic developments go hand-in-hand as an embryo grows; as their names suggest, we believe the processes to be under genetic control. It will be obvious that they could suffer interference by outside factors or by adverse conditions developing within embryonic cell systems. Effects of such interference could be drastic, even lethal, or of a more subtle nature. They could lead to abnormalities of development such as are found more frequently in man than in animals because of man's ability to care for his young. Congenital abnormalities are now the third most frequent cause of death during the first year of life.

FOR FURTHER READING

Marshall's Physiology of Reproduction. Vol. I, part I (1956) and Vol. II (1952). Edited by A. S. Parkes

The Facts of Life. C. D. Darlington. George Allen and Unwin, 1953

Vertebrate Sex Cycles. W. S. Bullough. Methuen, 1951

Analysis of Development. B. H. Willier, P. A. Weiss, and V. Hamburger. W. B. Saunders, 1955

CHAPTER 7

HIS LIFE AS AN EMBRYO

> 'Sir,' replied Dr Slop, 'it would astonish you to know what improvements we have made of late years in all branches of obstetrical knowledge, but particularly in that one single point of the safe and expeditious extraction of the foetus, – which has received such lights, that, for my part (holding up his hands), I declare I wonder how the world has – .' 'I wish,' quoth my uncle Toby, 'you had seen what prodigious armies we had in Flanders.'

LAURENCE STERNE wrote the words above about the middle of the eighteenth century, and in the two hundred years since then extraction of the foetus has become even safer, though perhaps only a little more expeditious. As a result even such a seasoned warrior as Uncle Toby would have been amazed at the exceedingly prodigious armies that have been arrayed in Flanders on more than one occasion since 1760.

Embryology is the study of the changes that occur in the early life of an organism from the time of fertilization until the time adult form is assumed. There are many reasons for such a study; historically it arose from a desire to explain the cause of abnormalities such as hare-lip and 'monsters' such as extreme forms of Siamese twins. Considerable advances have been made in recent years in teratology (*teratos*, a monster) and in unravelling the many causes of foetal deformity. We should now considerably modify the causes given in a passage written by the French surgeon, Ambroise Paré, in the sixteenth century:

> There are reckoned up many causes of monsters; the first whereof is the glory of God, that his immense power may be manifested to those which are ignorant of it ... Another cause is, that God may punish men's wickednesse, or show signs of punishment at hand ... The third cause is, an abundance of seed and overflowing matter ... If, on the contrary, the seed be anything deficient in quantity, some or more members will be wanting, or more short and decrepite ... the force of imagination hath much power over the infant ... Monsters are bred and caused by the straightnesse of the womb ... by the ill placing

of the mother, lying downe or any other site of the body in the time of her being with child ... By the injury of hereditary diseases, infants grow monstrous, for crooke-backt produce crooke-backt, lame produce lame, flat-nosed their like ... Monsters are occasioned by the craft and subtelty of the Devill.

The passage does, however, suggest a second reason for studying embryonic life; to understand interaction of hereditary factors and those of the internal and external environment of foetuses. Embryology should throw light on how genetic effects are produced. It also allows us to compare the origin of similar structures in embryos of different species – a study of homologous embryonic organs. It may well help to explain steps in the processes of evolution in that phylogeny is but modified ontogeny (p. 24). There are also many puzzling philosophical aspects on which to ponder; Karl von Baer rightly called embryology 'that true torch for the investigation of organic life.'

Embryology can be descriptive in its approach, recording appearances at different stages of development in a form of historical research. Changes are first described in only one species, then in related species, and eventually as a review of any process in all animals. Recently an experimental approach has been applied to various problems but so far it has had to be limited to experiments on non-mammalian embryos, at least during the earliest stages. It is possible to carry out simple surgical operations on invertebrate and lower vertebrate eggs and embryos to determine potentialities of various zones and to investigate factors controlling development. Wilhelm His encouraged the quantitatively minded embryologist with the statement: 'The ultimate aim of embryology is the mathematical derivation of the adult from the distribution of growth in the germ.'

The history of embryology indicates that early workers, with limited material and primitive techniques, had two main attitudes towards what controlled development. Some took the view that the fertilized egg possessed hidden within it all the many characteristics of the adult and that development represented their growth and unfolding until they became visible. More than one considered that they could see a little animal or homunculus curled up inside the egg or sperm – they would thus have supported the theory of in the first few weeks of human embryonic life that it would take much more than this chapter to cover all that is known.

It is essential to realize that each horizon in development is not a fixed or static stage. Every geologist finds particular fossils or distinguishing features in his 'geological horizons', yet he does not imagine that they mark the end of a stage in evolution. Streeter remarked that it is necessary to emphasize the importance of thinking about an embryo as a living organism 'which in its time takes on many guises, always progressing from the smaller and simpler to the larger and more complex'. He intended to publish descriptions of the earliest age groups after the later ones, but his death prevented this. Hertig and Rock have, however, taken over the task and indefatigably continue to fill the storehouse of our knowledge. The early horizons are ten in number and cover the first 23 days of the life of the human embryo. The age of each embryo is estimated from what can be discovered of the time of ovulation. There is evidence that the viability of a mammalian ovum is measured only in hours and thus it is probable that estimations of embryonic age made in this way are fairly accurate. These first ten horizons can be tabulated thus:

Horizon I One-cell fertilized egg.
II Segmenting egg.
III Free blastocyst.
IV Implanting ovum.
V Ovum implanted, but still avillous.
VI Primitive villi, distinct yolk sac.
VII Branching villi, axis of germ disc defined.
VIII Hensen's node, primitive groove.
IX Neural folds, elongated notochord.
X Early somites present.

Recovery of human ova and early embryonic stages is difficult and fortuitous (p. 125). Few embryologists have even seen a human ovum or blastocyst; it is not surprising that when one is found it is described carefully. The author will always remember the desperate tension in a certain laboratory when one valuable and at that time unique stage was accidentally lost. Descriptions of the one-cell stage and segmenting eggs were given in the last chapter; by the fourth day after fertilization the free blastocyst stage (Horizon III) has been reached.

The free blastocyst is small at first in all mammals; it is 0·09 to 0·1 mm. in diameter in man. It consists of a hollow sphere of cells one layer thick with an embryonic knot inside at one pole. Four and a half days after fertilization a human blastocyst contains just over 100 cells. Even at this early stage one can detect a division of labour taking place amongst its cells. Its single-layered covering is called the *trophoblast* and is destined to give rise to membranes and placenta that surround and nourish the growing embryo. The embryonic knot (inner cell mass) will develop steadily into an embryo.

The young blastocyst is nourished by diffusion of foodstuffs through the trophoblast. In mammals it reaches the cavity of the uterus between the fourth and ninth day after ovulation; it arrives there on the fourth to fifth day in man. The corpus luteum in the ovary (p. 96) has by then reached its fullest activity and caused transformation of the uterine lining so that the latter secretes material (uterine milk) nutritious to the blastocyst. The zona pellucida (p. 114) usually ruptures and is lost when the blastocyst reaches the uterus: the blastocyst can now 'implant'. This term signifies a process of attachment of the trophoblast to the maternal uterine tissues (Horizon IV). Several types of implantation are recognized but all depend on an initial contact being made between trophoblast cells and uterine epithelial lining. What follows depends on the species of mammal. In pigs, sheep, cows, horses, dogs, and cats the blastocyst enlarges rapidly and expands so much that it soon fills the greater part of the inside of the uterus. The area of contact between expanding trophoblast and uterine lining increases steadily. This method of implantation is called *central* or *superficial*. In man, chimpanzees, and certain bats the blastocyst becomes embedded in the uterine lining – *complete interstitial* implantation. This occurs partly as a result of 'burrowing in' and partly by enclosure within the uterine lining. In a third group of mammals that includes rats and mice the blastocyst enters a recess in the uterine cavity in which it becomes closed off and where it implants. This is known as *eccentric* implantation but can be considered to be a modified type of interstitial implantation.

Delayed Implantation

This curious phenomenon occurs in a number of apparently unrelated mammalian groups. They include marsupials, armadillos, martens, badgers, seals, and roe deer. The blastocyst reaches the uterine cavity in the normal way, but from then on there is a pause in development that can last many months and in badgers even up to a year. The blastocyst lies dormant, in an almost hibernatory state, in a recess in the uterus. The uterine lining undergoes little secretory change during the period of delay until in response to some ill-understood stimulus implantation suddenly occurs and development continues normally. It has often been maintained that a hormonal mechanism is responsible for delay. Badgers, however, can ovulate even while blastocysts have been present in the uterus for some months. It is also tempting to suggest from their appearance that the zona pellucida of these blastocysts is more resistant than that of other mammals and so prolongs the free blastocyst stage. Delayed implantation can result in birth of young at the same time every year, often at a time most favourable for the newborn. It has never been reported in Primates or in man.

Before and After Implantation

Horizon IV is reserved for the stage of blastocyst attachment (4½–7 days after fertilization). No normal examples of this stage have so far been recovered. Implantation proper begins 5½ to 6 days after fertilization and the blastocyst rapidly embeds in the uterine lining. Glandular activity increases and as soon as implantation occurs there is marked increase in blood flow and intracellular accumulation of fluid (oedema). These changes lead rapidly to those of a 'decidual reaction'. This involves enlargement of connective tissue cells with glycogen and fat. There are also changes in intercellular substances that probably make the lining more resistant to invading trophoblast. The changes serve the twofold purpose of providing nutriment for the young embryo and yet also of containing invasive propensities of trophoblast cells. They may also prevent excessive haemorrhage from ruptured maternal vessels that might dislodge the embryo. The reaction of the lining therefore prevents too deep initial penetration and thus ensures successful implantation and survival. A mutual interaction is presumed to occur between foetal and maternal tissues. In certain experimental animals a decidual reaction, often very marked, can be caused even by introduction of glass beads into the uterine cavity at the right time in their cycles. The large number of incomplete or faulty examples of implantation that have been reported suggests that many factors may influence this interaction.

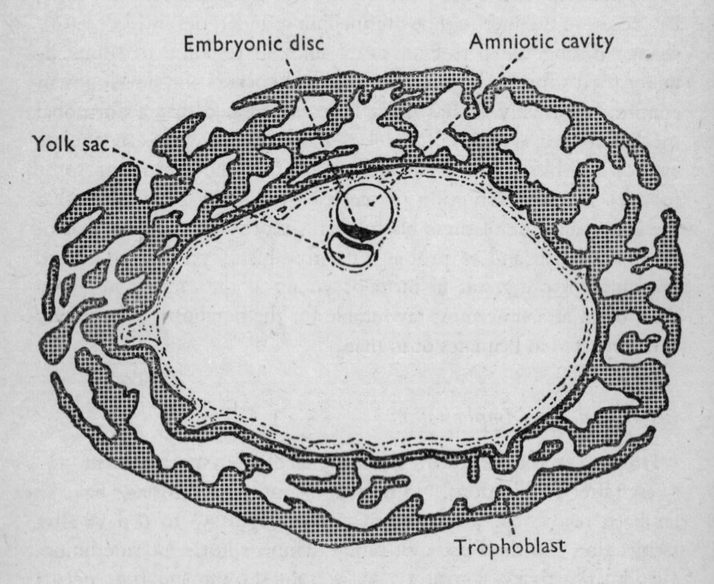

FIG. 9. Section through an early human embryonic disc and chorionic sac. (Horizon VI.) See Plate IX.

Horizon V has been subdivided by Hertig and Rock into three phases. The blastocyst retains an almost solid form during the first phase; the trophoblast becomes two-layered during the second; by the third the blastocyst has become hollowed out by certain cavities. The trophoblast divides into an outer *syncytio*-trophoblast (so-called because it seems to be a multinucleated layer lacking individual cell membranes) and an inner *cyto*-trophoblast (often called after Theodor

Langhans who described it in 1870). Both layers produce hormones, one of which it is suggested has an important function relating to a fate that threatens the young embryo – its expulsion from the uterus at the menstruation that should shortly take place. The menstrual flow that would be expected some 14 days after ovulation is in fact suppressed. There is evidence from several sources that it is a hormone from the cyto-trophoblast (a chorionic gonadotrophin) that acts on the maternal ovary or pituitary or both organs to cause menstrual suppression. This hormone is soon excreted in biologically detectable quantities in maternal urine; methods have been devised for demonstrating its presence and form valuable pregnancy tests. It is not known for certain that the trophoblast of any other mammal produces a gonadotrophin comparable to that of man, although it is too early to call it a unique human characteristic. There is evidence that the mare's trophoblast may stimulate the endometrium to produce a comparable hormone; thus we are not yet quite sure precisely how embryos of every mammalian species weather early hormonal storms and other inclemencies.

The syncytio-trophoblast possesses enzymes capable of destroying maternal tissue with which it comes in contact. Some other factor may also cause the death and liquefaction of maternal cells that occur close to the trophoblast. Tissue death results in formation of material called *histiotrophe* (nourishment by tissue) that is nutritious to the embryo. Implantation is well advanced by the 12th day after fertilization and the embryo is veritably a parasite within its mother.

Small projections develop on the outside of the trophoblast during Horizon VI. These are primitive *villi*. Their appearance increases the surface absorptive area of the trophoblast: in the next chapter it will be seen that they develop into the placenta, becoming complicated in form and gaining blood vessels that link up with those of the embryo.

Changes in the Embryo

The embryonic knot becomes transformed during Horizon VII into a flattened, pear-shaped disc. This is brought about by appearance of two cavities within the blastocyst; details of their formation differ in various mammals. They are called the *amniotic* and *yolk sac* cavities (Fig. 9). Between them lies the *germinal disc* composed of two layers of cells. That on the floor of the amniotic cavity is called the *ectodermal* layer; that on the under-aspect of the disc is the *endodermal* layer. They are the first of what von Baer christened *germ layers*: they are found in all vertebrate embryos. A third layer, the *mesodermal*, soon appears between the other two. It is technically known as secondary mesoderm to distinguish it from primary mesodermal cells that take part in formation of foetal membranes (p. 149).

To understand what happens during Horizon VIII we must imagine that we can look down into the amniotic cavity of a human embryo about 15–16 days old. We should see below us the upper ectodermal surface of the pear-shaped germinal disc; its broad end marks the front or head end. A mid-line longitudinal furrow that extends along most of the disc is called the neural groove because it is destined to develop into neural tissue of brain and spinal cord. A small node is present at the hind end of the neural groove; it was first described by a German embryologist, Viktor Hensen. Behind this node a mid-line streak marks the site of formation of secondary mesoderm below the surface ectoderm. Study of vertebrate embryos suggests that cells formed here migrate forwards to provide embryonic connective tissue.

A tube or column of cells originates from a point close to Hensen's node and burrows forwards beneath the neural groove towards the head end of the disc. This is the *notochordal* process, a slender, mid-line, hollow rod of cells which clearly divides the disc into a left and a right side. It indicates a future bilateral symmetry shown by all vertebrate embryos and marks the earliest stage in development of a backbone. Possession of a notochord sometime or other in life by an animal means that it can be classified as a *Chordate*. In lower, free-swimming Chordates, such as *Amphioxus*, the notochord remains as a long, flexible, and elastic rod. Its main function in such an animal can be compared to that of a strut preventing the animal from being telescoped. The largest sub-phylum of the Chordata is the Vertebrata, and in them the notochord is absorbed into and replaced by the spinal column. The notochord elongates during Horizon IX and in Horizon X mesodermal cells derived mainly from the primitive streak region come to lie on each side of it.

Two important developments take place in this mesoderm. It

first becomes segmented into a series of blocks called *somites*. Segmentation starts near the head end and continues towards the tail end until eventually some 44 somites are formed. The significance of the somites is that they illustrate the basic construction of much of a vertebrate embryo. Somitic segmentation (metamerism) primarily involves the muscular system but also affects other features. It is reflected in the serial arrangement in mammals of ribs, vertebrae, intercostal nerves, and skin segments of the trunk. Much modification of basic segmental pattern has occurred in other parts of the body, but it is possible to discern evidence of a primitive segmentation in the anatomy of the limbs, the head, and the vascular system. Knowledge of details of modifications in the basic segmental pattern in various regions can be very helpful in understanding adult structure and even in elucidating how certain disease processes affect the human body.

The second important change in somitic mesoderm in Horizon x involves formation of a split in the outer edges of each somite so that it becomes divided like a sandwich. The upper layer will necessarily come to lie on the inner aspect of the ectoderm; the lower layer will become applied to the endoderm. There is thus a cavity left between the two layers on each side of the germinal disc. It is to become the *coelom* which is later sub-divided into important body cavities. It is obvious that organs which move or change their shape inside the body must be able to do so without damaging themselves or neighbouring organs. Heart, lungs, and abdominal viscera became invaginated, as it were, into a double-layered sac. It is as if a fist were pushed into a balloon so that one layer of the balloon covers the fist close to the skin and the other lies outside it. The heart is invaginated into its particular sub-division of the coelom, the pericardial cavity. The two layers of the pericardium are separated by a little fluid and so enables the heart to fill and empty safely. Lungs are invaginated into pleural cavities, but in elephants both layers are closely attached to the thoracic cage. Abdominal viscera are completely or partially invaginated into a peritoneal cavity that is made complicated in form by many folds, mesenteries, and recesses. One large recess is found in mammals behind the stomach and is called a *lesser sac* of peritoneum. Its significance is that it allows the stomach to fill and empty freely; a requisite of warm-bloodedness is that of being able to eat after quite short intervals to sustain metabolic rate and body temperature.

All the sub-divisions of the coelomic cavity are at first in communication in a young embryo. Later they become anatomically separated and, apart from certain developmental abnormalities, remain so throughout life. Separation of the sub-divisions is related to development of folding of the germinal disc.

Folding of the Early Embryo

Folding or 'tucking under' occurs in the head and tail regions and at the sides of the germinal disc. Mesoderm called septum transversum and the primitive heart tubes first develop in the head region.

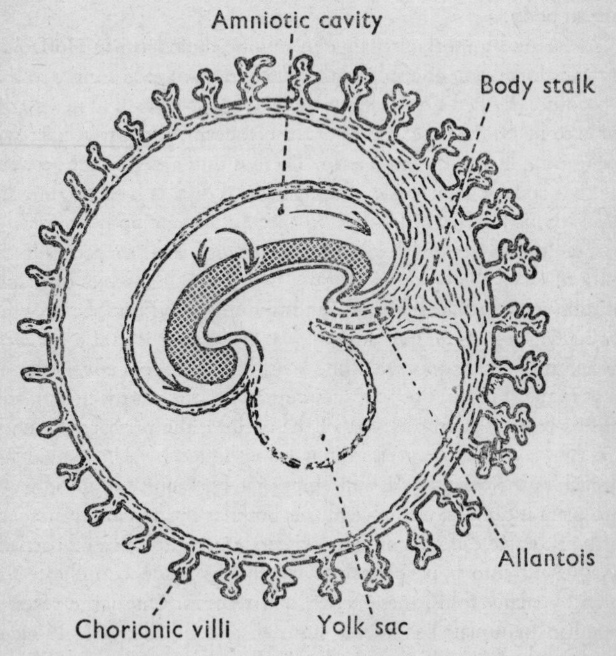

FIG. 10. Arrangement of the embryonic membranes and body stalk in a young human embryo. It also indicates how head, tail, and side folds develop.

Folding of the embryo results in these structures coming to lie beneath the head: the septum transversum cuts across the coelom as the diaphragm. It thus helps divide pleural from peritoneal cavities. Folding in the tail region provides room for development of openings for alimentary and urogenital systems and for a tail in those species that have one. Folding at the sides of the disc encloses the digestive tube and viscera that will develop from endodermally lined yolk sac. The inner layer of mesoderm (see above) of each side closes round the gut tube to provide its muscle and connective tissue. The outer layer, together with ectoderm, closes in front of the now almost tubular embryo to form the tissues of the anterior thoracic and abdominal walls.

Folding processes result in the young embryo 'rising up' in the amniotic cavity (Fig. 10). The amnion ceases to be attached to the edges of the disc and is swept round until it surrounds a stalk left between the embryo and the developing placenta – the stalk is the *umbilical cord*. It is possessed by all Eutherian mammals and is evidence of true intra-uterine life with a placental attachment. The embryo elongates more rapidly than the amniotic cavity enlarges in diameter: thus it develops a marked curvature and is 'doubled up'.

Pharyngeal Bars

The human embryo is by this time 2·5–3·0 mm. in C.R. length and is 24 ± 1 days old (Horizon XI). Young embryos are curled up (Plate XI) and are measured in a straight line from Crown to Rump – thus C.R. length – as is used below in the various Horizons. Thirteen to twenty paired somites are present. Folding in the head region results in the heart coming to lie below the head with the front, narrowed part of the yolk sac (foregut) extending between them (Fig. 11). A number of interesting pharyngeal arches develop on each side of this primitive mouth cavity. In fishes, salamanders, and tadpoles they are called *gill bars* and have slits between them that permit passage of water. Gills have a respiratory function in these animals; oxygen passes from water to blood within their vessels. Pharyngeal arches or bars do not have a respiratory function in reptiles, birds, or mammals, nor are there slits between the arches. In mammalian embryos derivatives of pharyngeal arches contribute to structures in face and jaws, ears, tongue, larynx, and to several endocrine organs in the neck. Each pharyngeal arch has ectoderm outside, an endodermal lining and cartilage, muscle, blood vessels, and nerves within it. Analysis of the fates of the various arch components is essential for

FIG. 11. How the umbilical cord develops from the body stalk in Fig. 10.

understanding adult anatomy in the head and neck. It also throws much light on evolution of jaws, auditory mechanisms, and endocrine organs.

Temporary existence of pharyngeal arches has frequently been used to support theories of recapitulation, i.e. 'that embryos of higher forms pass through stages resembling adults of lower forms'

(Haeckel, p. 24). Such theories are now only considered helpful after some modification. It has been said that there are two kinds of embryologists; those that *look at* embryos and those than *think about* them. The former have advanced the subject; the latter have only raised difficulties. Pharyngeal bars in mammals are not gills: they represent a structural groundwork occurring in vertebrate embryos which are used in some to build gills and in others to make jaws and other structures. '... we may safely deduce from the similarity of this arrangement in all classes of vertebrates ... that they inherit their pattern of growth through some one common protovertebrate ancestor, of fish-like general character though not exactly like any present-day fish ... The descendants, as they evolved into various classes, necessarily inherited such a pattern, but they worked it over into new forms suitable for their needs' (G. W. Corner).

Three to Seven Weeks

Streeter's Horizons XII to XXIV cover the time during human embryology when the great organ systems develop. It is the time of organogenesis: a chapter on each organ would not cover all that is known. Details that are peculiarly human are too recondite for this brief review and we must be content to list only a few outwardly discernible features (see Fig. 12 and Plates X–XIII).

Horizon XII 3·2–3·8 mm., 26 ± 1 days old. Three pharyngeal bars present.

Horizon XIII 4·0–5·0 mm., 28 ± 1 days old. Arm and leg buds just formed.

Horizon XIV 6·0–7·0 mm., 28–30 days old. Leg buds fin-like, ear and eye defined.

Horizon XV 7·0–8·0 mm., 31–32 days old. Head large, nostrils forming, hand plate present.

Horizon XVI 8·0–11·0 mm., 33 ± 1 days old. Main parts of brain formed; thigh, leg, and foot regions recognizable.

Horizon XVII 11·0–13·6 mm., 35 ± 1 days old. Head much larger, facial processes present; digital rays in hand.

Horizon XVIII 14·5–16·0 mm , 37 ± 1 days old. Body a more unified mass. Toe rays present; eyelid folds, tip of nose and ear hillocks discernible.

Horizon XIX 17·0–20·0 mm., 39 ± 1 days old. Trunk region starts to straighten out.

Horizon XX 21–23 mm., 41 ± 1 days old. Limbs increased in length and stubby fingers present.

Horizon XXI 24 mm., 43 ± 1 days old. Fingers longer, toes present.

Horizon XXII 25–27 mm., 45 ± 1 days old. Eyelids starting to cover eyeballs; ear assuming definitive form.

Horizon XXIII 28–30 mm., 47 ± 1 days old. Head bending into erect attitude; neck more apparent; limbs longer.

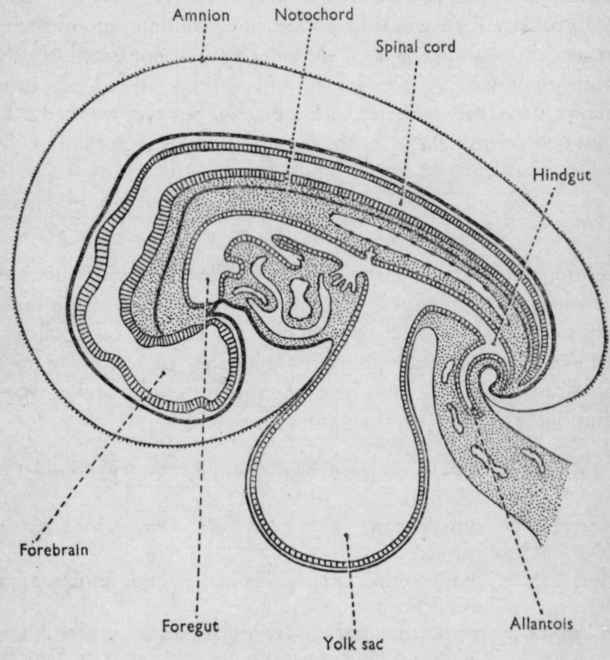

FIG. 12. Arrangement of the main parts of a human embryo about five weeks old.

Eight weeks after fertilization a human embryo is some 40 mm. in *C.R.* length. It now has an unmistakably human appearance. The head is bulging and round (Plate XII), the forehead high, indicating an already relatively large brain. The face is flat, the nose small, but suggestions of a definite chin can be discerned. The ear has a shell-like pinna in miniature. The thorax is barrel-shaped and squat, the abdomen rotund and protuberant. The forelimb is more developed than the hind, but already certain characteristic features of fingers and toes are observable. The rudimentary tail has disappeared and there is a rounded rump. All these external features indicate that their owner must rank in a group high among Primates, but it is only its large brain that 'predicts that this being is destined to feel, think and strive beyond all other species that live on earth'.

Growth of the Foetus

The term foetus is applied to an embryo when it has acquired all the characteristics that can be recognized in later life. This stage is reached by the end of the second month in human embryos. The foetal period is thus mainly one of growth with certain alterations in shape and proportion. Figs. 9–11 show how a foetus grows and Plates X–XIII show its appearances at different ages.

Fusion of eyelids over the eyeball occurs during the third month. Most of the primary ossification centres appear in bones and the first signs of hair and nails are seen. The face assumes a more human appearance during the fourth and fifth months; the skin glands become active. The foetus can now move powerfully enough for the mother to appreciate 'quickening'. Eyebrows are present and eyelids are no longer fused by the seventh month; head hair is present. Children born prematurely at this time (or even a little earlier) can survive with careful nursing.

A full-term child weighs on the average 7½ lb. (3,400 g.) but the weight can vary from 6 lb. (2,700 g.) to over 10 lb. (4,500 g.). Length from crown of head to heel is 20–21 inches (50–53 cm.) and C.R. length is 12–13 inches (30–33 cm.). Circumference of the head is about 13 inches (33 cm.).

A human neonate has a 'chubby' appearance and its head appears unduly large relative to the body. The head is often distorted in shape, having a 'sugar-loaf' form because of moulding during passage through the birth canal. Moulding is quite normal and persists for less than a week. The face is broad and cheeks bulge owing to a pad of fat in each that facilitates sucking at the breast. The nose is broad and squat and the facial region is relatively small compared with the rest of the large head. Jaws are small, devoid of erupted teeth (except, rarely, lower central incisors) and a distinct chin can be felt. The neck is apparently short and there are marked circular creases in its skin. The bones of the neck (cervical vertebrae) are, however, relatively long at birth. Shoulders are set high on the thorax as if in a fixed shrug. This, and the fat neck and a tendency for the head to fall forward, give a shortnecked appearance.

The thorax is more barrel-shaped, the heart relatively larger and higher within it, than in the adult. The abdomen is plump and distended owing to the relatively large liver – it occupies about half the abdominal cavity – and because marked elongation due to occur later in the lumbar spine has not begun. The 'small of the back' and the loins are therefore hardly discernible. Arms and legs are about equal in length; the leg steadily elongates from birth onwards. Testes are usually in the scrotum.

The human neonate is born with hair on its head and often some hair or a few single stiff hairs on other parts of its body. This is primary hair, *lanugo*; it is shed during the few weeks following birth and is replaced by secondary hair that may not be of exactly similar colour. Lanugo is usually first shed from the back of the head, rubbed away by nodding movements. A new-born child is covered to varying degrees by a white cheese-like substance of fatty consistency, *vernix caseosa*; it is washed off at the first bath. It is composed of dead skin cells mixed with sebum and is said to protect foetal skin from amniotic fluid. Vernix may break loose from the skin and be swallowed, sometimes with shed lanugo hairs, when a foetus drinks amniotic fluid. Finger nails reach the level of the tip of the pulp of the fingers by the end of a full-term pregnancy. All neonates are blue-eyed; other eye colours develop by six months as more pigment is laid down in the iris.

FOR FURTHER READING

Ourselves Unborn. G. W. Corner. Yale University Press, 1944

Principles of Embryology. C. H. Waddington. George Allen and Unwin, 1956

Analysis of Development. B. H. Willier, P. A. Weiss, and V. Hamburger. W. B. Saunders Co., 1955
Embryos and Ancestors. G. R. de Beer. Oxford University Press, 1951
Human Embryology W. J. Hamilton, J. D. Boyd, and H. W. Mossman. Heffer, 2nd Ed., 1952

CHAPTER 8

HIS NUTRITION BEFORE BIRTH

THE parts played by the uterine tube and the uterine glands in providing secretions nutritious to the cleaving egg and blastocyst have already been mentioned. It has also been shown how the blastocyst obtains foodstuffs by diffusion as it invades the endometrium. From about the third week after fertilization foetal blood vessels first make their appearance, both inside the embryo and outside in the membranes surrounding it. The stage is now reached for the development of an organ, the placenta, that acts as an intermediary between the foetal and maternal circulations. The placenta shows a diversity of form in mammals greater than that of any other organ and is thus particularly difficult to define.

The term placenta (a Latin word meaning cake-like in form) was given to the discoid human after-birth by the Italian anatomist Columbus about four hundred years ago. In its present meaning it is applied to 'any intimate apposition or fusion of the foetal organs to the maternal (or paternal) tissues for physiological exchange'. This is the definition of the American anatomist H. W. Mossman, who has placed us so much in his debt by his investigations of the structure of the placenta. The extended definition of the term allows us to include all connexions, sometimes quite curious, between developing young and mother (or even father) in a wide variety of animals. It even enables us to consider relationships in certain invertebrates and lower vertebrates as well as those in highly specialized mammals.

The placenta has always been considered as a somewhat mysterious structure. Man has approached it with the practical attitude of the midwife, but albeit with curiosity as to why it should be reputed to increase the growth and yield of a vine when buried underneath. Many natural historians have wondered why certain female mammals eat the placenta after birth. Several speakers at recent international conferences have been unable to explain its complex structure and its growing number of functions that have been revealed by modern methods of investigation.

It was formerly thought that the placenta was simply a structure that acted as an intermediary organ between mother and foetus and allowed gases and foodstuffs to diffuse from maternal to foetal blood. Products of metabolism from the foetus returned across the placenta to be broken down and excreted by the mother. Recent research has shown, however, that the placenta, besides providing a transfer service, has a number of other functions, many of which are not yet well understood, but are apparently very important to the foetus. It acts as a barrier to prevent potentially toxic substance reaching the embryo, as an endocrine organ and as a storage organ.

In essence the placenta involves an arrangement of tissue in which maternal blood comes into very close relation with foetal blood, but the two blood streams do not normally ever mix. They are separated by a layer of tissue known as the placental membrane or 'barrier', often composed of both foetal and maternal tissue, and it is across this that substances passing to and from the foetus must travel. It is now clear that the placental membrane has a structure more complex than that of a simple intervening layer in the form of a semi-permeable membrane that allows some substances, and obstructs others, in their passage from one blood stream to the other. The placenta is an organ 'in its own right', with a metabolism of its own and capable of manufacturing certain substances. It not only passes on all types of foodstuffs, keeping some for its own use, but also has some products of its own that are essential for survival of the foetus.

The placenta differs both in its gross and in its fine structure in various groups of mammals. These differences have been the basis of several attempts to classify and compare the various forms, and this has led to arguments about the relative efficiency of each type. Many consider that the placenta exhibits generalized and specialized features, some of which may be hazardous or even detrimental to embryonic life. To the foetus, however, an efficient and satisfactory placenta is one that serves it successfully until term, and fortunately that nearly always happens.

CHARACTERISTICS OF THE HUMAN PLACENTA

A number of adjectives are used to describe the manner of development, the form, and fine structure of any placenta. We shall first consider those that can be applied to the human placenta with a brief comment on their significance.

Shedding of the Placenta

The human placenta is *caducous* and *deciduate*. These terms imply that the placenta is shed at term (*caducere* means to fall away or to be shed) and that in its separation from the uterine wall some maternal tissue (*decidua*) is also torn away. The decidua is the inner lining or endometrium of the pregnant uterus (see p. 129).

It might appear a strange waste that so useful an organ should be shed and discarded at the end of its life. Extrusion from the uterus occurs after the birth of the child; but separation starts early in labour and contractions of the uterine muscle cause shearing forces in the placental bed. After expulsion a raw, bleeding area is left at the placental site on the uterine wall. Up to a pint of maternal blood may normally be lost from this site at the time of labour; eventually the vessels become occluded and blood clots on the surface. There is a slight loss of blood and fluid for a few days of the *puerperium* (*puer* = a boy, and *parere* = to bear) and this constitutes the lochia. At first the lochia is red, but after about four days it becomes brown. By the tenth day it is yellowish-white or almost colourless and consists principally of secretions from the cervical glands and cellular debris. The lochia ceases about the middle of the third week, but repair at the placental site is still incomplete. Shedding the placenta, and the damage it causes to maternal tissues, is potentially dangerous. This is particularly true when birth is assisted, because infection may be introduced. Man may be the only mammal that can act as midwife to himself, but it is hardly a hundred years since he first realized the inherent dangers. Micro-organisms are found in the human uterine cavity one day after birth, but fortunately most are harmless. In the past, when man had no knowledge of bacteria, pathogenic organisms frequently gained access to the raw surface of the placental site.

They were literally carried to the female reproductive tract on the hands and clothing of the accoucheur. We little realize nowadays how devastating were the ravages of puerperal fever, and rightly we remember the name of Semmelweiss, a Hungarian physician who demonstrated the need for antisepsis during childbirth.

Many mammals shed their placenta; some even eat it and so return to the maternal organism much needed substances such as the iron that is occasionally stored there. In other mammals the placenta is not shed (the contra-deciduate type) but degenerates and is absorbed by maternal tissues. In the non-deciduate mammals (the pig, the horse, the whale, and also the lemurs) the placenta is shed, but without any of the decidua. There are risks for the maternal mammal with all these types of placental fate, but to the human foetus with the deciduate type there are certain advantages. The placenta separates so easily that there is little chance of tearing of the cord and blood loss from the foetus. Separation results in the placenta being squeezed by the contracting uterus and a considerable quantity of blood is returned to the foetus before the cord is cut.

Placental Form

The human placenta, and that of the great apes, is discoid in shape; at birth it is a flattened, circular disc like a dinner plate. The human full term placenta is nine inches in diameter, about an inch thick and weighs a pound (Plate XIV). On its outer, or maternal aspect, there are 16–20 lobes or cotyledons, separated by clefts in which lie septa of maternal tissue, some of these come away with the shed placenta. These lobular cotyledons fit into corresponding depressions in the wall of the uterus. From the edge of the disc a membranous sac arises and surrounds the foetus. Careful inspection shows that the sac has two layers: the outer layer is continuous with the substance of the placental disc, the inner one (the *amnion*) can be separated from the foetal aspect of the disc and is reflected onto the umbilical cord (see Fig. 13). The outer layer is the *chorion* (Greek for skin), a name first given to it by Galen by analogy with the skin of a grape. It is derived from the original outer covering of the blastocyst – the trophoblast (see p. 128). Part of it has developed a large number of processes, or villi, on its outer surface (chorion frondosum) and it is these which become the cake-like placenta. In the villi foetal connective or mesodermal tissue forms the supporting tissue or core of the villi, and also gives rise to blood vessels. It is this connective tissue and the trophoblast covering which really constitute the chorion. In the

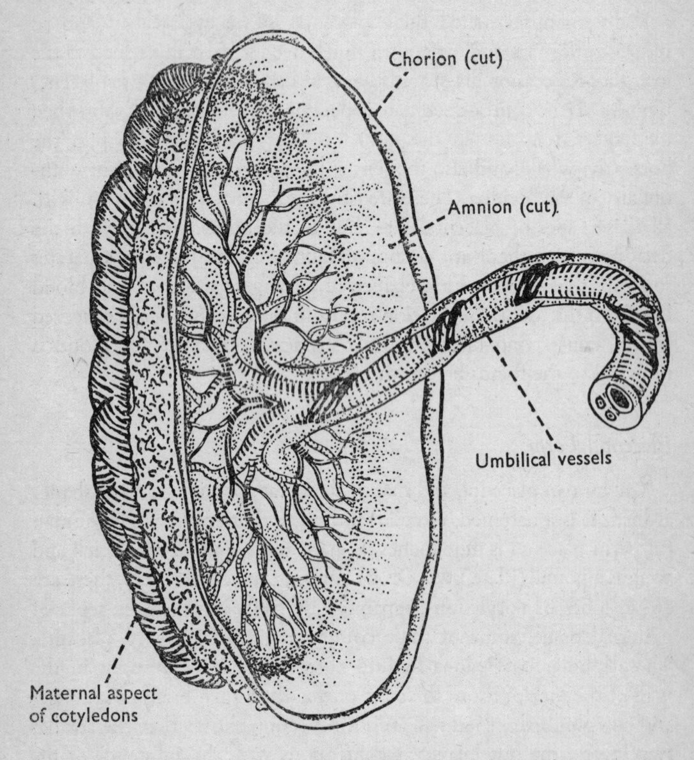

FIG. 13. Main parts of a human full-term placenta. See Plate XIV.

thin part of the chorionic sac, attached to the margins of the main disc, these two layers are fused and appear almost as one. No villi are present, therefore this part is called the chorion laeve (*laeve* means bald). Another way of illustrating what has happened is to imagine that at implantation only that part of the trophoblast near the uterine wall develops villi, while the remainder is pushed out into the uterine lumen as the embryo increases in size.

Both the form of the placenta, and the arrangement of the villi, differ in the various groups of mammals. The appearances often vary at different stages of pregnancy. When fully developed, we can recognize the following forms. A *diffuse* placenta, found in the pig, the horse and the whale, possesses villi, or folds that resemble villi, distributed evenly over the whole of the chorion. The villi may be restricted to a limited number of areas called *cotyledons* (thus cotyledonary placenta); in some species of deer there are few cotyledons (5–8) whereas the goat and the cow have many (120–180). The villi of each cotyledon fit into crypts in specialized portions of the uterus called caruncles, and thus a series of little placentae or *placentomes* are formed. These may look like flattened discs, oval plates, elongated ovoids, or hollowed-out cups. In many Carnivora the placenta is *annular* or *zonary* and is like a 'muff' about the middle of the chorionic sac. In Platyrrhine and Catarrhine monkeys and in the Tree Shrew the placenta is *bi-discoidal* with the two discs placed on opposite sides of the uterine cavity. Women occasionally have bidiscoidal, and rarely diffuse or annular placentae. In lemurs the placenta is diffuse and strikingly resembles that found in certain ungulates; this is another reason why lemurs cannot seriously be considered immediate relatives of man (p. 38). Tarsiers, however, have a discoidal placenta which in many ways resembles that of man.

Placental form is obviously correlated with the type of uterus, whether it be single or double horned and whether there are caruncles or whether the endometrium is glandular throughout. It is also a reflection of the genetic constitution in each species, but is of little help in evolutionary classification. Placentomes can be so large that they interfere with labour, as in Sika deer. A discoid placenta can develop over the mouth of the uterus (the opening to the cervical canal); this condition is called placenta praevia.

Placental Villi

Villi as well as placentae exhibit many shapes. They are long and filiform in many deer and fit into straight crypts in the caruncle. In reindeer each main stem villus has many side branches like a Christmas tree. In the goat the villi branch frequently to form tufts. Branching may be so complicated in some mammals that a three dimensional lattice-work is formed. The placental mass is thus sponge-like and the arrangement of villi is labyrinthine. The villi may fit into sockets or crypts in the uterus, as described above, but the degree of persistence of maternal tissue varies. In some mammals the uterine lining remains intact and lies in close contact with the surface of the villi. In others there is a varying amount of destruction and in yet others the maternal tissue is eroded until maternal blood escapes and percolates through the labyrinth of spaces between the villi.

The arrangement of the villi in man has been difficult to define precisely, partly because there is much variation, and partly because perfectly preserved uteri with the placentae in position are difficult to obtain. It has been suggested that the villi are arranged in a digitate manner like fronds of seaweed, with maternal blood circulating through the intervillous lakes. Others have described a series of thick main stem villi passing through the mass of the placenta and from which many side branches are given off. These are turned back so that the appearance is similar to that of many inverted willow trees. More recently the view has developed that the villi may at times appear as described above, but that more frequently tips of adjacent villi fuse together as they develop, with eventual formation of a sponge-like or *labyrinthine* arrangement.

Allantois

There are other membranes taking part in the formation of the mammalian placenta besides the chorion and amnion. In some species a large, sausage-shaped, fluid-filled sac is found within the chorion. This is called the allantois and is initially an outgrowth from the hind end of the embryonic gut (Fig. 10). The latter is at first a common chamber for lower ends of developing alimentary and urogenital systems. It is called a *cloaca* from a Latin word meaning a sewer. The cloaca later separates into the anal canal and the *urogenital sinus* which is destined to develop into the bladder and most of the urethra. The allantois retains connexion with the urogenital sinus by a hollow tube that enters the embryo at the umbilicus. It is not certain whether part of the urinary bladder is developed from the allantoic stalk, which usually atrophies. Remnants of its existence can be seen in the adult in the form of a strand of connective tissue, the *urachus*. It passes from the apex of the bladder to the umbilicus, and sometimes cyst-like swellings develop within this strand. The allantois is lined by endodermal cells similar to those lining the yolk sac. From the time it starts to grow out from the hindgut it carries mesoderm with it on its outside. This allantoic mesoderm becomes vascularized and if the allantois grows out far enough to reach the chorion its blood vessels become those of the placenta. We speak therefore of a *chorio-allantoic* placenta and we mean by it *the* placenta – that is the structure commonly called the after-birth whose characteristics we have been describing.

The allantois is well-developed in birds; it is very vascular and essential for respiration, absorption, and excretion. Its form varies in Marsupials, in which it may or may not reach the chorion to form a type of chorio-allantoic placenta. In Eutherian mammals it is occasionally very large, as in Carnivora, whales, lemurs, horses, and ruminants, and may contain much fluid. The allantoic fluid is probably excreted by the foetus either directly via the developing bladder, or from the allantoic vessels. In Primates, including man, the endodermal allantois is small or absent, but as already indicated its mesoderm plays such an important part in forming blood vessels that we describe the human placenta as chorio-allantoic.

Yolk sac

The fourth foetal membrane in mammals is derived from the yolk sac (see p. 131). In birds it is developed by extension of endoderm about the yolk, with mesoderm following later and becoming vascular; it provides a means of mobilizing yolk and conveying it as food to the embryo. In some mammals, despite the reduction of yolk, the endoderm of the yolk sac grows out and comes into contact with the chorion. This is a non-vascular yolk-sac placenta and it occurs in many rodents, the armadillo, and bats. There is fusion or intimate apposition of the bilaminar layer with uterine tissues and physiological exchange occurs by diffusion.

In most marsupials, in mammals such as squirrels and Insectivores mesoderm extends between the yolk-sac endoderm and the chorion.

Vascularization of mesoderm occurs and blood circulates through the trilaminar structure to and from the embryo. This primitive type of yolk-sac placenta is the *chorio-vitelline* placenta. In the Eutheria it is very variable in size and importance, sometimes simple and bilaminar, sometimes trilaminar and vascular, and often transitory, being replaced by the chorio-allantoic placenta. In most rodents affairs are complicated in that the yolk sac becomes 'inverted' and eventually, owing to the breakdown of the bilaminar part, the vascularized endodermal part comes in direct communication with the uterine lumen. Recently it has been shown by experiment that this curious phenomenon may play a part in transfer of antibodies and perhaps food substances from mother to embryo. In Primates the history of the yolk sac is again variable, but a chorio-vitelline placenta cannot be formed because a large extra-embryonic coelom prevents the yolk sac from coming in contact with the chorion. The yolk sac is largest in the marmosets. The small yolk sac in man (Fig. 11) is covered by vascularized mesoderm and is important as a site of blood formation in early embryonic life and also as the site of origin of germ cells.

Fine Structure

Variations in fine structure of the chorio-allantoic placenta, as seen through the light microscope, were used by the German placentologist Otto Grosser and later by the American embryologist H. W. Mossman as a means of classification. They examined 'the intimacy of contact between the chorion and the maternal tissues and thereby ... the thickness and constitution of the membrane separating the maternal and foetal blood streams'.

Four main types of histological relationship have been recognized; other types have been described but are not generally accepted. It is assumed that the chorion is always an intact, continuous layer, however thin. The name of the type of maternal tissue found in apposition to the chorion is placed before the word chorion to describe each type of relationship. Thus *epitheliochorial* indicates that the maternal uterine epithelium lies in contact with chorion; such a relationship is found in the non-deciduate, diffuse type of placenta. Six layers of cells or tissue separate the two blood streams, and thus form the 'thickest' type of placental membrane. Theoretically every type of placenta commences by being epitheliochorial in that this is the relationship that pertains when trophoblast first comes into contact with maternal epithelium. There are no blood vessels in the chorion at this early stage, and so this is not an argument that an epitheliochorial type of placenta is necessarily primitive.

The *syndesmochorial* relationship implies that maternal epithelium has been destroyed to a varying degree and the chorion is thus in contact with maternal connective tissue. It is found in placentae of ruminants, sheep and goats, and perhaps the cow. It reflects, therefore, an apparent thinning of tissues intervening between the two bloodstreams. There is some evidence that maternal epithelium may be continually repaired and destroyed again as pregnancy advances. In the *endotheliochorial* type the chorion eats through or destroys maternal epithelium and connective tissue until it comes into contact with the endothelial lining of maternal blood vessels, although strands of connective tissue are often left surrounding each capillary. This arrangement is typical of Carnivora, some Insectivora, tree shrews, and some bats. The fourth type is called *haemochorial*: the trophoblast destroys even the endothelial lining of the maternal blood vessels and thus maternal blood escapes to bathe the outer surfaces of villi. A haemochorial placenta is found in lower types of rodents, hedgehogs, monkeys, apes, and man. Two varieties of haemochorial placenta are described; one is the labyrinthine type, in which villi are arranged in lamellae with maternal blood percolating through narrow capillary-like channels (as in rodents), the second is the villous type in which villi float more freely in a pool of blood. The labyrinthine type is usually considered more primitive, and in Primates all variations are found between it and the villous type.

The distinguished embryologist, J. P. Hill (1873–1954), considered that four stages could be defined in Primate placentation: (*a*) a *Lemuroid* stage – in which the placenta is non-deciduate and epitheliochorial; (*b*) a *Tarsioid* stage – discoid or localized, deciduate, and haemochorial, with peculiar features distinguishing it from the placenta of monkeys and some characteristics of vascularization not unlike those of the human placenta; (*c*) a *Pithecoid* stage in which implantation is superficial and in which a bi-discoidal, labyrinthine, and haemochorial placenta develops; (*d*) an *Anthropoid* stage with a deciduate, discoidal, villous, and haemochorial placenta. Man is, of course, included in the fourth stage, but many consider that the placenta is labyrinthine.

Hazards of a Haemochorial Placenta

It is unfortunate that study of the placenta has thrown so little light on the evolution of Primates. It shows that man displays some primitive features in placental development, and in placental structure, although there are also some specialized characteristics. Many consider that there are some theoretical disadvantages associated with the haemochorial relationship, but man's reproductive rate suggests they cannot be very serious. There is evidence that circulation of blood through the intervillous space is slow, and that formation of localized clots of maternal blood is not uncommon. Maternal arteries leading through uterine tissue into the intervillous space are remarkably coiled, show curious changes in their inner linings, and have narrow nozzle-like openings; these anatomical features could lead to considerable slowing of blood flow. Most of the blood returning from the intervillous space was believed to drain into a 'marginal' sinus at the edge of the placenta and thence to the uterine veins. The existence of a marginal sinus has not been confirmed and it appears that blood leaves the intervillous space into numerous uterine veins opening near maternal septa that separate the main cotyledonary masses. The openings of these veins are wide enough to admit the tips of villi and may thus get blocked, leading to stagnation of blood flow (J. D. Boyd and W. J. Hamilton).

Slowness of circulation rate in a haemochorial placenta may result in insufficient oxygen reaching the foetus. It is known that foetal haemoglobin has a marked affinity for oxygen and that other physiological mechanisms encourage the transfer of oxygen and may compensate for the slowness of the maternal blood flow. Yet it appears that the foetus lives in a state of relative oxygen lack, rather like that experienced by a man in climbing a high mountain. Some features of foetal blood such as the frequently increased number of red cells (polycythaemia), their large size (macrocytosis), and the fact that it 'resembles in many respects ... blood that has been subjected to an effective continuous and extremely potent stimulus to blood formation' may be responses to an insufficient quantity of oxygen crossing the placenta. Therefore it could be argued that an intra-uterine existence any longer than that necessary for development of a neonate capable of surviving after birth becomes increasingly dangerous as time passes. Prematurity and postmaturity are both un-desirable to a foetus.

Placental Transfer

The placenta performs for the foetus the functions of respiration, food absorption, and excretion. It has a large surface area in contact with maternal tissue or blood to carry out these functions. The villi of a full term human placenta have a surface area of about ten square metres. The cells covering the villi possess minute processes on their surfaces called *microvilli*. They can just be seen with the light micro-scope as a 'brush border' to the chorionic cells. The electron micro-scope demonstrates them in the form of slender protoplasmic strands, often with dilated ends (Plate xv).

Many substances pass unaltered through the placental membrane; some, such as iron, glycogen, and fat are stored, others are modified during transmission and others are aided across the membrane. Many substances never normally pass across. Oxygen and carbon dioxide pass in either direction by diffusion under pressure, but efficiency of oxygen transfer is about one twentieth of that across the lung. Sugars, lipoids, and proteins do not cross by simple diffusion and various enzyme systems may be involved. Amino acids can cross the placental membrane slowly, even when the concentration in foetal is higher than in maternal blood. Transfer against the gradient can also occur with other substances.

Certain poisons and drugs pass easily across the placenta, including anaesthetics and alcohol. Much research has been done recently with radio-active isotopes of those elements that normally traverse the placenta. It is generally too dangerous to experiment with such sub-stances during human pregnancy and so such work is most frequently carried out on experimental animals. It is also possible to 'label' maternal red cells with radio-active isotopes and, after injecting them back into the maternal circulation, to find out if there is any mixing of the labelled cells with foetal ones. Normally, no mixing occurs, but in certain pathological conditions there is some evidence that it does.

The Placental Barrier

The placenta must, therefore, be traversed by a considerable number of substances and the type of research indicated above, as well as chemical analysis, histochemical preparations, and other methods, all indicate that the placental membrane acts as a barrier more permeable to some substances than others. It contains a number of enzymes that play an important part in its transfer mechanisms for providing energy necessary for its work.

There is no doubt that the placenta acts as a most effective barrier against transmission of bacteria. Organisms are believed to be able to pass to the foetus only after producing a lesion in the placenta. Some viruses, or toxic substances elaborated by them, can cross the barrier and may interfere with developmental processes. Proteins in immunological quantities can cross as unaltered molecules, as can many antibodies. The *Rh* agglutinogen (p. 61) passes from foetal to maternal side and the subsequently formed antibody (isoagglutinin) can pass back to the foetus. It may return in quantities sufficient to cause much destruction of foetal blood. It is for this reason that no *Rh* negative woman should be transfused with *Rh* positive blood. In at least 10 per cent of all pregnancies conditions are such that isoimmunization by *Rh* factor could occur. Blood-destroying disease in all its forms, however, only complicates 0·25 per cent of pregnancies and even more rarely is it very severe.

Both layers of trophoblast produce hormones: the placenta is therefore an endocrine gland. The human cytotrophoblast is believed to be the source of probably more than one gonadotrophin (p. 131). It may produce slightly different gonadotrophins at different stages of pregnancy.

The human syncytiotrophoblast secretes oestrogens and progestins. To what extent placentae of other mammals secrete hormones is not fully known. The placental hormones pass into the maternal circulation and influence maternal endocrine organs; they may play some part in controlling the onset of labour. If so, the placenta has another function in that it influences the length of gestation, perhaps more so in man than in other mammals.

The placenta also acts as a barrier against maternal hormones, although some can cross and cause changes in foetal organs. Madame Dantschakoff has vividly discussed the importance of the placenta in preventing male foetuses being swamped with female oestrogens. 'Truly', she writes, 'nature has taken especial pains over the male sex.'

FOR FURTHER READING

Chapters on placentation in *Marshall's Physiology of Reproduction*. Vol. II, 1952

'Comparative morphogenesis of the foetal membranes and accessory uterine structures'. H. W. Mossman. *Contr. Carneg. Instn. Embryol.* 26, 129, 1937

'The Developmental History of the Primates'. J. P. Hill. *Phil. Trans. roy. Soc. Lond.* B. 221. **45**, 1932

Gestation. Ed. L. B. Flexner. Josiah Macy Foundation, 1954

CHAPTER 9

HIS UPRIGHT GAIT

Each has his own tree of ancestors, but at the top of all sits Probably Arboreal!

R. L. STEVENSON

OUR ancestors 'probably came down from the trees more than a million years ago, and may have gone through a more or less quadrupedal phase before a change in pelvic shape made bipedal running and the emancipation of the hands possible. The great development of the brain probably occurred quite soon after adoption of bipedal posture.' (J. B. S. Haldane.)

We do not yet know in detail the successive stages through which man passed before he walked upright with ease. The Miocene and Pliocene apes were probably arboreal, but could almost certainly progress along the ground. *Proconsul major* (p. 47) of the Early Miocene was about the size of a gorilla; it could only have moved safely in the lower branches and for this and other reasons several authorities have suggested that it was mainly terrestrial. The evolution of upright posture can be associated with disappearance of thick forests and their replacement with small woods separated by tracts of open scrub or savanna. Such countryside might well have existed in Kenya in the Miocene according to the examination of fossil insects, fruits and seeds from there made by L. S. B. Leakey. Study of the morphological pattern displayed by the hip bone and much that is available of the lower limb skeleton of the Australopithecinae (p. 48) does not show a pattern of features that indicates either progression on four legs or brachiation. It is reasonable to infer that the Australopithecinae had become adapted to bipedal posture and locomotion, but not as perfectly as man (W. E. Le Gros Clark). Paradoxically, perhaps, it may have been efforts to *retain* an arboreal way of life that resulted in the appearance of upright posture; this would enable more rapid and effective passage across ground between two woods. We can therefore suggest with some confidence that at least one place where man's ancestors stood and walked upright was Africa and that they showed attempts at doing so sometime during the Miocene.

Pronograde, Orthograde, and Plantigrade

Mammals can progress on ground, and even in trees, in two main ways. The trunk or body may be parallel to the ground, *pronograde*, or vertical to the ground, *orthograde*. Man is therefore orthograde, and furthermore, because he walks on the soles of his feet, he is *plantigrade*. Cattle and horses walk on the tips of two, or one, modified digits in each limb.

Upright posture, or ability to stand for varying lengths of time on two hind legs, is exhibited by a number of mammals. The kangaroo, a marsupial, bounds on two hind legs, using the tail as a third limb for balancing. Everyone has seen a bear 'stand up' to beg for a bun, or a dog doing its tricks 'walking' on its hind legs; but it is in monkeys and apes that bipedalism is even better developed. Monkeys can, and often do, run short distances on their hind legs; chimpanzees and gorillas can stand up against the bars of their cages. It has even been suggested that the tracks of the 'Abominable Snowman' were made by a langur running or walking for a short distance. No mammal is capable of bipedal gait to an extent that, as one anatomist phrased it, 'it could go for a nine mile route march with boots on and pack on its back'. Among birds, however, an ostrich might well defeat man in this respect!

Anatomical modifications associated with upright posture, and with bipedal gait, are found throughout the body, but are particularly evident in the skeleton. So much so that it is sometimes possible to state from examination of even a single bone that its possessor could well have walked upright on its hind legs. One of the chief desiderata in bipedalism is ability to balance the head so that the eyes 'look where one is going' and are maintained in a plane horizontal to the horizon. To achieve this with a skeleton of articulated bones requires a number of related modifications of the pronograde mammalian pattern; it is not enough to make a tetrapod's skeleton 'stand up'. We are not trying to derive a human skeleton from that of a tetrapod, but rather to discern characteristics of the skeleton that must be present in that of upright man.

Man's Foot

The human foot is so characteristic, and the print of the bare foot of a man on sand so recognizable, that Robinson Crusoe was in no doubt that his island was shared by another of his species. A glance at Man Friday's foot-print revealed its human characteristics. The big toe, or *hallux*, is larger and nearly always projects beyond the other toes. Occasionally the second toe is longer – a Graecian foot. The other toes are all smaller, the little toe so receded that it often lacks a nail. The footprint shows that weight is borne on the heel, a ridge along the outer side of the sole, on thickened skin at the bases of the toes, but principally on the 'ball' of the foot, though to a lesser degree on the under-surfaces of the tips of the toes. It is very much as if each foot were in the form of a flexible tripod, the heel being one base, the outer margin of the sole being the second, and the ball of the foot, aided by the big toe, being the third. Balancing on one foot one can feel the three areas pressed firmly against the ground or sole of the shoe. The development of hard, dead skin in these regions after much walking indicates that they are weight-bearing.

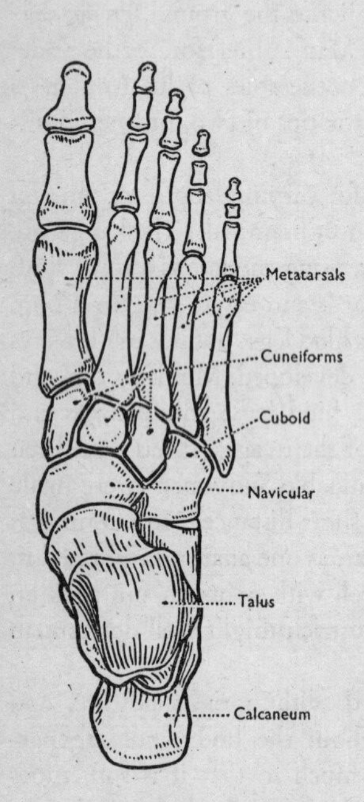

FIG. 14. Arrangement of the bones of the human foot as seen from above.

The skeleton of the foot is not made, however, of struts of bone in the form of a tripod. It consists of a number of 'blocks' of bone (tarsal bones) articulated together with the ankle joint between one of them, the talus, and the bones of the leg. The tarsal bones are arranged in a broad arch extended and expanded by five longer bones (metatarsals) and the shorter phalanges. Figs. 14 and 15 show

how the bones of a foot are articulated and give their names. It will be seen that the bones fit naturally together so that a marked longitudinal arch is made along the inner side of the foot. There is a less marked longitudinal arch along the outer edge, and a third, transverse one across the heads of the five rod-like metatarsals. These are the three main 'arches of the foot'; an ancient Arabian definition of a beautiful girl states that her 'feet are so arched that little streams can run beneath'.

The arched form of the foot is maintained by several factors; there are short interosseous ligaments, strong short and long plantar liga-

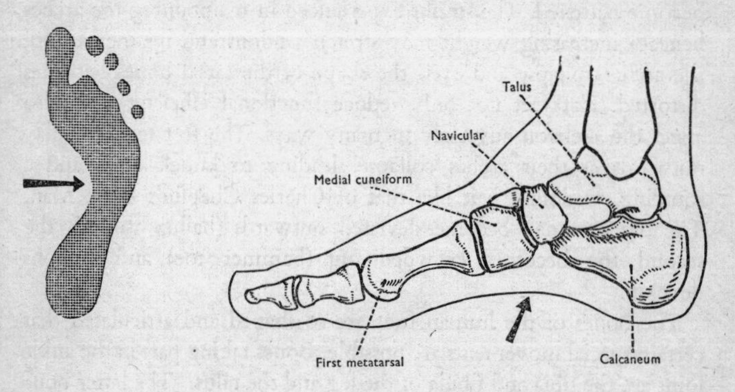

FIG. 15. Bones in the human foot seen from the inner side. The arrows mark the medial longitudinal arch.

ments, and a special ligament called the 'spring' or 'check' ligament below the head of the talus. This ligament does not in fact give the foot its springiness; that is obtained by short muscles of the foot as well as by action of calf muscles whose tendons pass round the ankle to be inserted into tarsals, metatarsals, and phalanges. All the muscles and the thick plantar band or aponeurosis immediately beneath the skin of the sole also help maintain the arches.

The arches perform several functions useful in standing and walking. They ensure that weight is distributed evenly over the sole, a principle similar to that behind use of an arch in building. They allow the foot to be used as a flexible but strong lever and result in springiness in the stride. Running or jumping do not shock or jar the body when it can land on an arched foot. There is sufficient space beneath the arch for small muscles, tendons, and blood vessels without their being compressed.

Man has not evolved bipedalism without being liable to pay a premium, and certain potential weaknesses and disadvantages accompany it. The visiting anatomist from another planet mentioned in Chapter 4 might have commented that characters associated with man's bipedalism had not evolved sufficiently – that he stood upright too early. Man's foot is one of his unique features, but it is not functionally infallible. The arches of his foot may, for several reasons, become flattened. The strains experienced in maintaining the arches beneath increasing weight may stretch tendons and ligaments until the arches collapse and even the shape of the tarsal bones becomes distorted. Flat feet not only reduce functional efficiency but also affect the skeleton adversely in many ways. The feet tend to splay outwards as their arches collapse, leading to knock-knees and a shuffling, waddling gait like that of Charles Chaplin's Little Man. The big toe may become deviated outwards (hallux valgus), the second toe becomes crowded out (hammer toe) and bunions develop.

The bones of the human foot are so shaped and articulated that certain special movements are possible. Bones taking part in the ankle joint are the tibia and fibula of the leg and the talus. The latter bone is called by zoologists the astragulus, and it is in a way a pity that the word has now been abandoned by human anatomists. The astragalus got its name at the time of the Trojan War, when the besiegers used to play dice with the bodies of cervical vertebrae of animals they had eaten. Similarly shaped bones were recovered from hind limbs of sheep and goats, although two curved surfaces reduced the scoring sides to four. The Greek for 'to play dice' is *astragalein*, and so the bone got its name; later the word was transferred to the human bone. The talus articulates with the lower ends of the tibia and fibula in the manner of a hinge, the talus being able to rock in the socket made by them (Fig. 15). The socket is deepened at the sides by flanges of bone projecting downwards from the fibula on the outer side and from the tibia on the inner side of the ankle. This ensures that there is almost a 'grip' exercised by tibia and fibula on the talus. It prevents any movement of the talus other than to and fro rocking (except in

A Bush-Baby (*Galago*) taken by Professor H. Butler, University of Khartoum.

A Rhesus monkey (*Macaca*) with 6-month-old male young.

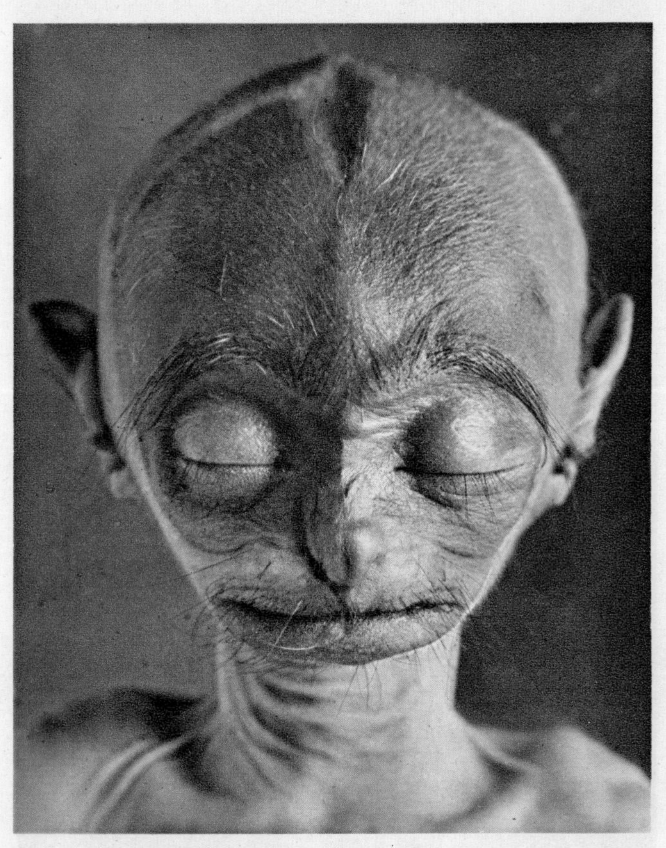

Head of a 5½-month-old male Gibbon foetus (*Hylobates*). The foetus was 25·5 cm. in body length. (*Reproduced by permission of Dr H. Steiner*).

Three year old male Chimpanzee (*Pan*).

Bushman, a lowland Gorilla (*Gorilla*) that died in Lincoln Park Zoo on 1 January 1951, aged 22 years. The body weighed 500 lb. (*Reproduced by permission of Dr P. E. Steiner*).

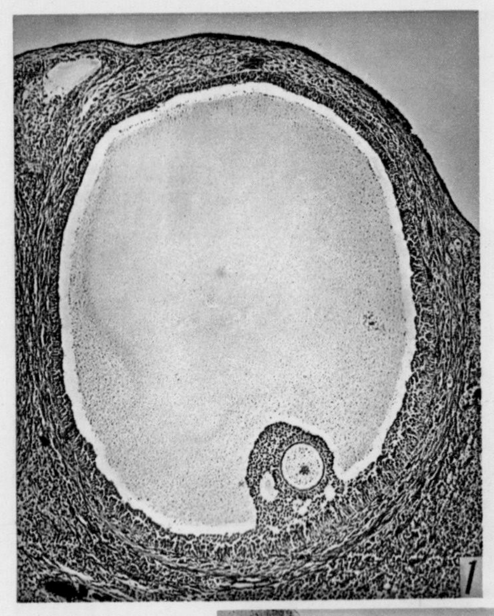

1. Photomicrograph of ovarian follicle and oocyte. × 40.

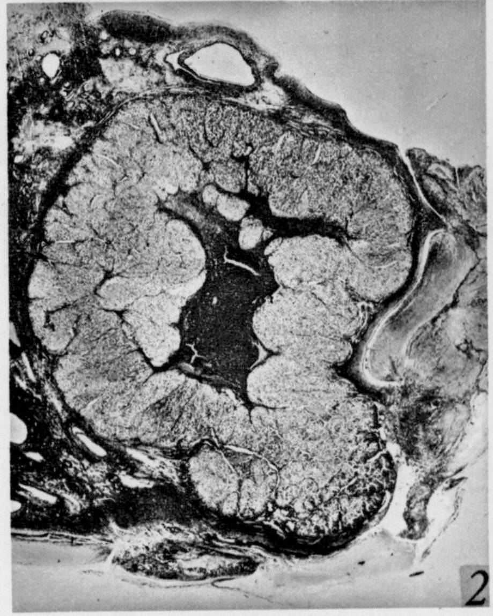

2. Photomicrograph of 6-week-old corpus luteum. × 4.

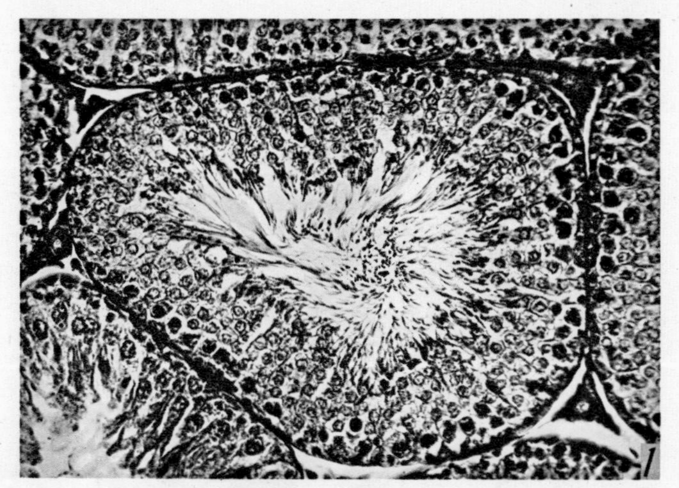

1. Photomicrograph of tubules of testis. × 200.

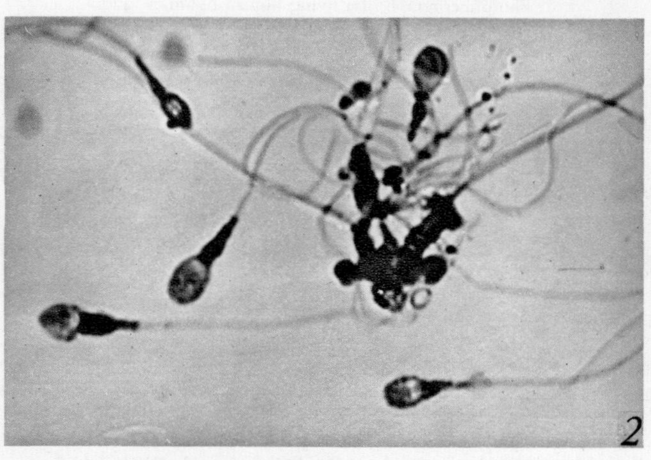

2. Photomicrograph of human spermatozoa. × 1400.

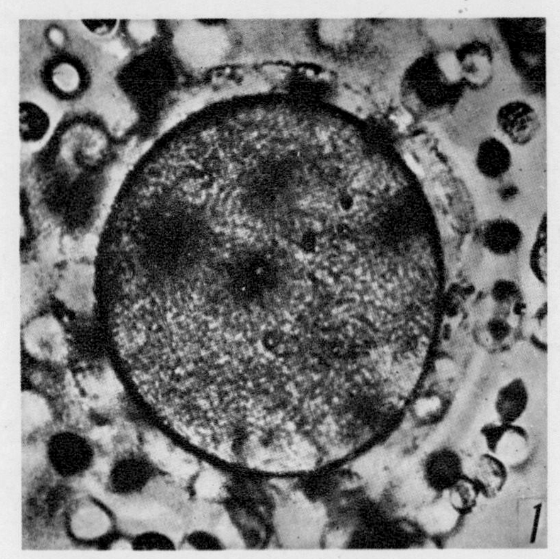

1. Photomicrograph of a living human ovum. × 420. (*Reproduced by permission of Prof. W. J. Hamilton.*)

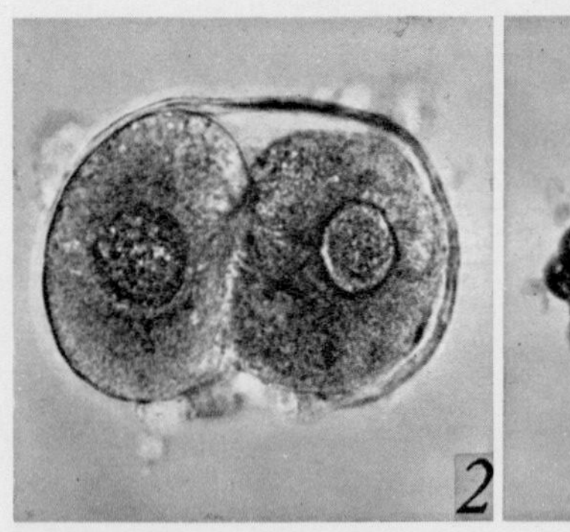

2. Photomicrograph of a section of an intact two-cell segmenting human egg. Carnegie 8698. × 320. (*Reproduced by permission of Drs A. T. Hertig and J. Rock.*)

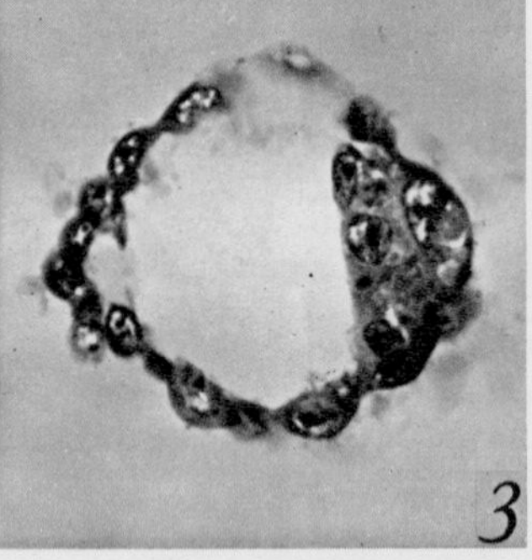

3. Photomicrograph of a mid-serial section of a 107-cell human blastocyst. Carnegie 8663. × 320. (*Reproduced by permission of Drs A. T. Hertig and J. Rock.*)

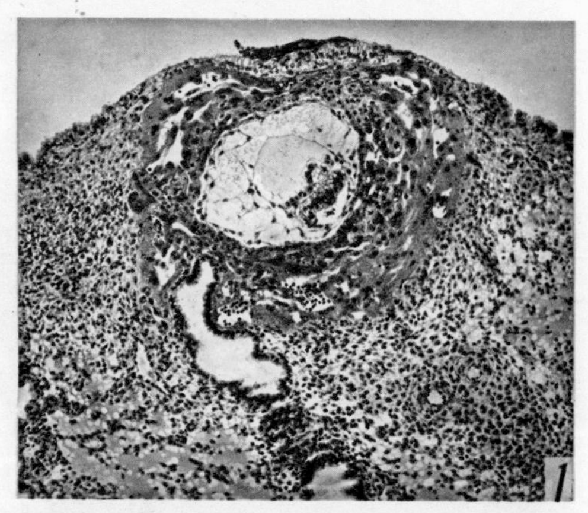

1. Photomicrograph of a mid-cross section of an implanting human ovum 11 days old (Horizon V). Carnegie 7699. × 60. (*Reproduced by permission of Drs A. T. Hertig and J. Rock.*)

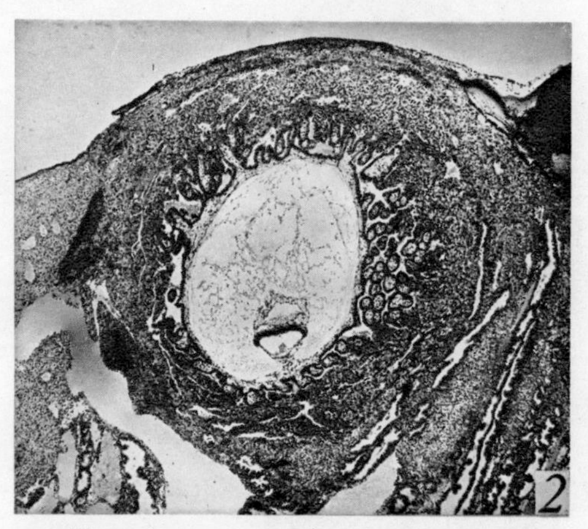

2. Photomicrograph of a section of an implanted human ovum 16 days old (Horizon VII). Carnegie 7802. × 18. (*Reproduced by permission of Drs A. T. Hertig and J. Rock.*)

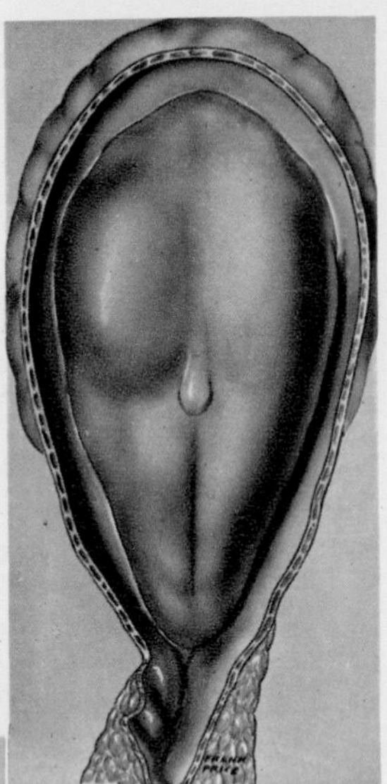

1. Drawing of human embryonic disc about 16 days old (from above). × *c.* 40.

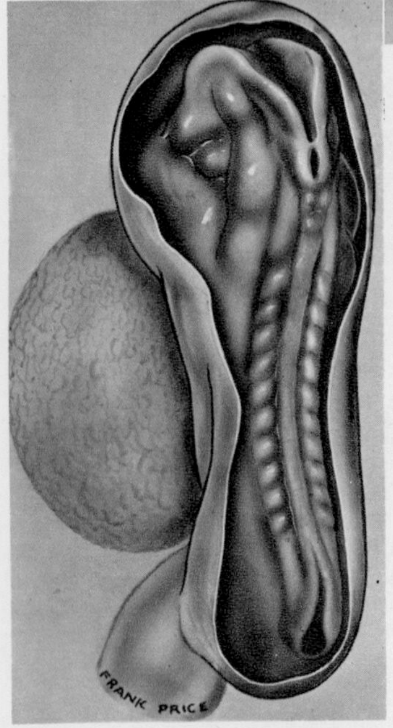

2. Drawing of a 10-somite human embryo about 23 days old. × 30.

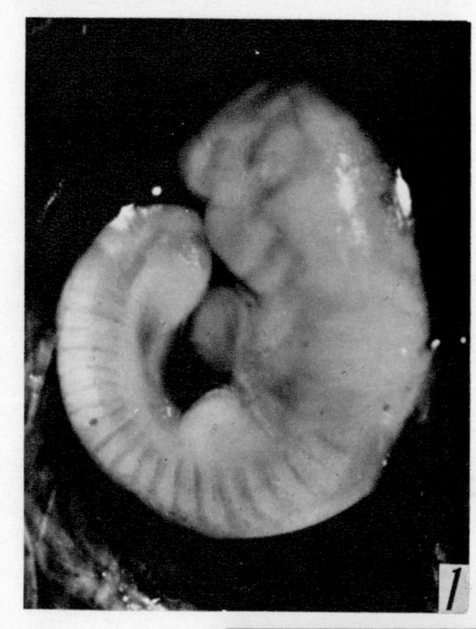

1. Photograph of a 5 mm. (C.R.) human embyro, $4\frac{1}{2}$ weeks old.

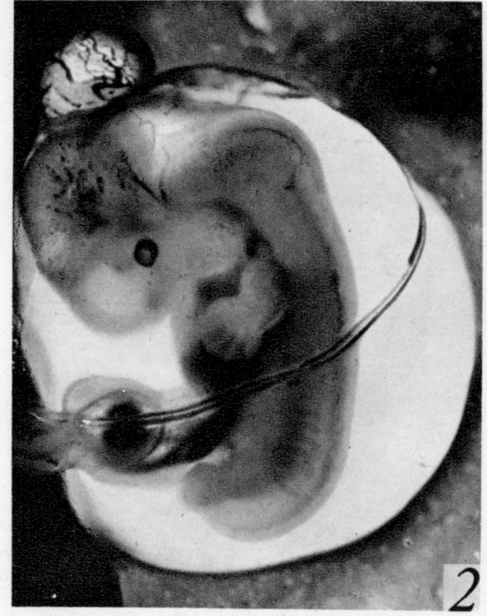

2. Photograph of a 15 mm. (C.R.) human embryo $6\frac{1}{2}$ weeks old.

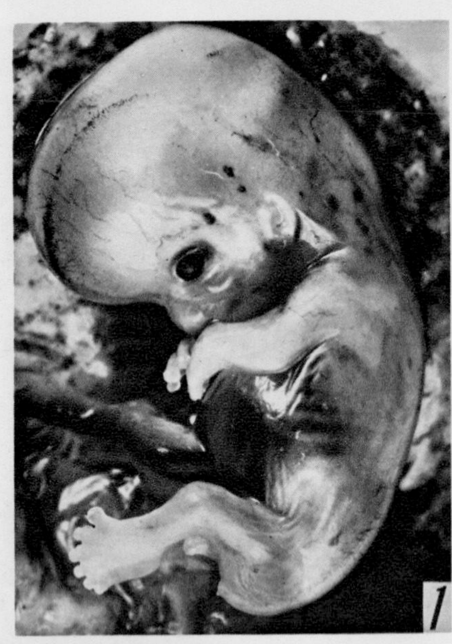

1. 25 mm. (C.R.) human embyro $7\frac{1}{2}$ weeks old.

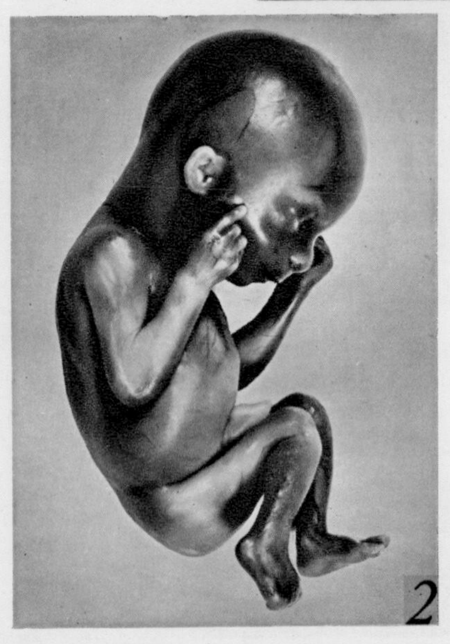

2. 90 mm. (C.R.) human embryo 13 weeks old.

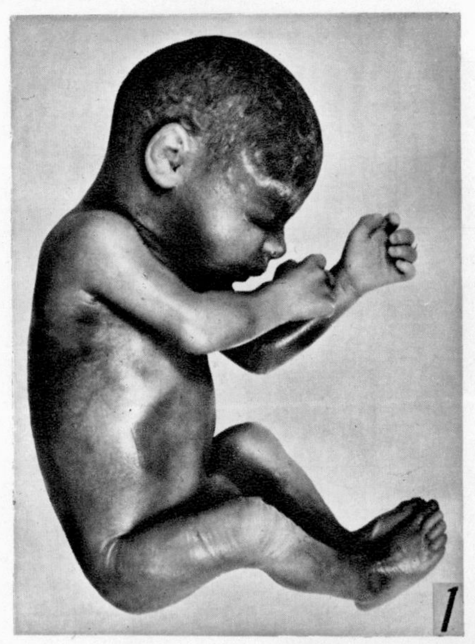

1. 200 mm. (C.R.) human embryo 7 months old.

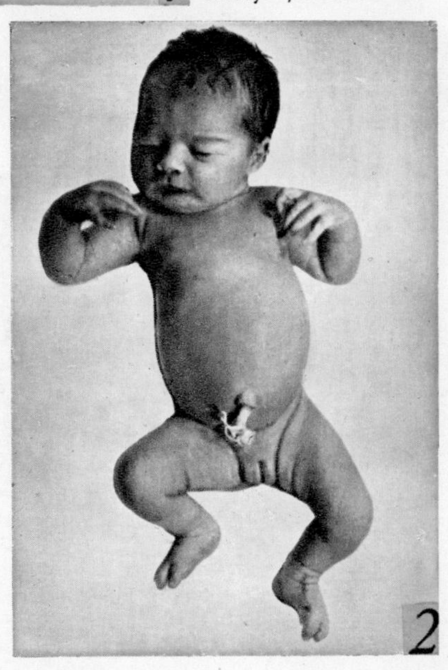

2. Full term human infant.

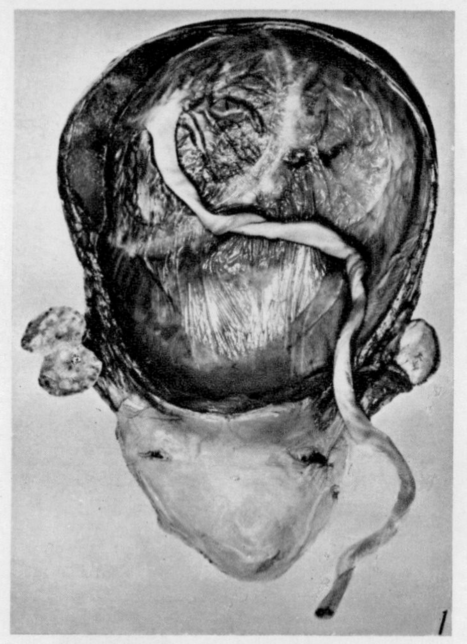

1. A full term human uterus with placenta *in situ*. $\times \frac{1}{8}$.

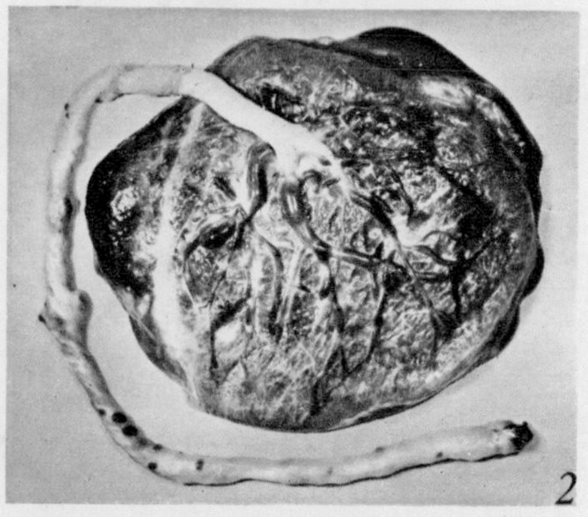

2. Foetal aspect of a full term human placenta after expulsion. $\times \frac{1}{5}$.

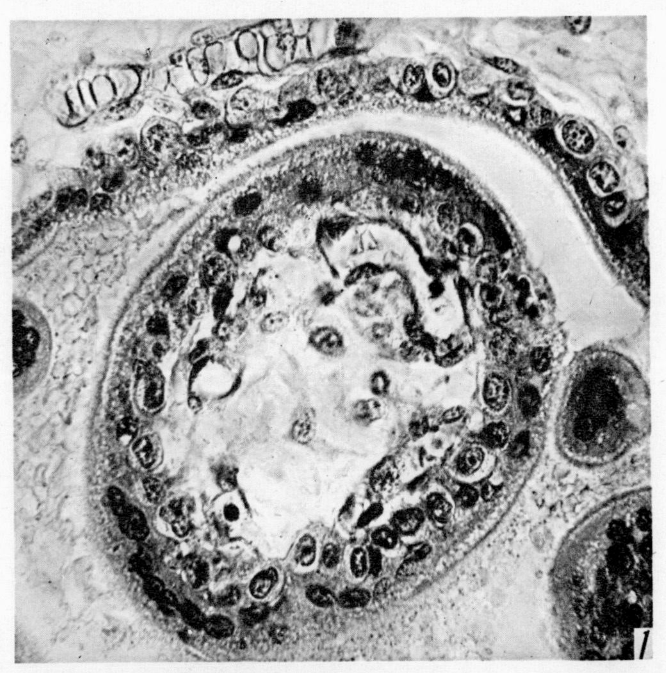

1. Photomicrograph of a cross-section of a human placental villus. × 530.

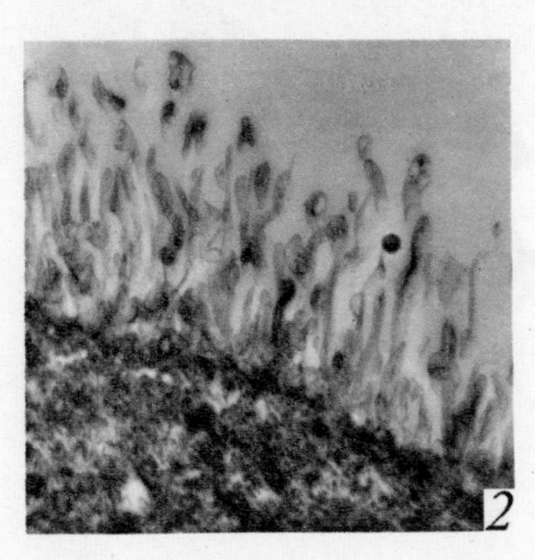

2. Electronmicrograph of microvilli on surface of placental villus. × 10,000.

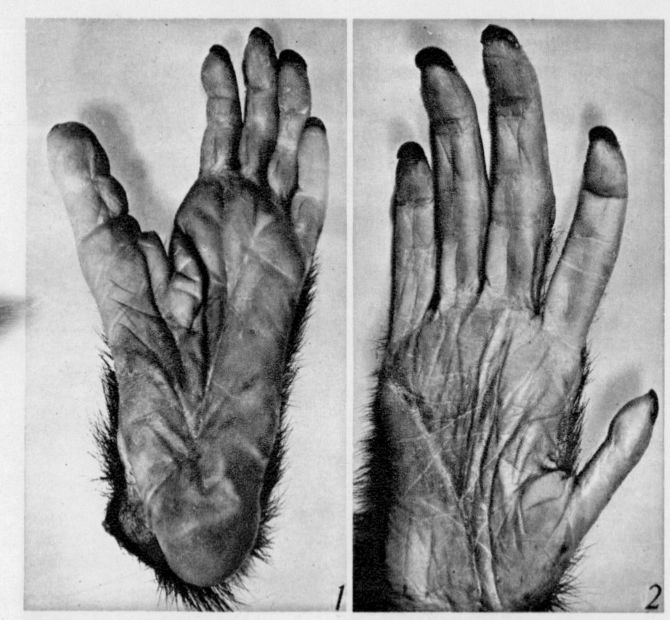

1 and 2. Foot and hand (right) of Chimpanzee in Plate IV.

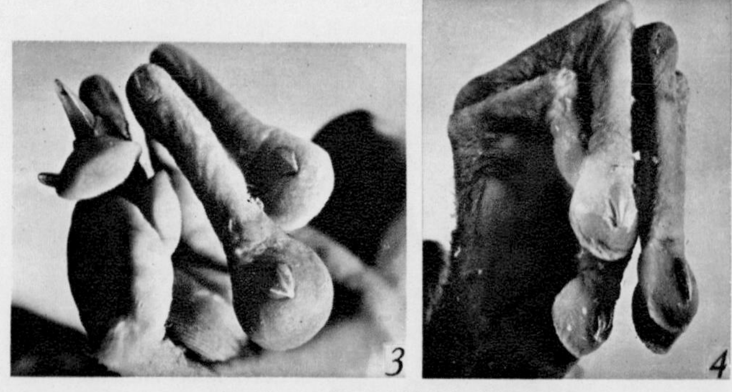

3 and 4. Foot and hand (right) of Tarsius.

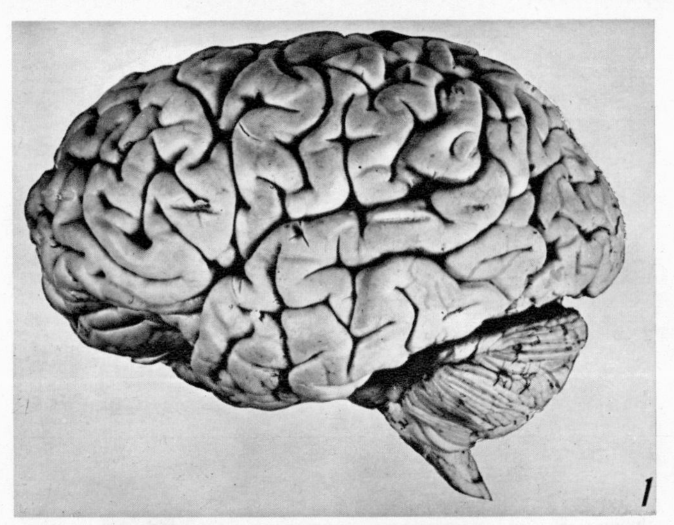

1. Lateral aspect of an adult human brain. × ½.

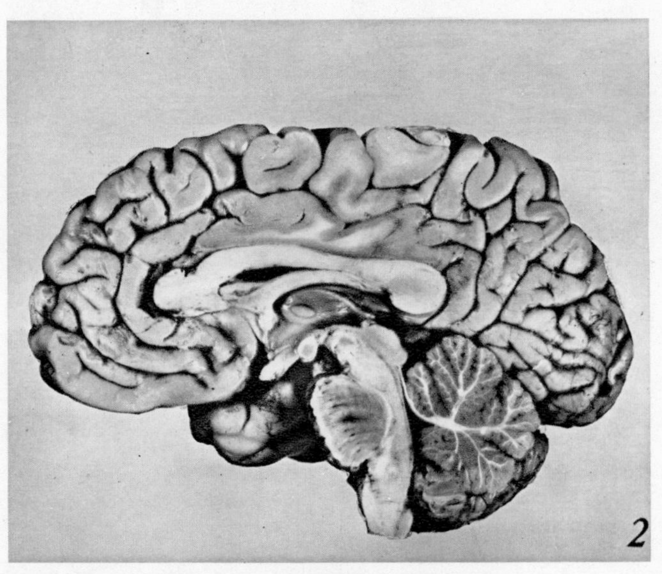

2. The inner aspect of a section through the middle of a human brain and brain stem. × ½.

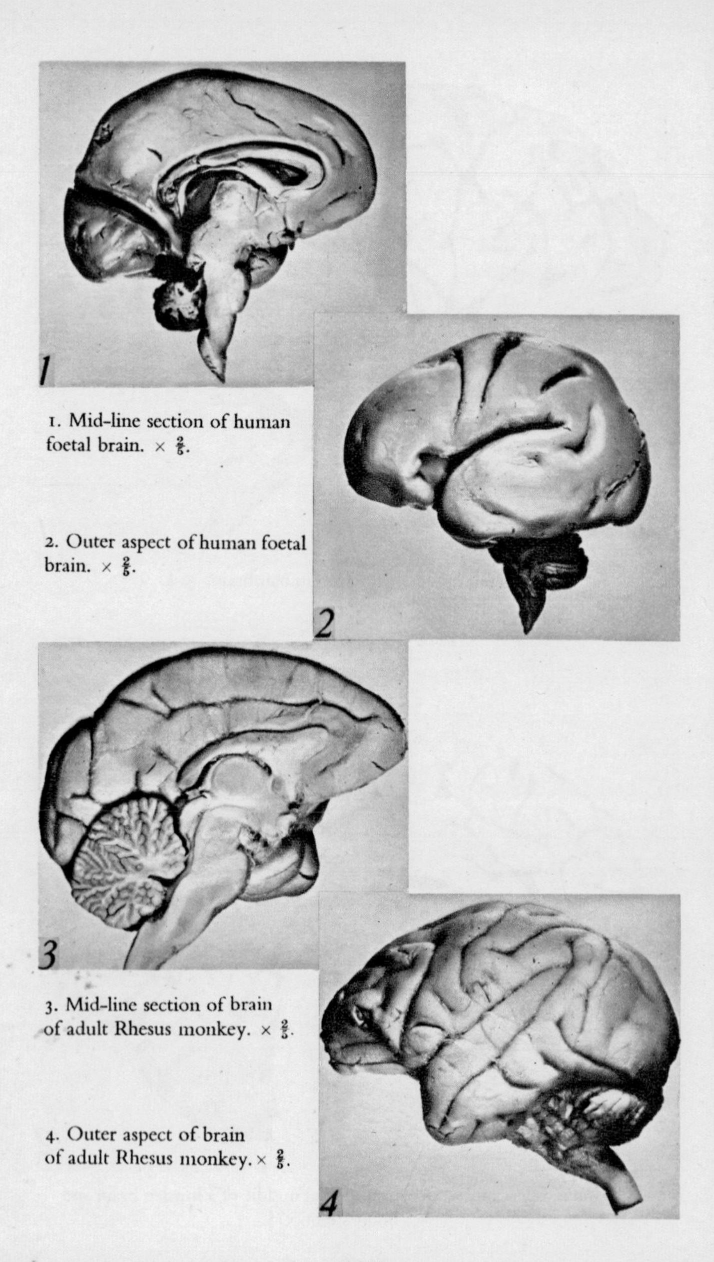

1. Mid-line section of human foetal brain. × $\frac{2}{5}$.

2. Outer aspect of human foetal brain. × $\frac{2}{5}$.

3. Mid-line section of brain of adult Rhesus monkey. × $\frac{2}{5}$.

4. Outer aspect of brain of adult Rhesus monkey. × $\frac{2}{5}$.

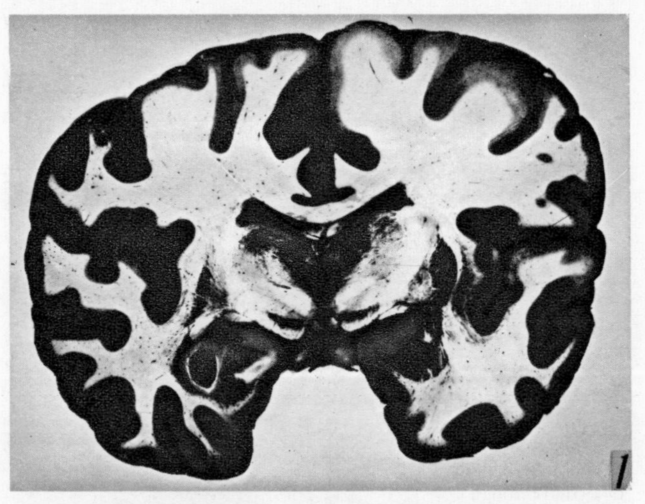

1. Transverse cross section of an adult human brain stained to show grey and white matter. × $\frac{3}{8}$

2. Photomicrograph of cerebral cortex stained to show neurones. × 120.

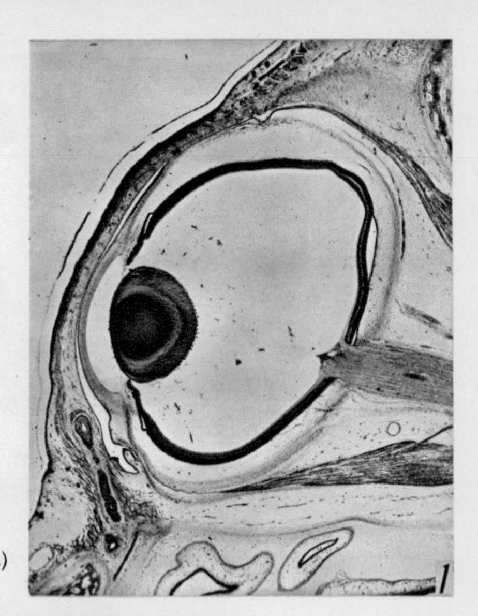

1. Photomicrograph of section through human foetal (54 mm.) eye. × 11.

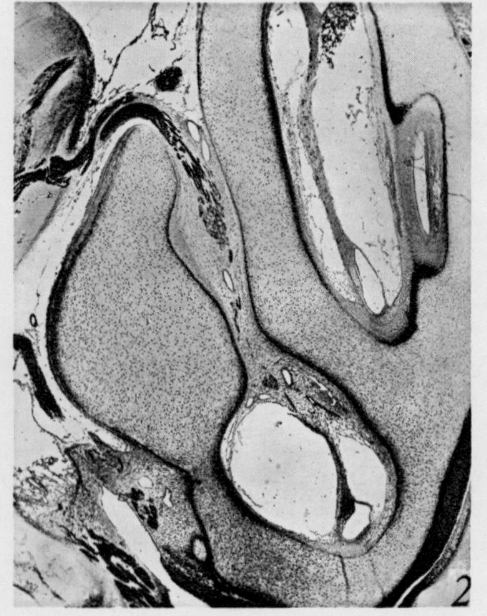

2. Photomicrograph of section through human foetal (85 mm.) cochlea showing auditory nerve fibres. × 20.

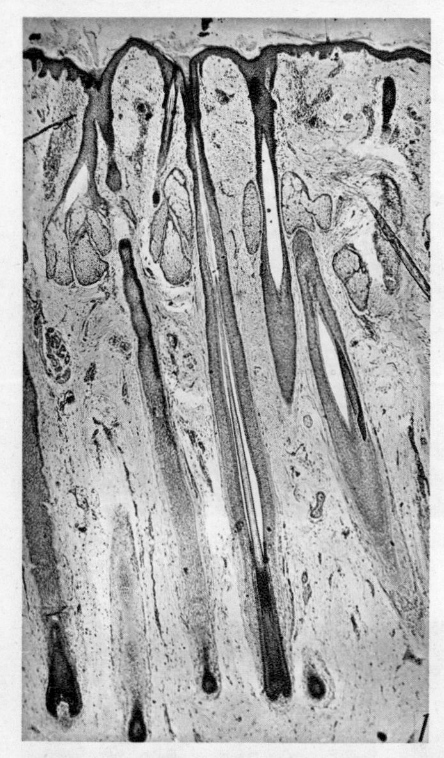

1. Photomicrograph of section of human scalp. × 18.

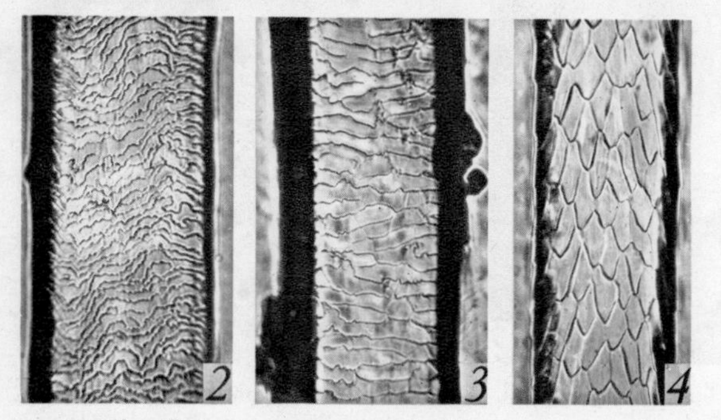

2, 3, and 4. Scale patterns on outside of human, goat, and rat hairs. × 120.

1. Epidermal ridges on human palm. × 4.5.

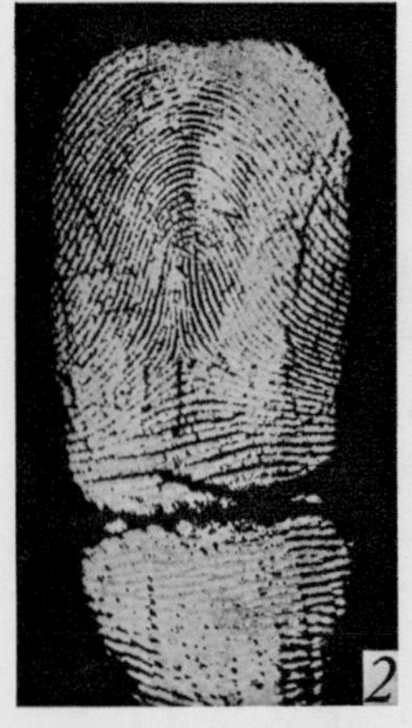

2. Human finger print.

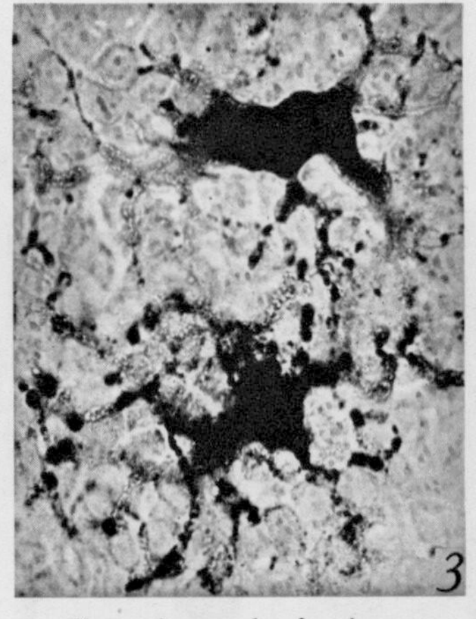

3. Photomicrograph of melanocytes in human skin. × 615. (*Reproduced by permission of Dr G. Szabo.*)

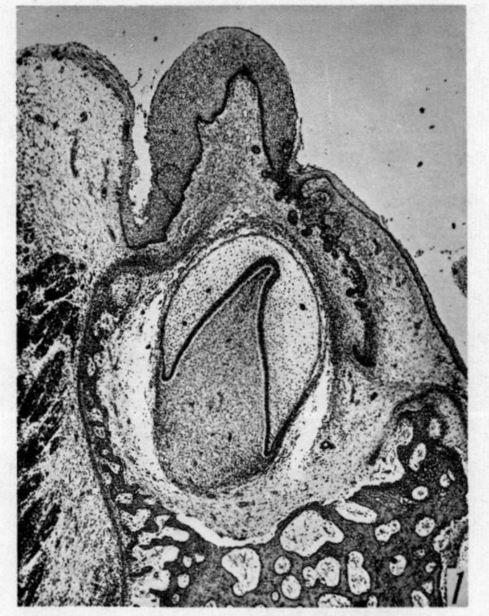

1. Photomicrograph of section through a human foetal (5 month) lower incisor tooth. × 22.

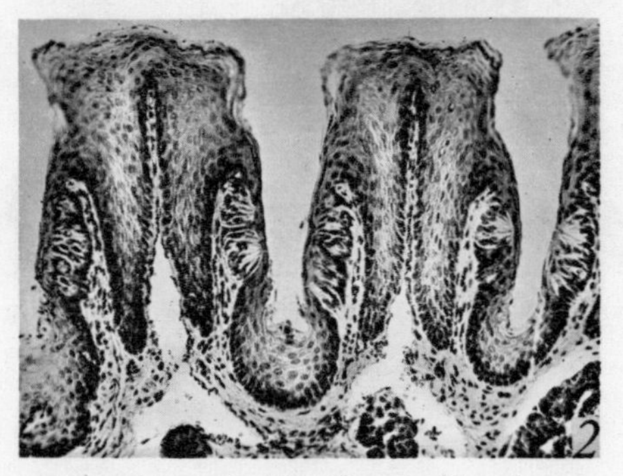

2. Photomicrograph of fungiform papillae of tongue stained to show taste buds. × 160.

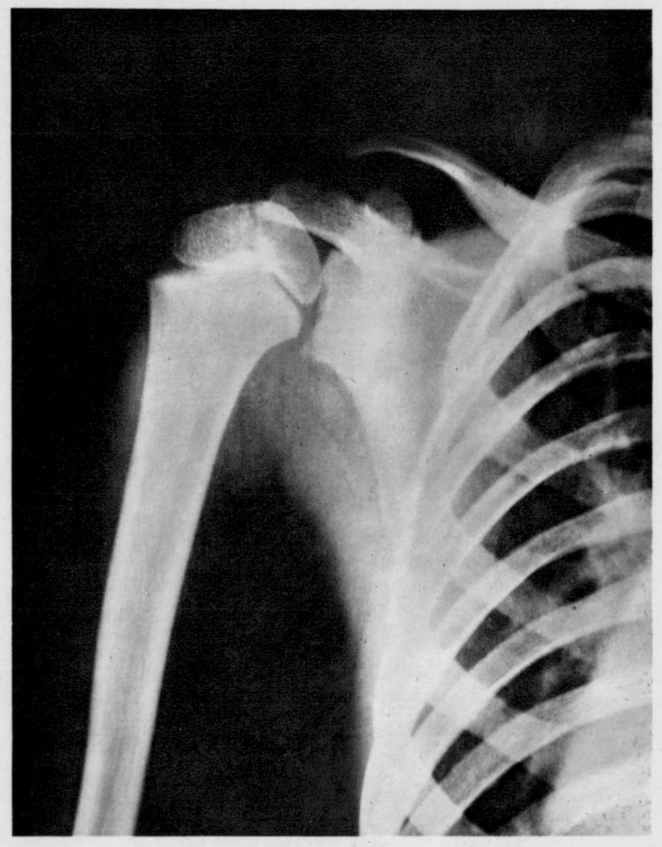

Reproduction of X-ray film of the shoulder of a 3-year-old girl to show epiphyses of upper end of humerus.

certain positions of the talus). The ankle joint is therefore particularly well constructed only to allow flexion (plantar-flexion) and extension (dorsiflexion) of the foot. There has been some confusion in description of movements at the ankle joint and the terms in brackets more accurately describe them.

Movement at the ankle joint is obviously of primary importance in walking; in taking a step the ankle joint of the foot remaining on the ground is plantar-flexed. That of the advancing foot is first dorsiflexed and then plantar-flexed when it is placed on the ground in front of the body. As the body swings over it the joint becomes dorsiflexed again. The articular surface of the talus is wedge-shaped so that it is broader in front; thus the 'grip' exerted by the tibia and fibula is increased as the ankle joint becomes dorsiflexed. This is useful in preventing the leg going forwards and leaving the talus behind in jumping or when coming to a sudden stop. There are, however, certain disadvantages in this grip-like function of the tibia and fibula at the joint. The bone at the sides of the downward projecting flanges is somewhat reinforced and can be felt immediately under the skin of the ankle where elevations so formed are called *malleoli*. The word means 'little hammers' and malleoli got their names from the way they get knocked against things. Forcible sideways twisting of the foot may result in fracture of one or both malleoli and even dislocation of the ankle joint. This may happen while ski-ing or from slipping off the edge of a high pavement. The fracture-dislocation is known as Pott's fracture after an English surgeon, Percival Pott (1714–88), who first described it. He fell from his horse in 1756 in what is now the Old Kent Road and broke his tibia: there is some doubt whether he sustained a type of fracture now called after him.

Every reader must have heard of skating on the inner or outer edge of an ice-skate. Ability to perform these exercises depends on existence of joints in the foot that allow the sole to be turned inwards with its inner edge elevated. The movement is called *inversion* and is most marked when accompanied by plantar-flexion of the foot at the ankle joint. The opposite movement, turning the sole so that it faces outwards with its outer edge elevated, is called *eversion* but is more limited in range. The movements take place at joints between calcaneum and talus, and between these two bones and navicular and cuboid. They are brought about by groups of muscles called *invertors* and *evertors*. Those that invert and also plantar-flex, such as *tibialis posterior* (Fig. 16), are characteristically large in man. This is partly because man's centre of gravity lies in front of the ankle joint in the erect attitude; a tendency for man to tip forwards is countered by contraction of plantar-flexors. Ability to invert and evert the foot enables man to walk *round* mountains, over uneven ground and to perform subtle flicks with his feet when he is a 'footballing man'. Of the two movements that of eversion is distinctly human and is brought about by a group of *peroneal* muscles arising from the outer side of the fibula. One of them, *peroneus longus*, has a tendon that stretches round the outer side of the ankle and passes across the under surface of the foot to reach the base of the metatarsal of the big toe. This muscle not only everts the foot, but also exaggerates the transverse arch.

Man's Knee Joint

The large human knee joint is particularly well adapted for weight bearing and locomotion. The ends of the bones taking part are expanded and arranged as a hinge; movement at the joint is modified in that some rotation can occur. A large sesamoid bone called the patella (Latin – a limpet) develops in the tendon of the *quadriceps femoris* where it lies against the lower end of the femur (Fig. 16). The articulating surfaces of the femur and tibia do not fit well and two thin crescentic (semilunar) cartilages lie between them. These cartilages facilitate movements, distribute pressure, and act as shock absorbers. Rotary movement occurs during the final straightening of the joint. With the foot on the ground the inner side of the femur continues to move after the outer side has stopped; the bones are 'screwed home' and the joint is then said to be 'locked'. This makes the knee more secure as a weight-bearing strut. Unlocking is brought about by a muscle from the back of the tibia, the *popliteus*, that rotates the femur when the foot is firmly on the ground or the tibia with the foot in the air. The muscle is peculiarly large in man (Fig. 16).

The semilunar cartilages move with the tibia, but must change their shape during rotatory movements. In violent movements parts of the cartilages may be caught between the moving bones so tightly that they are torn or wrenched from their attachments. Evolution has provided man with an excellent knee joint, but his social exercises and the demands of his will occasionally require a performance that too severely tests his anatomy.

Walking

Few methods of locomotion in animals are simple, and walking on two legs is probably one of the more complex. The movement starts with the weight being transferred to one leg; the body and thus its

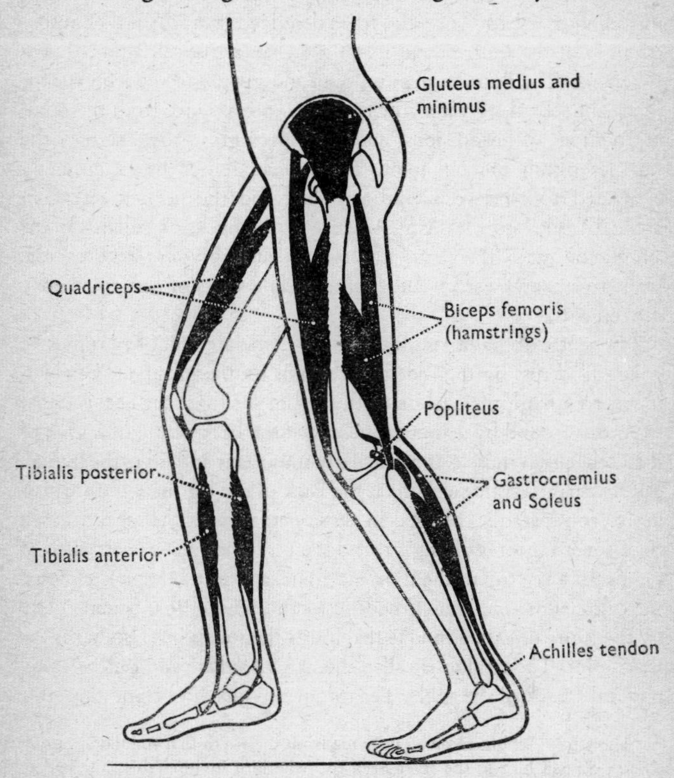

FIG. 16. Positions of some of the muscles involved in walking. See also Fig. 17.

centre of gravity incline forwards and the other leg is advanced a step. Several important mechanisms allow this apparently simple act to occur, all leaving characteristic imprints on man's skeleton. Weight is transferred to one leg by sideways tilting of the pelvis; suppose the left leg is advanced, then muscles on the right, outer side of the loin contract and tilt the left side of the pelvis so that weight is taken off the left leg. The muscles are called *gluteus medius* and *minimus* and they pass from the ilium of the hip-bone to the greater trochanter of the femur (Fig. 16); the word trochanter is derived from a Greek word meaning 'runner'. The gluteal muscles, including the *gluteus maximus*, to be described later, form the muscular mass of the buttock and make it a characteristically human protuberance. The ilium in man is broad and gives wide attachment for these muscles; the greater trochanter is some distance from the point of rotation at the hip joint and thus gives great advantage to the muscles tilting the hip joint. The human femur has a distinctly elongated neck between head and shaft and the neck is set at an angle of 120° to the shaft. Absence of the neck, or collapse of its angulation with the shaft, is a serious disability and reduces the walk to an awkward waddle rather than a series of easy oscillatory movements.

The centre of gravity is moved forward as the result of a propulsive 'take off' thrust by the foot that remains on the ground. Weight is transferred from the heel on to the ball of the foot; the heel is raised from the ground by action of muscles at the back of the calf. One of these, the *soleus* muscle, is particularly important and gives the human calf its characteristic swelling at the back of the leg. It is, not surprisingly, considerably enlarged in those native races that spend much time squatting or walking great distances. The soleus is attached at the back to the top of the tibia and fibula and to the large heel bone, the calcaneum. The muscle ends in a stout tendon that is joined also by the *gastrocnemius*, a muscle that assists the soleus but also flexes the knee joint. The tendon is called the *tendo Achillis** and can be easily felt at the back of the ankle. The calcaneum juts out behind the ankle

*The tendo Achillis received its name from the myth that Achilles' mother, Thetis, dipped him in the river Styx to make him invulnerable. She had to hold him by the tendon and thus Achilles' heel became the fatal spot where Paris shot him.

joint and so the calf muscles can exert a strong thrust when the heel is elevated.

The foot must be rigid as the 'take-off' develops. This is brought about by long tendons passing to the tarsal bones from other leg muscles and also by small muscles in the foot. The knee joint must

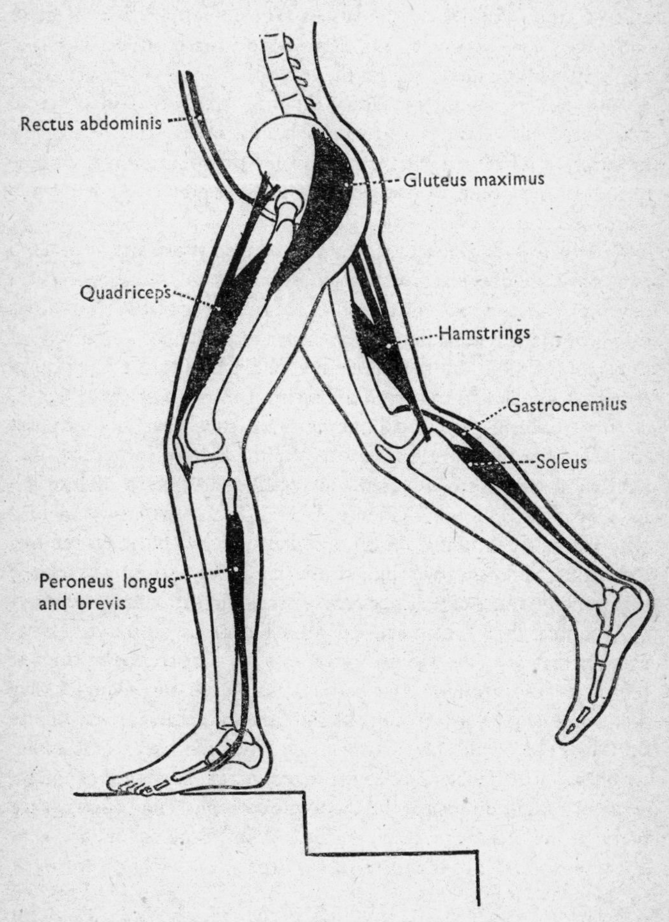

FIG. 17. Positions of muscles involved in walking. It shows the action of gluteus maximus in straightening (extending) the hip joint in walking up steps.

also be firm so that the developing thrust will not just bend it. Rigidity is ensured by contraction of certain thigh muscles, in particular by the four-headed *quadriceps femoris* muscle in the front of the thigh. It is a well developed muscle in man with a bone, the patella, in its tendon. Bones that develop in tendons are called *sesamoid*, the patella being the largest. The tendon of the quadriceps continues over the patella to be attached to a marked tuberosity that can be felt on the upper part of the front of the tibia. This part of the quadriceps tendon can be tapped in the resting limb in order to stretch receptor endings and bring about a reflex 'knee jerk'. The quadriceps and muscles at the back of the thigh, *hamstrings*, all help to fix the knee joint. Thrust from the take-off propels the body forwards and also raises it a little.

The leg to be advanced is now free to swing forwards. It does so partly because of the action of gravity and partly because of impetus developed by the take-off thrust. It is lifted clear of the ground by tilting of the pelvis, flexion of the knee and hip joints, and by elevation (dorsiflexion) of the foot. The latter movement is brought about by muscles arising from the front of the tibia of which *tibialis anterior* is one of the most important. Its tendon can be easily felt beneath the skin where it is covered by the 'tongue' of a shoe, particularly if the foot is inverted and dorsiflexed. Tibialis anterior has more work to do if one's shoes are heavy or caked with mud. A man who plays three rounds of golf on a heavy, hilly course on the first day of his holiday may well inflame the thin sheath enclosing its tendon (tenosynovitis) and experience pain on walking, particularly uphill.

As soon as the leg has swung past the line of the centre of gravity, muscles that brought about elevation of the foot relax and the sole returns to the ground. The pelvis rotates with the swinging leg, increasing its forward movement, and giving a characteristic side to side 'wobble' to the body when seen from the back. This rotary wobble can be deliberately exaggerated, particularly in women because of certain differences in pelvic proportions. The weight of the body is now transferred on to the leg in front. Both its foot and knee must be held rigid as the forward momentum of the body comes on to them; once more the quadriceps contract to keep the knee extended. Its importance will be particularly appreciated after walking *downhill* for some distance; the muscle soon starts to ache.

The body now moves easily forwards, swinging over the foot that is on the ground. Weight is taken first on the heel and then on the ball of the foot. The leg left behind now exerts a propelling force similar to that which initiated the first step and the series of movements is repeated. In running and sprinting the movements are greater; the body leans forward more and the heel does not touch the ground. In walking uphill, or in climbing stairs, the *gluteus maximus* (p. 164) plays an important part in raising the body on the leg. A foot is placed on a stair and the muscle straightens (extends) the hip joint; the knee is straightened at the same time and so the body is raised. As already stated, a large gluteus maximus and rounded buttocks are peculiarly human.

The Human Pelvis

Adoption of upright posture could hardly avoid numerous alterations in the pelvis. Its bones are essential for locomotion and its muscles are involved in walking and balancing the body in the upright position. It transmits weight from spinal column to limbs: its floor supports viscera as do muscles of the abdominal wall that stretch between the pelvis and the thoracic cage. The external genitalia are attached to it and it has to be constructed so that urine can escape from it through the urethra and faeces through the rectum and anal canal. It must also allow passage of a 7½ lb. baby at childbirth without disarrangement of maternal anatomy or damage to the baby. It is true that the 'most hypercritical of anatomists and surgeons must be forced to agree that structure and function have been mated in the pelvic region with considerable ingenuity. It is equally true that it is difficult to suggest a better anatomy for the region.' Even so certain deficiencies in pelvic structure can cause much aggravation to modern man, probably more than to prehistoric man because of differences in his way of life.

The pelvis of man has a peculiarly expanded upper part, the ilium, which helps to support viscera and gives a wide area for attachment of muscles. The front pubic region is set high in relation to the sacrum; this gives better advantage to certain muscles (adductors) that draw the legs together. This increases his agility on his legs and enables him to ride astride a horse or saddle with greater ease than could an ape. The lower, 'true' part of the pelvis is large, capacious, and has a characteristic outline. In the erect attitude it forms the lowest part of the abdominal cavity and the French word *bassin* for pelvis aptly describes its form. Yet it is its basin-like form and function that are so incompatible with a need for large openings through its floor. The bony floor of the pelvis is deficient and the opening is closed by a muscular and fascial pelvic diaphragm that is perforated by urinary, alimentary, and reproductive ducts. The *levator ani* muscle is the most important component of the pelvic diaphragm and is slung from each side of the pelvis as a hammock to support viscera. It has numerous functions but none is more important than that of retaining and supporting viscera. There is constant pressure on the pelvic diaphragm in the erect attitude, even while standing still, and it increases even with the slightest movement of the arms. Pressure increases fivefold on bending down to pick up a heavy object; if the movement is violent or sudden, pressure rises tenfold. Blowing up a balloon, or explosive coughing, also raises the pressure. Muscles surrounding the abdomen contract during these activities, increase the intra-abdominal pressure, and squeeze the contents into the pelvis. Every straining movement compresses abdominal viscera; they are composed mainly of water and they therefore act as water-hammers seeking out weak points in the containing walls. There will be a constant tendency for organs to slide out or prolapse from the pelvis, or, if the weak point be small, to protrude or herniate through the opening.

Man's Backbone

'The human spine is a mechanism of the utmost complexity; between the sacrum and the skull are incorporated twenty-four vertebrae, each provided with three short levers – the spinous and (two) transverse processes; each lever is furnished with, not a single muscle, but a group of them (416 in all).' The writer of this sentence, the late Sir Arthur Keith, then continued by discussing many ways in which the spine of man is adapted to his upright posture and pointed out that there were many weaknesses in these adaptations. On the whole, however, man's spine serves him remarkably well.

The human vertebral column is a long axial pillar composed of vertebrae held together by intervening fibro-cartilaginous discs and ligaments that give it a considerable degree of flexibility. It extends from the tip of the coccyx, which can be felt through the skin in the cleft between the buttocks, to the atlas vertebra upon which the skull is balanced. It is 8 inches long at birth and is then formed of 33 separate bones. It is about 28 inches long in an adult man (24 inches in an adult woman), in whom it is formed of only 26 separate bones: those of the lower end become fused into the sacrum (5) and coccyx (4). The spine shows remarkable constancy in its length and is said to be the least variable component of stature. It contracts, however, by 3–4 per cent between getting up in the morning and going to bed at night and it is a little longer after lying down for any length of time. The healthy adult spine can bear a third of a ton without being crushed.

The vertebrae exhibit considerable differences in shape and mobility in the various regions of the spine and not surprisingly they are associated with different functions in each region. A typical vertebra has a weight-bearing body and an arch enclosing the vertebral canal. Within the latter lies the spinal cord, the nerve roots, and their covering membranes, the meninges. The arch has articular processes above and below, transverse processes at the side, and a spine (thus spinal column) at the back. The spines are not as large or as long as they are in mammals in which the vertebral column forms a girder horizontal to the ground. The bodies of the vertebrae, except those of the coccyx, sacrum, and atlas, are separated by intervertebral discs. These are thick enough to account for one quarter of the length of the column. Each disc consists of a thick fibro-cartilaginous outer part (*annulus fibrosus*); its densely packed fibres are arranged in concentric rings and stretch obliquely between two vertebral bodies with opposite obliquities in each layer. A soft, almost gelatinous substance is found in the centre of each disc in young and middle-aged individuals. It is called the *nucleus pulposus* and is believed to be derived in part from the notochord (p. 132). It varies in its composition throughout life until in old age it loses water and becomes fibro-cartilaginous throughout. The discs act as shock absorbers, or as water-cushions, tending to equalize distribution of pressure over the surfaces of vertebrae. They permit one vertebra to rock on another to degrees dependent on the arrangement of the articular processes. The changes in the discs in old age reduce considerably the flexibility of the spine.

Intervertebral discs are somewhat wedge-shaped to conform with spinal curvature. The nucleus pulposus is under some pressure and occasionally it ruptures its surroundings to protrude or herniate in various directions. This is the anatomical basis of a 'slipped disc'; should protrusion occur posteriorly it may press on a spinal nerve. Slipped discs are rare in mammals and although it is not unlikely that they are caused by factors additional to that of posture they represent another potential disadvantage of bipedalism.

Spinal curvatures. Looked at from the side the adult human spine exhibits characteristic curvatures that give it the appearance of two S's stretched out one above the other. Two are concave in one direction, two in the other. The spine of a foetus, and of a child at birth, has only curvatures that are concave forwards. The upper of these *primary curvatures* is larger and is made by cervical, thoracic, and lumbar vertebrae; the short lower one is made by sacral and coccygeal vertebrae. The *secondary curvatures* are convex forwards and develop as a child adopts an upright posture; they are called compensatory curvatures because they develop as the intervertebral discs become wedge-shaped. The secondary cervical curvature appears two to three months after birth, at the time when the child is able to lift its head unaided, and is well established by nine months when a child sits playing in its cot. This curvature is indeed an earnest of an intention to adopt upright posture and to walk erect; it results in the head being brought to the vertical with the eyes looking towards the horizon. It requires muscular effort to maintain the head erect despite reduction in size and weight of the facial skeleton. Forward positioning of the foramen magnum and occipital condyles in man enable his skull to sit more securely on his spine. Anyone who has tried to go to sleep sitting upright will recall a sudden jerking back to consciousness as his head falls towards his chest.

The other secondary curve is in the *lumbar* region. Its point of maximum curvature is almost opposite the umbilicus and it extends to the articulation of the last lumbar vertebra with the sacrum. The curve is best seen in children and in women in whom fashion occasionally decrees that it be artificially exaggerated. The lumbar curve is characteristic of the human species.

The lumbar region of the human spine forms a flexible lever on which the whole weight of the upper part of the body is poised. The graceful carriage of the body would be lost were the lumbar curve not present; the position of the centre of gravity would be altered and there would be a distinct tendency to topple over backwards. The lumbar spine is not too long, otherwise the body would sway; it is not too short, or there would be insufficient room in front of it for the abdominal viscera. It is not so slight that it is unable to bear the body's weight, nor is it so stout that sideways bending is prohibited. Walking on two feet demands that the loins be long or the advantage of muscles moving the legs will be the less. The primitive mammalian number of lumbar vertebrae is three or less, whereas in man there are usually five. It can be argued that orthograde posture demands a shortening of the lumbar region, simply for economy of muscular effort, and this seems to have occurred in orthograde apes. There is, however, a tendency for a lengthening of the human lumbar region, shown by the rapid growth and elongation of the lumbar vertebrae during the first two years of a child's life. It would seem that there is in association with human plantigrade posture, not only curvature of the lumbar spine, but lengthening of it and of the loins as well. Freeing of the first sacral vertebra to give a sixth lumbar is found in 8 per cent of human skeletons, whereas the opposite condition of sacralization of a fifth lumbar vertebra is less than half as common.

The sacro-coccygeal curve follows below the lumbar curve. It is concave forwards and represents the original lower primary curve. The sacrum in many races, particularly in women, is often at right angles to the lumbar spine. Backward tilting of the sacrum provides a wide area for attachment of the large muscle mass (sacrospinalis of the erector spinae) that keeps the body upright. Downward pressure of the weight of the upper part of the body tends to depress the front of the sacrum towards the ground and at the same time to rotate its coccygeal end upwards. This is prevented by strong ligaments of the sacro-iliac joint and by others that pass from sacrum to hip-bone (sacro-spinous and sacro-tuberous). There is also a tendency for the lumbar spine to be driven forwards and downwards off the sacrum into the pelvis. This is prevented by the way the articular processes on the last lumbar vertebra are gripped within those of the sacrum. This type of dislocation is called spondylolisthesis from *spondylos*, a vertebra and *olisthanein*, to slip. The rarity of the condition is a clear indication of how well the mechanism of the spine is constructed; it only occurs as a result of some violent force or when there is maldevelopment of vertebrae.

There is some normal side to side curvature of a spine looked at from in front. It is called *scoliosis* and deviates to the left in right-handed people. Shortness of one leg exaggerates scoliosis. Abnormal curvatures may result from collapse of the bodies of vertebrae (*kyphosis* or hunch-back) or of the arches (*lordosis*).

Upright Posture and Man's Abdomen

Parts of the alimentary tract and many of its associated viscera are almost entirely enclosed within a peritoneal covering and retain contact with the abdominal walls only by double-layered mesenteries. Other parts, such as most of the duodenum and both kidneys, are 'plastered', as it were, against the back wall with peritoneum covering only their front aspects. There is usually some anchoring connective tissue, but this does not immobilize them completely as they can move up and down an inch or more during respiratory and postural movements. Those parts of the alimentary canal with peritoneal mesenteries are not, however, held in place by them. Anyone unfortunate enough to have seen a large wound of the abdominal wall with viscera extruded will know that in the intact body mesenteries are not taut. It is the muscles and fibrous sheets or aponeuroses of the abdominal wall that retain and support man's viscera. Musculature of the flank is arranged in three layers that blend into fibrous aponeuroses at the front. The muscles are the external and internal *oblique* and the *transversus* of each side; their fibres run in different directions, either obliquely or transversely as a living corset girding the abdomen. The fibrous sheets from these muscles blend and split in front to form a sheath that encloses each of the two vertically placed, strap-like muscles (the *recti*). The *rectus sheath* of one side is connected to that of the other by a central toughened fibrous band called the *linea alba*. The abdominal wall is therefore composed partly of muscle (mainly above the umbilicus) and partly of fibrous aponeuroses (mainly below the umbilicus and in the mid-line); both parts exert a retentive function.

The lumbar curve ensures that the abdominal wall is so set in the erect attitude that it lies more beneath than in front of the lower abdomen. The outline of the front of the abdomen is not (-shaped but _-shaped and thus the lowest part, attached to the pelvis, has directly to support viscera. Middle age is associated with slackening and sagging of the lower abdominal wall and its retaining and supporting functions are further tested by increase in weight. Its efficiency is also potentially weakened by openings of the passage (inguinal canal) to the scrotum. The spermatic cord lies in the inguinal canal and peritoneum and viscera may be forced down it to produce one of the types of inguinal hernia. Upright posture seeks out the weaknesses in man's structure and surgeons will always be needed to repair or strengthen these anatomical defects when they become apparent.

Freedom of the Upper Limb

It is not just in the legs and trunk that there are modifications associated with bipedalism. The front limbs may well have become freed for carrying out skilled movements, but they have to be carried wherever man goes. Each arm and shoulder weigh some 10 lb., and for the arm to be free in its movements it must not be attached to the body by many rigid bony struts. The suspensory mechanism of the shoulder region must be muscular. When we examine the flattened, broad-shouldered back of man we see that it is the large *trapezius* muscles that play the most important role. Looked at from behind, his neck splays out at its root as if a monk's cowl of muscle lay just beneath the skin. This appearance is given by the upper fibres of each trapezius muscle that stretch from the back of the skull and neck to the shoulder girdle. The old name for the muscles was *musculus cuculli*, from *cucullus*, a cowl. They are assisted in their postural action by other muscles deeper in the neck; all are constantly at work maintaining or fixing the position of the shoulders. It has often been remarked that these muscles do not seem adequate for their purpose. A child appears to have a short, bull neck, yet the cervical spine is relatively longer at birth than at any other time:

it is the child's shoulders that are set high. There is a progressive dropping in level of the shoulders as a child grows into adulthood.

We have seen that man's upper limb shows few anatomical specializations (p. 82), yet the freedom and mobility of his shoulder joint and whole limb are remarkable. The human hand can be brought into almost any position. The *number* of positions in which the hand can be placed to do its work is unique and, because of limb proportions, is probably unequalled in the Primates. We have space only to discuss one muscle that enables such freedom of positioning and we unhesitatingly choose the *serratus anterior*. It arises from the side of the thoracic cage and is attached to the hind edge of the shoulder blade. Contraction of the muscle can cause movement forwards of the scapula round the thorax as in pointing, reaching, pushing, and punching. It can also rotate the scapula, as in reaching upwards or fixing a back collar stud. Some men, but not all, can touch the fingers of one hand when that arm is doubled up in the small of the back, with the fingers of the other reaching down from behind the head.

There are many other adaptations, skeletal and otherwise, associated with upright posture and bipedalism, but lack of space forbids their ennumeration; some are mentioned in other chapters.

FOR FURTHER READING

Structure and Function as seen in the Foot. F. Wood Jones. Baillière, Tindall and Cox, 1944

CHAPTER 10

HIS LARGE BRAIN

IN the last chapter we saw that there was reason to believe that the brain of man's ancestors enlarged shortly after they left the trees. Man's large brain is his greatest anatomical peculiarity and its evolution has often been closely associated with his bipedalism. Erect posture freed the forelimbs, allowing them to become refined and mobile. Associations between hands and brain became more intricate; development of precise control of finger positioning was initiated. A new positioning of the skull more centrally above the vertebral column was linked with recession of the face and jaws. The vault of the skull no longer possessed massive ridges for attachment of powerful masticatory and postural muscles. It was 'free' to enlarge and encase a rapidly expanding cerebral cortex in a characteristically rounded calvaria (p. 75). Increase in size of cortex enabled development within it of many more nerve cells or neurones. The number of associations that could be learnt became ever increasing and *ipso facto* was born the possibility of development of man's intellect.

Basic Pattern of Nervous Systems

Any nervous system found in an animal can be analysed into several components. Perhaps the analysis can be better understood if we compare the nervous system in a higher animal with an electrical system found in a modern ship. In fact many biologists have been happy to consider that fundamental patterns of nervous activity can be compared favourably with the way in which man-made electrical devices work. Construction of machines that 'think' has helped us to understand circuits in the nervous system.

It will be quite clear that any animal must have several forms of device to detect information about the outside world around it. A ship can receive wireless messages from the shore and can detect radar signals reflected from an iceberg ahead. Such devices could well be called *receptors*, and in a ship they are the aerials or antennae; in an animal they are sensory endings in skin, eye, ear, and nose, etc. These endings provide information about the world outside or external to the animal, and thus are called *exteroceptors*. A further set of endings gives information about the position of the body and its various parts; these are sensory endings in joints, tendons, and muscles. They are called *proprioceptive* endings; *proprius* means 'pertaining to oneself'.

The generalized endings in skin, the special sense organs, the internal receptors, and the proprioceptive endings provide sensitive mechanisms that are capable of being stimulated in various ways. The result of the stimulus is initiation of a nervous impulse that travels along a nerve fibre as electric currents pass along wires in a ship. The latter is conducted along the particular nerves leaving the sense organs and thence to spinal cord or brain. There are a very large number of sensory nerves and together they constitute the *afferent* side of a nervous system. In adult anatomy sensory nerves are found in nearly all cranial nerves, brain, brain-stem, spinal cord, and in segmentally arranged spinal nerves (except possibly one).

Returning to the analogy with a modern ship it could be said that signals or instructions sent to the engine room or to mechanisms controlling the rudder are effective orders demanding positive action. In a nervous system nerve fibres that pass to muscles and glands are called *motor* or *efferent* fibres. They leave the brain by some cranial nerves and all spinal nerves, and pass to *effector* endings that initiate movements in muscles, and promote secretion by glands.

Such an arrangement of afferent and efferent fibres and their associated nerve cells is found in the most primitive type of nervous system, but there is also a third component. This is called an *intercalated* nerve cell and it and its kind are destined in evolution to be of ever-increasing importance. Afferent and efferent components increase in number and complexity with increase in size and divergence of form in animals; increase in quantity of intercalated nerve cells is even greater. The function of intercalated nerve cells is to regulate the efferent side of a nervous system in the light of any 'information' they may be endowed with or may have acquired, and to modify its response in association with activities of the animal generally, Multiplication and increasing complexity of intercalated nerve cells, and their concentration in definite regions result in establishment of a *central nervous system* composed of brain and spinal cord. Innumerable intercalated neurones are arranged in groups or 'levels' within brain and cord and thus complex connexions and circuits can develop between and within each level of nerve cells. In a ship it could be considered that the 'brains' of the system, whether human or mechanical, interpret wireless messages, soundings, and information obtained from radar in the light of what is already known about behaviour of ships, or what has been learnt about navigation, and of what is best for that ship in its immediate environment.

Nervous tissue consists of three main components, *grey matter* composed of nerve cells or neurones, *white matter* composed of nerve fibres which conduct nerve impulses, and connecting tissue or *neuroglia* that supports and binds together all components. Nerve fibres are long processes that arise from neurones.

Development of Nervous Systems

One of the most fascinating aspects of neuroanatomy concerns the study of the way that nerves get properly arranged in an animal, that is to say, how an embryo gets 'wired up' by nerves. Stages in development of a human brain are fairly complex, and for obvious reasons little is known of development of function in association with structural changes. In Chapter 7 the earliest appearance of a brain in a human embryo was described in Horizon IX as a development of neural folds. These rise up as two waves of tissue and fuse along the mid-line of the germinal disc. A long centrally placed hollow tube, the fluid-filled *neural tube*, is thus formed. At first it is open at each end, anterior and posterior neuropores, but the openings soon close (by 25 somite stage, Horizon XII). The neural tube is bent in conformity with embryonic curvature and is supported below by the notochord (p. 132) except at its very tip. Three swellings develop in the front part of the hollow neural tube called forebrain, midbrain, and hindbrain vesicles. They will develop into cerebral hemispheres, upper brain stem, pons, cerebellum, and medulla: the rest of the neural tube will become the spinal cord. The hollow spaces within each vesicle give rise to cavities within the adult brain and cord; they are called *ventricles* in the brain, and a small central cana persists in the spinal cord. The fluid within them is called cerebrospinal fluid. It is formed continuously from delicate fringe-like whorls of blood vessels invaginated into the roofs of the ventricles. It leaves the ventricular system by openings in the roof of the ventricle formed from the hindbrain vesicle (fourth ventricle) to enter a *sub-arachnoid* space between arachnoid and pia mater. These are the delicate inner two membranes (meninges) that envelop all mammalian brains; the tough outermost one is called dura mater. Meninges protect the central nervous system and the cerebrospinal fluid provides a water jacket that allows of slight changes in shape of the brain, cushions it against shock and may provide nutriment.

Early in embryonic life the forebrain vesicle develops on each side a rapidly growing diverticulum. Each diverticulum will develop into a cerebral hemisphere, the hollow in the hemisphere formed by enlargement of the diverticulum being the *lateral* ventricle. The latter retains its embryonic connexion with the cavity of the forebrain vesicle, or *third* ventricle as the small interventricular foramen (of Monro*). It was incidentally near the region of the third ventricle that Herophilus (died 280 B.C.) considered the seat of emotional life to be situated. Even by the second month of embryonic life this great enlargement of the forebrain region gives human embryos a characteristic appearance (p. 138).

There are no nerves in embryos at this and several later stages and until after the neural tube has closed there is no indication that they will appear. Afferent nerves develop from a group of cells known as *neural crest* cells and efferent motor nerves develop by a process of outgrowth from neurones developing within the neural tube.

Neural Crest Cells and Development of Nerve Fibres

Neural crest cells are circumscribed groups of cells that fail to be incorporated in the dorsal part of the closing neural tube and are left between fused dorsal ectoderm and neural tube. They give rise to a

*Three Alexander Monros, grandfather, father, and son, successively occupied the chair of Anatomy in Edinburgh University from 1720 to 1846. It was Monro Secundus (1733–1817) who described the interventricular foramen, and who probably made the greatest contribution to anatomical knowledge.

wide variety of structures and their exact fates are not yet completely known. It is clear that they do give rise to ganglia of sensory nerves and Fig. 18 shows how this may happen. They are difficult to discern in the head end of an embryo but certain areas of ectoderm maintain intimate connexion with the neural tube in the form of sensory *placodes*. These play an important part in forming nerves of special senses (olfactory, optic, and auditory) and are probably homologous with neural crest tissue proper.

Neural crest cells become segmentally arranged along each side of

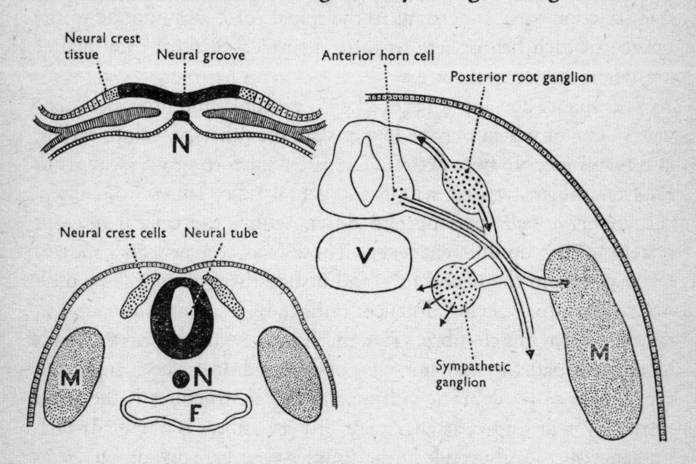

FIG. 18. How neural crest tissue and spinal nerves develop. N: notochord; V: vertebra; M: mesoderm; becoming segmental myotome. F: foregut.

the neural tube and each cell develops two processes to become bipolar neurones (later unipolar). One process grows peripherally until it reaches an area of ectoderm and is thus in a position to innervate skin that eventually develops from that area. The second process grows inwards towards the neural tube and enters it on its dorsal aspect. In this way groups of neural crest cells innervate the skin and other structures and at the same time find connexions within the developing spinal cord and brain stem.

Motor nerves develop in a different manner in that they are formed as a result of outgrowth of processes direct from the neural tube. The latter is at first composed of only a few cells, but soon *neuroblasts* start to develop from germinal cells that also give rise to neuroglia and cells lining the ventricles. Development of increasing numbers of neuroblasts causes the central nervous system to increase in size and gradually neuroblasts come to be arranged in characteristic places at each level. They are arranged in a distorted H about the central canal in the spinal cord, and the fibre tracts extending up and down the cord lie outside them. Neuroblasts in the brain aggregate into a number of masses or nuclei in the walls of the ventricles, and in contradistinction to arrangements in the spinal cord, also migrate to the surface of each hemisphere to form a surface cloak of grey matter known as the cerebral cortex.

Neuroblasts develop a series of fine protoplasmic processes (dendrites), one of which may be longer than the others, develops earlier, and forms a nerve fibre (axon). The latter starts to grow away from each neuroblast, at first within the neural tube. Fibres from intercalated nerve cells pass up and down within the central nervous system to link up different levels. Those of motor neurones start to grow out from the neural tube and invade the embryo. They push out steadily for varying distances until they reach a termination in relation to a muscle-fibre. The mechanisms guiding nerve fibres along their pathways are not fully understood. It has been suggested that guidance by contact with neighbouring structures is the main means by which final arrangement of nerve fibres is obtained; such guidance may easily result in the simpler arrangements of nerves, as those supplying thoracic musculature in a definite segmental pattern. Other factors may well be involved in governing the more complex pathways established in brachial and other complex nerve plexuses, or by the wandering vagus nerve. It is easy to ascribe development of such complexities to early instructions of heredity, to action of local electrical forces, or to some specific chemical affinities between nerve fibre and that structure upon which it will terminate, but it is difficult to see how to analyse these factors experimentally. It is probable that when a particular fibre reaches its destination and makes final contact some change occurs in the cell body, specifying that each cell has taken on its particular function. Thereafter it is effectively capable of taking part in building up of patterns of excitation as other neurones develop their specificity. Peripheral nerve fibres possess outer sheaths, *neurilemmal* cells, and it has been suggested that these play a part in guiding nerve fibres to their appropriate terminations. It seems generally agreed, however, that the central axon precedes outgrowth of the sheath. Neurilemmal cells do, however, take part in regeneration of peripheral fibres.

Nerve fibres may be naked axons, may have a neurilemmal sheath and also may have a *myelin* sheath. Myelin is a fatty substance laid down about an axon and myelinated fibres are found inside and outside the central nervous system. Electron microscopy shows that myelin is wrapped about an axon in many layers, possibly as a result of enrolling activities of the neurilemmal cells. The myelin sheath is interrupted at intervals by nodes; in experiments it can be shown that a nerve impulse 'leaps' from node to node. It is not clear what is the exact function of myelin, but myelinization of fibres is not completed at birth in man, but continues until the age of five. Even after this growth of a fibre can continue for many years.

Parts of the Brain

The head end of the neural tube indicates more distinctive features than other parts of the central nervous system from the time of its earliest appearance.

Usefulness of enlargement of the head-end of the neural tube is not difficult to associate with other structural developments. Locomotion involves progress, even if in a random direction, and the leading end of an elongated animal will be exposed to new surroundings more frequently than any other part. The head-end is thus better placed for assessing change, and will receive more information and will be in a position more advantageous for regulating and influencing the rest of the body. Evolutionary advent of special senses of taste, smell, sight, and hearing and appearance of jaws proclaim and demand increased numbers of intercalated nerve cells in the head region. This necessitates abundant connexions between nerve cells of trunk and limb levels, and thus there follows desirability of numerous links of connecting tracts of fibres up and down the brain and spinal cord.

Fore-, mid-, and hind-brain vesicles each have a particular fate. The hind-brain is continuous with the spinal cord and together with the mid-brain forms the brain-stem. Derivatives of the hind-brain are numerous and its structure is markedly different from that of the spinal cord. There is no definite arrangement of grey matter in central columns with an outer sheath of ascending and descending fibre tracts, but there are scattered aggregations of neurones and both longitudinal and transverse bands of fibres. Some of the longitudinal

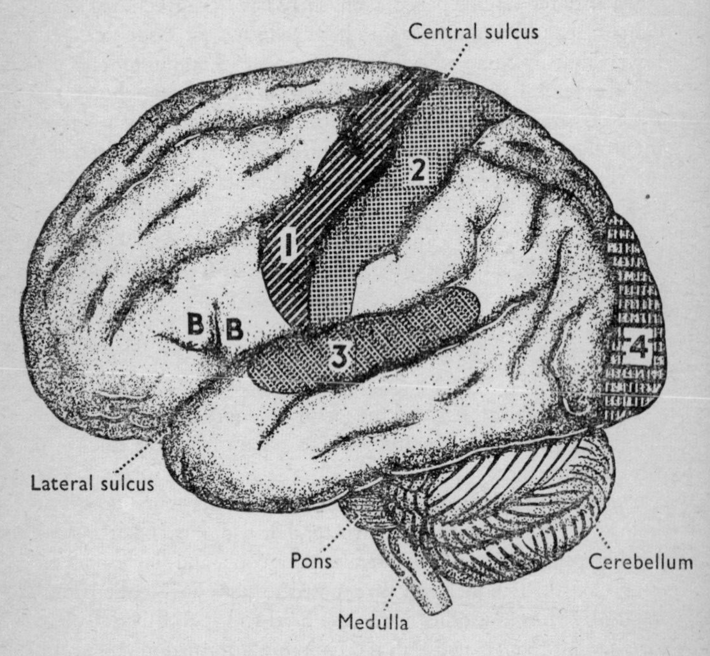

FIG. 19. Outer aspect (left side) of a human brain. 1: the motor area; 2: the sensory area; 3: the auditory area; 4: the visual area; B: Broca's speech centre. See Plate XVII.

fibres traverse the hind-brain in passing from cord to brain or *vice versa* and there display a strange phenomenon of 'crossing over' (decussation) from one side to the other. No really satisfactory explanation of decussation has yet been given; it may have evolved to facilitate 'steering' mechanisms in lower marine vertebrates. Other fibre tracts end or originate in neuronal groups in the hind-brain.

The main component parts of the hind-brain are the medulla oblongata, the pons, and the cerebellum. The medulla contains neurones and fibre tracts associated with certain cranial nerves. Central mechanisms within it control activities of the heart, respiratory apparatus, alimentary canal and its derivatives. They also innervate derivatives of pharyngeal arches concerned in development of tongue, pharynx, and larynx, and are much concerned with balancing

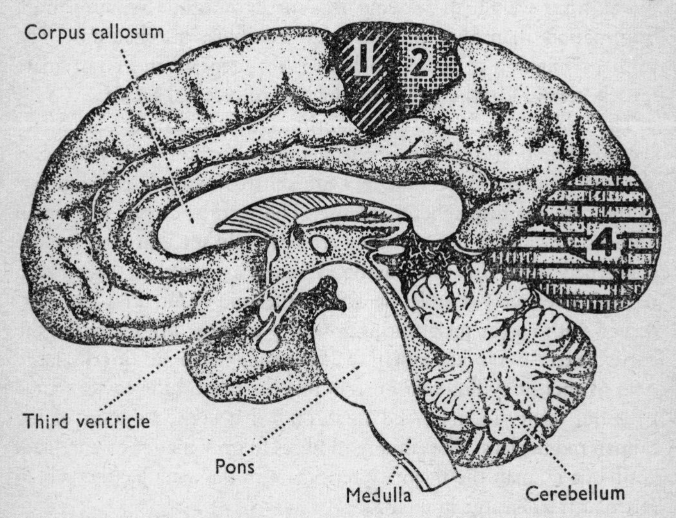

FIG. 20. Mid-line section through a human brain (right side). See Fig. 19 and Plate XVII.

mechanisms. The pons links cerebral hemispheres, mid-brain, cerebellum, and medulla. It is most highly developed in man and its size is a reflection of the complexity of his movements. Those involved in speech, writing, and playing musical instruments demand rich integration between visual, auditory, and cerebral mechanisms.

No subdivision of the mammalian brain displays such morphological diversity as does the cerebellum. Numerous interpretations of its morphology have been attempted; nowadays it is considered to have two fundamental components, a corpus cerebelli and a flocculonodular lobe (J. Jansen). The largest cerebellum is found in the whale, in which it is 20 per cent of total brain weight. In man it weighs about 150 g. which represents 11 per cent of brain weight. Parts of the corpus cerebelli (middle lobe of Elliott Smith) are much enlarged in man to form neo-cerebellar tissue. This is particularly associated with enlargement of the cerebral cortex and the supply of proprioceptive information. Vestibular information is received mainly in the flocculonodular lobe. This assists in maintenance of upright posture, but shifting weight or moving legs in that attitude requires more information than that provided by vestibular mechanisms. The primary function of the cerebellum is to integrate and co-ordinate muscle action. It is the great 'modulator' of cerebral activity.

The mid-brain of man retains a primitive form. Lower vertebrates show elaboration of its roof or *tectum* in association with visual and auditory centres. These functions are shifted forwards in mammals as the cerebral hemispheres enlarge. The tectum carries four small hillocks, or *colliculi*, upon it; they are relatively small in man and are concerned with visual and auditory reflex activities in the cervical region. The two *red nuclei* lie within the mid-brain; they are concerned with motor mechanisms accessory to those originating in the cortex (extra-pyramidal systems). It contains two kinds of cells, large ones of ancient evolutionary origin that are plentiful in lower mammals but scanty in man, and small ones that compose most of the human red nucleus. The latter send fibres to grey matter of the spinal cord but in man the majority terminate in the medulla (the rubroreticular tract is large in man).

The cerebral hemispheres are 'supported' on the mid-brain; fibres passing to and from them traverse its *cerebral peduncles*. Each hemisphere has several masses of grey matter within it called *basal ganglia*. Fibres pass amongst (*internal capsule*) and around the basal ganglia on their pathways to and from the cortex of one hemisphere, the spinal cord, the other hemisphere and parts of the same hemisphere. Each hemisphere is connected by the remnants (diencephalon) of the original fore-brain vesicle. The lower part becomes the *hypothalamus*, an important constellation of nuclei having nervous and vascular connexions with the pituitary (p.247). Over its roof develops the main bundle of fibres (corpus callosum) that cross from one hemisphere to the other (commissural fibres). In its upper wall develops each *thalamus*; they are large subdivided sensory relay stations. Those nuclear groups (ventrolateral) concerned in the relay to the cortex of all modalities of sensation from the body are particularly developed in man.

There is no space to describe the anatomy of the spinal cord or the autonomic system with its sympathetic and parasympathetic divisions. Those characteristics that could be claimed as being peculiarly human are for expert neurologists.

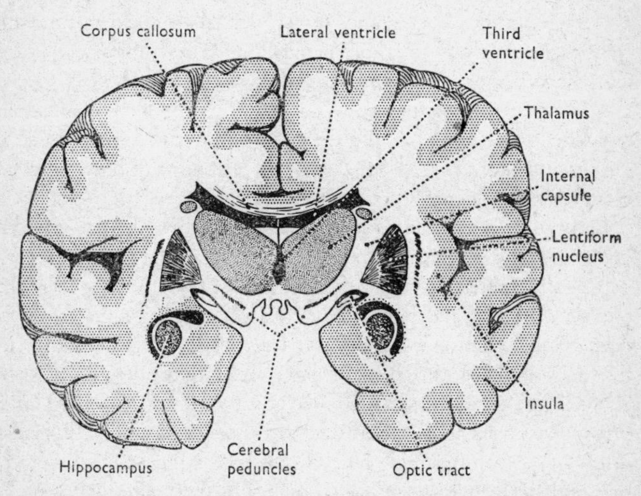

FIG. 21. Transverse section through a human brain near the middle. Compare with Plate XIX.

Man's Cerebral Cortex

The human cerebral cortex forms a layer of grey matter, varying in thickness from 1·25 to 3 mm., spread over the whole surface of each hemisphere. Its total extent is about 1,145 cm^2 and its volume about 300 cm^3 (D. A. Sholl). It is often called the pallium or mantle, and in man it is the 'highest' part of the nervous system, dominating the activities of all other parts. The pallium of lower vertebrates is almost entirely concerned with olfactory matters (archipallium), but the mammalian cortex displays a *neopallium*, composing in man the far greater proportion of the pallium, and it receives many other kinds of sensory impulse. The pallium in lower vertebrates lies deeper within the cerebral hemisphere, but with evolution of mammals the grey matter, except that of the basal ganglia, tends to move towards the surface. Migration of nerve cells to the surface is also seen during early embryology of the human brain. There is at first a marginal zone free of nuclei on the surface. This soon becomes invaded by developing nerve cells from the deeper germinal cells, first at a point that corresponds to the parietal area, and then rapidly over the whole surface of the neopallium. The embryonic parietal area shows a more precocious rate of development than other areas. It is the first part of the neocortex to receive sensory connexions, and since these are from the thalamus and convey impulses from sensory receptors, it seems that early establishment of body sense has considerable influence over cortical development.

Embryonic mammalian cerebral cortex rapidly exhibits a number of significant developments between the 6th and 12th week of intrauterine life. It steadily increases in thickness, owing partly to multiplication of cells and partly to arrival of new migrants from the deeper layer. Neurones in the cortex thus become stratified, a process that does not cease until birth or even later. It is usual to describe six layers in the cortex; the outer three are more distinct in the human brain. The layers are differentiated by characteristics of cells peculiar to each layer; for example layer V possesses large or medium-sized pyramidal cells with axons descending into the white matter of the hemisphere.

Certain types of cell may be recognized; those with descending axons that reach the white matter beneath and that continue either to lower parts of the nervous system (projection fibres) or to other regions of the cortex (association fibres); those with axons that ascend and ramify, in one or more layers nearer the surface; those with horizontal axons that remain in one layer; those with short axons that ramify within the immediate proximity of the cell. The last type is found in great profusion in every layer of the human cortex and in some areas outnumbers cells with descending axons. A Spanish histologist, Santiago Ramon y Cajal (1852–1934), whose work has done much to elucidate anatomical arrangements in the cortex, maintained that the presence in the human cortex of characteristically large numbers of cells with short axons is an anatomical expression of the subtlety and delicacy of function of man's brain.

Man soon suspected that the cerebral hemispheres were the seat of his intelligence. Early anatomists, however, ascribed important functions to pumping activities by the fluid-filled ventricles. Descartes (1596–1650) thought the pineal (p. 249) a link between brain and soul. Thomas Willis (1621–75) may probably be considered the father of scientific neurology and he realized the necessity for team work. He was helped in his investigations of the brain by Sir Christopher Wren (p. 190) and Richard Lower, an early experimenter in blood transfusion (p. 59). Willis realized that the substance of the hemisphere was the source of volitional activity and he produced experimental evidence as proof. A hundred years had to pass before the next contribution, that by a medical student, Francesco Gennari of Parma, who saw a well marked white line in the occipital region of the cortex. He thought it designated particular functional significance to an area which we now know is the visual cortex. This observation was confirmed by Jules Baillarger (1806–90) in France, to whom we owe the first description of stratification of the cortex into its six layers of regionally varying thickness. He also described two white lines in the cortex, the outer of which corresponded to that of Gennari. Baillarger endeavoured to apply his discovery to an investigation of brains of insane persons, but, as was to be realized repeatedly during the ensuing century, the methods employed were far too gross to detect any differences specific to insanity.

The early nineteenth century saw the coining of a word that became in some respects far too popular. It was phrenology (from *phrenos*, a frenzy) and it was intended to mean the study of the science of the mind. It came more to mean a hoped-for association of bumps on the surface of the head with an underlying development of certain parts of the brain. This unfortunate assumption has to be laid at the feet of Franz Joseph Gall (1758–1828), a Viennese physician, and for a time his views were very popular. They brought him great wealth and influence until his teaching was suppressed on the grounds of its danger to religion; yet Gall's concept that function could be localized in the cerebral cortex did not deserve to be as utterly discredited as it was by those who maintained that the brain functioned as a whole and could not be differentiated into 'thirty-three' parts.

Flourens in 1824 showed by extirpation methods that the cerebrum was definitely concerned with certain perceptual and volitional functions. A clinician at The London Hospital, John Hughlings Jackson (1835–1911), made observations on epileptiform seizures associated with localized lesions on the surface of the cortex (1863). He suggested that certain regions of the brain controlled certain limb movements. In 1898 he enunciated his ideas on evolution in the nervous system of pathways gradually increasing in complexity as the level ascended from spinal cord and brain stem to motor areas in the cortex and to the most complex regions of all in the anterior part of the brain (pre-frontal region). Hughlings Jackson's observations were supported by that of the French surgeon and anthropologist Paul Broca who noted that a discrete lesion in a particular region of the frontal lobe on the left side in right-handed people produced loss of speech (p. 209). R. Fritsch and E. Hitzig (1870) applied electric currents to the surface of the brain and for the first time by this method caused an anaesthetized animal to move its leg when a certain motor area was stimulated on the opposite side of the cortex. Their work was extended by Sir David Ferrier (1843–1928) who showed similar effects by electrical stimulation and extirpation in brains of Primates and mammals. The results of these discoveries are to be compared with statements by Gall; the latter maintained that because a certain region of the head felt enlarged in some pickpockets it marked increased acquisitiveness; in fact beneath this region lies the motor cortex. The methods used by Fritsch and Hitzig have been much extended in recent years and were critically discussed by Sir Charles Sherrington and W. Penfield. The surgical work of the latter has provided much information. Techniques have been devised to measure patterns of electrical activity in the brain (H. Berger) and in small volumes of cortex. Effects on behaviour of animals of removal of small pieces of cortex have been studied by K. S. Lashley. Techniques involving insertion of mica strips and numerous metal wires have been developed by C. Sperry. Others have devised more specific techniques for determining normal and degenerative characteristics of cortical neurones and nerve fibres. The discovery by J. Z. Young of particularly large nerve fibres in squids has led to advances in our knowledge of nerve conduction.

Numerous maps have been made of neurone distribution in the

cortex; the best known are those of the 'cortical cartographers', A. W. Campbell, K. Brodman, and C. von Economo. More recently, K. S. Lashley and G. Clark have critically examined difficulties inherent in making maps of cytoarchitecture. They found it difficult to assume 'that every recognizable difference in cortical structure represents a functional differentiation'.

Estimates have been made of the total number of neurones in the cortex of Primates (G. A. Shariff). Tarsius is estimated to have 310 million, a marmoset 270 million, *Cercopithecus* 2,500 million, a chimpanzee 5,500 million, and man 6,900 million. Packing density, neurone size, proportions of specific types of neurones present in different parts of the cortex, fibre length and distribution and other quantitative aspects of cortical organization are critically discussed in the book by D. A. Sholl quoted at the end of the chapter. Those interested in analogies between animals and communication systems and in construction of ingenious toy animals that 'learn' should consult some of the other books mentioned. Finally we quote from Professor Lashley '... all of the neurones of the cortex must be in constant activity and integration must consist of complex patterns of interaction and not of conduction over relatively isolated paths'.

Blood Supply of the Brain

Grey matter in a human brain is particularly well supplied with blood vessels. Nervous tissue needs oxygen; it is said that each minute a quantity of blood nearly equalling the weight of the brain should circulate through it. About one third of the blood leaving the left ventricle in a resting man passes to the brain. Blood reaches the brain through two internal carotid and two vertebral arteries. Carotid is derived from *karos*, a stupefaction; Aristotle believed that compression of a carotid artery resulted in deep sleep. Curtis (1551) first showed, however, that in some mammals ligature of *both* carotids did not produce sleep or stupor. This is because in certain mammals only vertebral arteries carry blood to the brain. Instantaneous suppression of blood flow to a human brain results in unconsciousness in about seven seconds. Irreversible changes occur in nervous tissue shortly afterwards.

The two vertebral arteries unite as they enter the skull to form the basilar artery. This divides again and its branches, together with those of the internal carotids, form a circle of arteries, at the base of the brain. This circulus arteriosus was described by Thomas Willis (1621–75) and illustrated by Sir Christopher Wren. The latter is remembered for his architectural genius, but he was also an anatomist and studied medicine at Oxford. In some mammals, such as cattle, branches of the vertebral arteries enter into formation of a network of arteries (rete mirabile) at the base of the brain. Small but vital central and basal arteries leave the circle of Willis and penetrate the base of the brain. Certain central arteries leave each middle cerebral artery to supply the main fibre tracts (internal capsule) passing to and from the brain. Man is peculiarly prone to lesions of these vessels; and they will obviously cause much disability. They are often called 'arteries of cerebral haemorrhage' and are associated with the name of Jean Martin Charcot (1825–93), a famous French neurologist.

Large cerebral arteries (anterior, middle, and posterior) leave the circle of Willis and encompass the brain. They give off numerous cortical branches that penetrate the cortex to varying depths and anastomose to varying degrees. The primitive pattern was that of a simple looped system; to meet the needs of an enlarging brain it has been elaborated into either an arborization of paired vessels (opossum) or a reticular pattern as is found in Eutherian mammals (O. J. Lewis). A cubic millimetre of grey matter from a human brain may contain a quantity of capillaries that would extend for over a metre if put end to end. Blood from the brain drains into venous sinuses within the dura. In man the intra-cranial sinuses have a relatively simple pattern that eventually drains into each internal jugular vein. In seals the latter only drains face and neck and blood leaves the brain by sinuses that drain into a large extra-dural intravertebral vein. This lies dorsal to the spinal cord; blood leaves it to drain into a plexus of veins surrounding the kidneys. This remarkable modification is probably associated with presence of a muscle cuff on the posterior vena cava and with bradycardia that occurs when a seal dives (p. 83).

Brains of Primates

Brains of Lemurs have relatively small cerebral hemispheres that do not extend backwards to overlap the cerebellum. Areas associated with olfaction are large for a primate, but smaller than those of primitive mammals. The neopallium is smooth in some, but in others is quite markedly convoluted. Its occipital region is conspicuous, but not as relatively large as in Tarsius. The brain of an adult Tarsius weighs only 3–4 g., but relative to body weight it shows a distinct proportional increase. Its mid-brain is very large in association with importance of eye and ear reflexes.

In a macaque monkey the brain weighs from 60–70 g. and in all monkeys it is relatively larger than in lemurs and Tarsius. Cerebral hemispheres are so large that they overhang the cerebellum: olfactory parts are reduced. The neopallium is increased in area by marked foldings; certain fissures and sulci have special characteristics; a *lunate* sulcus clearly delimits the visual area. Catarrhine brains show in general more complicated fissuration patterns than those of Platyrrhines.

Brain weights of apes are as follows: gibbon, 80–140 g.; orang-utan, 300–390 g.; chimpanzee, 330–400 g.; gorilla, 380–430 g. Extension of the neopallium is more marked than in Catarrhines, but not as much as that of man. Certain well marked folds (*opercula*) develop in the lateral sulcus covering over an area of cortex known as the *insula*. The frontal one of these, however, develops only in man. Fissural pattern resembles that of man, but tertiary sulci are mostly lacking; the lunate sulcus or *Affenspalte* is deep. Chimpanzees show greatest differentiation of frontal lobes.

Development of cerebral cortex relative to that of the rest of the brain reaches a climax in man. Brain weight in Negroes averages 1,200 g. and in Whites 1,300 g.; it accounts for about 2·5 per cent of body weight. That of women's brains averages slightly less but is relative to their smaller bulk. Brain weight is not correlated with ability, though an adult weight less than 1,000 g. is not compatible with normal function. At birth a human brain weighs 325–350 g., by one year it weighs 800–900 g. and by the age of six to seven it has reached adult weight. The majority of the increase is due to completion of myelinization and development of full vascularity.

Fissuration is almost complete at birth and is even more complex than in apes; there is occasionally some evidence of handedness. Frontal and occipital lobes are particularly developed in man, as are association areas in parietal and lower temporal regions. The enlargement of the three latter areas is associated with man's dependence on sight, speech, and hearing (see the next chapter). Frontal lobe enlargement appears to be linked with man's characteristic exercise of caution, restraint, and inhibition in his actions. It may also be involved in his determination and concentration in prolonged pursuit of his desired ambitions.

Ah, but a man's reach should exceed his grasp,
Or what's a heaven for?

ROBERT BROWNING

FOR FURTHER READING

The Organization of the Cerebral Cortex. D. A. Sholl. Methuen, 1956
Design for a Brain. W. R. Ashby. Chapman and Hall, 1952
The Living Brain. W. Grey Walter. Duckworth, 1953
Minds and Machines. W. Sluckin. Penguin Books, 1954
The Organization of Behaviour. D. O. Hebb. Wiley, 1949
The Physical Background of Perception. E. D. Adrian. Clarendon Press, Oxford, 1947
Cybernetics or Control and Communication in the Animal and Machine. N. Wiener. Wiley, New York, 1948

CHAPTER II

HIS METHODS OF RECEIVING INFORMATION

A MAN'S brain receives information of two main varieties, that which tells him about himself, about the position of his limbs and the state of his organs, and that which informs him about his surroundings. Some of this information reaches consciousness, some reaches the lower centres in the brain. Three anatomical entities are necessary for such information to be appreciated. There must be some form of receptor, a sense-organ capable of responding to each stimulus. It may be one associated with general sensations of touch, pressure, temperature, and pain that can be felt in the skin, or it may be one concerned with special senses of sight, hearing, smell, taste, and balance that are appreciated in eye, ear, nose, tongue, and organs of balance. There are also proprioceptive sense-organs in tendons and muscles important for providing information about orientation of the body in space. Then there must be conducting pathways of nerve fibres leading from the sense-organs to convey nerve impulses initiated by their stimulation. These must reach some region of the nervous system that possesses a perceptive function and is capable of interpreting the signals received from the sense-organs.

Innervation of the Skin

Man can appreciate crude touch over all his skin, but delicacy and fineness of touch is limited to certain regions such as finger-tips and lips. The skin is also capable of appreciating pressure, changes of temperature, and pain. For the last sixty years four primary modalities of touch, cold, warmth, and pain have been thought to be associated with four specific types of nerve endings in the skin. M. von Frey (1894–96) suggested that there was therefore a punctate distribution of sensory 'spots' on the skin, each 'spot' having beneath a certain type of sense-organ.

The 'cold spots' on the skin were said to have beneath them groups of minute cylindrical bulbous corpuscles first described by W. Krause in 1859. They have a thin capsule that is pierced by a nerve fibre. The latter divides into a complicated plexus of thin fibrils within the nucleated semi-fluid contents of the corpuscle.

Tactile 'spots' are associated with underlying oval corpuscles having a capsule and penetrating nerve fibre, which pursues a spiral course to the tip of the corpuscle. Other fibres lose their sheaths some way before reaching the corpuscle and enter it to form networks of horizontal branches. Such endings were the first sensory end-organs in the skin to be described; they were seen by R. Wagner and G. Meissner in 1852. They have since been known as Meissner's corpuscles, but a number of authorities considered they were artefacts resulting from chemicals used on the skin to prepare sections. Evidence was then produced that was said to prove their existence; it was shown that the fibrils in them degenerated after a lesion affecting their nerve supply. Certain nerve fibres in the skin were believed to end on cells in the epidermis as knobs or discs, called Merkel's discs after the anatomist F. S. Merkel (1880). Recently it has become clear that they have so great a similarity to dendritic cells of the skin that Merkel, and others, were confusing these cells with what they believed to be special tactile elements.

Somewhat different corpuscles were described by an Italian histologist A. Ruffini (1898) and deemed to be associated with the sense of warmth. They consist of an oval, or spindle-shaped, closely woven network of nerve fibrils intermingled with small bundles of connective tissue. Ruffini observed so many types of capsulated endings intermediary in form between the above that he thought it rather hopeless to attempt a classification. Recently the application of more critical techniques, and the use of phase-contrast microscopy on fresh specimens, has suggested that many of the so-called organized and encapsulated end-organs are artefacts. A distorted and disrupted nerve ending may apparently present itself under various disguises. Encapsulated nerve endings are present in skin devoid of hair, in the finger tips, and in certain other places; there is none in hairy skin. They are of a multitude of shapes and complexities, but in each the nerve fibre divides into a plexus of fine filaments that end freely among the cells of the capsule.

Whatever may be the final answer to the way end-organs function it is generally agreed that skin is innervated through a plexus of medullated fibres situated in the dermis. The nerves get finer and finer as they near the epidermis and either lose their medullary sheaths or else they become extremely attenuated. After breaking

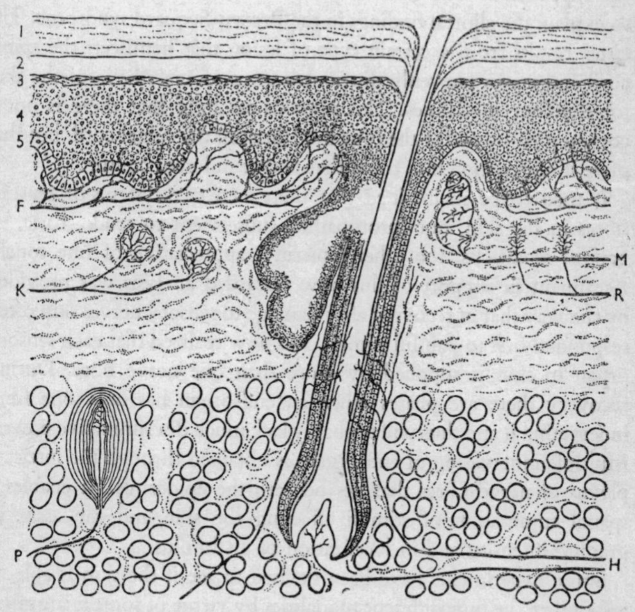

FIG. 22. Layers of the epidermis and sensory nerve endings in the skin. 1: stratum corneum; 2: s. lucidum; 3: s. granulosum; 4: s. aculeatum; 5: s. basale; F: free nerve endings and superficial plexus; H: free endings about hair follicle and in papilla; K: Krause's end bulbs; M: Meissner's oval corpuscles; P: Pacinian lamellated corpuscle; R: Ruffini's end organs.

up into arborizations they end as fine, naked filaments that lie free among the cell layers of the epidermis and in the dermis. Similar fibres end in relation to the cells of sweat glands and the coats of blood vessels larger than capillaries. It was maintained that these free nerve endings constituted the sole peripheral endings appreciative of pain, whereas other modalities were conveyed from the three types of corpuscle described above. The doubt that has been thrown on the existence of three such anatomically and functionally distinct types of end-organ suggests that the theory of punctate sensibility in the skin may have to be abandoned or modified. Sensory modalities appear to be segregated in the spinal cord: otherwise it is difficult to explain the clinical findings in the Brown-Séquard syndrome. The latter results from a certain type of lesion that hemisects the spinal cord and leaves unevenly distributed areas of anaesthesia of the skin for the four modalities. This suggests strongly that there is not a common pathway for the four modalities in the spinal cord, but that there is segregation into tracts that pursue different courses.

It used to be maintained that there were two systems of sensory fibres in the skin, one (protopathic) subservient to crude, basic, or painful sensations, the other (epicritic) appreciative of fine touch. Argument in support of this now discarded analysis was provided by the way that in recovery after damage to sensory nerves skin often responded first to painful stimuli. It is now realized that each sensory organ in skin is supplied by more than one nerve fibre. During recovery there are phases when an end-organ has only one fibre innervating it and thus will probably lack much discriminative power. Multiple innervation of end-organs is obtained through the intricate plexus of nerve fibres that lies beneath the epidermis. It enables a spatial summation of stimuli affecting the skin and can assist in grading intensity and in localization of a stimulus.

Some experiments have been devised to see if the skin is able to respond to the four different modalities by virtue of some anatomical pattern expressed through a particular distribution of end-organs and hairs. The results of these and other experiments concerned with examining how skin reacts to specific differences between its inner and outer surfaces lend encouragement to those who maintain that we should study such problems rather than accept the idea of a series of perhaps imaginary specific end-organs firing off at an appropriate stimulus.

Pacinian Corpuscles and other Endings

There is one striking capsule-like ending in the skin about the existence of which there is less controversy. This is the lamellated corpuscle that F. Pacini (1840) observed in deeper parts of the skin. They had been described earlier by A. Vater (1741) and are thus more correctly called Vater-Pacinian corpuscles. Each oval body consists of a series of layers arranged like coats of an onion, about a central core. A nerve fibre pierces one end, loses its sheath near the centre, and ends at the further end of the core in a dense network of fine filaments. The endings are present in the deep parts of the dermis, particularly of the hands and feet and also in relation to joints: there is good evidence that they subserve the pressure sense and perception of movement. They are developed by the eighth month of foetal life, but it is not known if they function sufficiently for the foetus to be aware of the compression to which it is subjected at childbirth.

Special sensory end-organs are present in the great majority of voluntary muscles and are capable of supplying information about the tension exerted on the contraction or stretching of a muscle. They are therefore important elements in obtaining balance and equilibration of the body and in providing information as to the degree of power put behind a movement. They play an important part in the complexities of neuro-muscular coordination. The endings are called neuro-muscular and neuro-tendinous spindles: in each case there is a multi-layered connective tissue capsule surrounding a core of specialized muscular and tendinous fibres. The latter are called intrafusal fibres, and in neuro-muscular spindles they exhibit some of the characteristics of embryonic muscle in that the intrafusal fibres are smaller with more cytoplasm and many nuclei and are less clearly striated than ordinary muscle fibres. The spindle shape of the organ is due to its enlargement in the middle by a fluid-filled space between the capsule and the core. Afferent and efferent nerve fibres supply the spindle; sensory fibres pierce it near the middle, lose their sheaths, and divide into a spirally or annularly arranged plexus of fine fibres. Some nerve fibres end in similar networks within muscle but are not related to capsulated spindles.

End-organs and subcutaneous nerve plexuses are linked to the central nervous system by sensory nerves. It was thought that they were specific in that each transmitted impulses related to a certain modality, and that there were pain, touch or hot and cold fibres. There are few anatomical differences between all the sensory fibres, except occasionally in their size. It is known that there are both fine and coarse fibres conducting 'pain impulses', the former at a slower speed than the latter. A transverse section of a main trunk from the skin plexus and end-organs shows considerable intermingling of sensory fibres, but, whether they do in fact originate from specific end-organs or convey patterns of impulses, there is sorting out of types of impulses as soon as the fibres enter the spinal cord.

Man's Eyes

Despite his large brain man would be lost without eyesight; yet it is his brain that enables him to interpret what he sees and gives a meaning to things seen. Man's two eyes perceive light, discriminate intensity, and appreciate colour. They also allow visual space perception; stereoscopic superimposition of two images is not a function of eyes but of the brain. To obtain it ocular functions must be integrated through brain activities.

Sensitivity to light is by no means confined to any one major group of animals. All cells are in some way sensitive to light. Development of screening pigment in invertebrates resulted in isolation of particularly sensitive cells. They are found as raised patches or pits on the animal's surface. Response in primitive eyespots is only to shadows that pass across the sensitive area. Later a transparent lens developed from ectoderm and focussed light onto the eyespots. In animals unable to move their eyes compound mosaic structures developed that enabled a wide range of vision (insects). Basic eye arrangement evolved early in vertebrate history but became modified in association with change of habit and environment.

Man's freely moveable eyeballs are set in complete sockets in his skull: closure of orbital sockets from the temporal fossae behind is a Primate feature. It is associated with both eyes being directed forwards. Each eyeball is moved by six extrinsic muscles (four recti and two oblique). Most are supplied by the third (oculomotor) cranial nerve. The superior oblique is supplied by the fourth (trochlear) cranial nerve and causes the eyeball to look downwards and outwards, giving a pathetic expression. The lateral rectus is innervated by the sixth (abducent) cranial nerve; it allows the sidelong glances of lovers and has been called the musculus amatorius.

The human eyeball is an irregular spheroid 24 mm. in average diameter. Its three coats consist of an outer *sclera* that is transparent in its front part as the *cornea*, an intermediate *choroid* modified in front as the *iris* with a central opening or *pupil*, and an inner *retina*. The sclera forms a tough, fibrous, protective covering for the eye-ball; in lower vertebrates it may be further strengthened by presence of cartilage or even bone. The cornea is a transparent multi-layered structure equal in area to one sixth of the total circumference of the

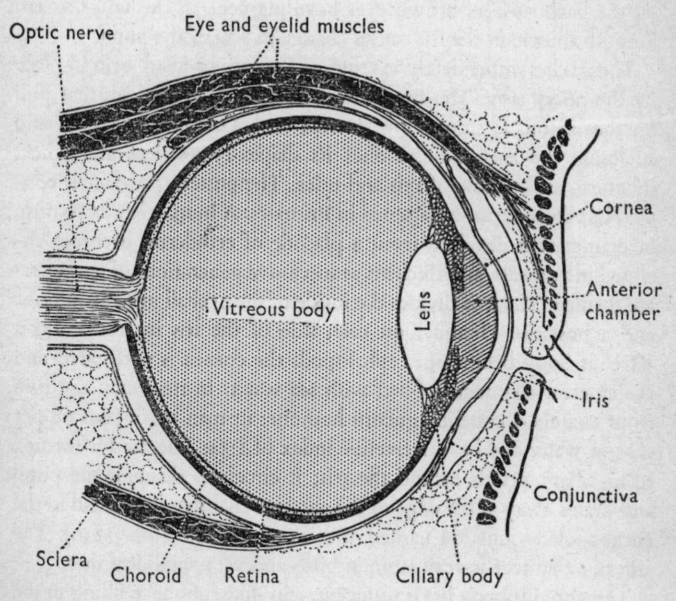

FIG. 23. Main parts of the eye. See also Plate XX.

human eyeball. It is curved to form a powerful lens; abnormal in-equality of curvature is called *astigmatism*. Whales and seals have a cornea with marked natural astigmatism. In some animals, sheep, chimpanzees, and many birds, the cornea is visibly pigmented; in no mammal is it normally vascularized.

The choroid is pigmented and well vascularized. Fishes possess a 'silvery membrane' in the choroid that gives their eyes a metallic lustre. A brilliantly coloured layer is seen on all or part of the choroid in many mammals but not in man. It is called the *tapetum* and is responsible for the green reflection from cats' eyes. Producing different coloured reflections it is present in Carnivora, cattle, horses, and whales with greatest intensity. The iris forms a contractile diaphragm about a central pupil that may be round as in man, oval as in seals, or slit-like as in cats. Its different colours are due to various arrangements of pigment within it; blue eyes have pigment only on the back surface, brown eyes have pigment all through the iris. Smooth muscle in the iris causes change in size of the pupil.

The iris lies immediately in front of the *lens*, both are held in place by the *ciliary body*. The latter also contains ciliary muscles that pull on the ligaments suspending (zonule of J. G. Zinn, 1727–59) and enclosing the lens and can alter its shape. Fishes' lens are almost spherical, as are those of rats and mice. The posterior surface is convex, but the anterior is flattened in Primates. A human lens is 10 mm. in diameter: it develops from a placode of ectoderm, becomes enclosed in a capsule, and thickens as successive generations of lens fibres are formed. The lens divides the inside of the eyeball into an anterior and a posterior chamber on each side of the iris in front, and a vitreous body behind. In cephalopods the cornea is perforated and the anterior chamber is filled with sea water. In mammals the two front chambers contain aqueous humour: in man it contains 98 per cent of water and has a refractive index of 1·34. The fluid is formed from ciliary vessels behind the iris; it circulates through the pupil and drains away at the edge of the anterior chamber by a canal in the corneo-scleral junction named after Friedrich Schlemm (1830). The anterior chamber is very large in birds and very small in fishes.

The vitreous body is a translucent, jelly-like substance filling in the space between lens and retina. In composition it resembles aqueous humour but contains as well a muco-protein that gives it a jelly-like consistency. In foetal life it is traversed by vessels (hyaloid) that supply the developing lens; these vessels degenerate later and the lens is nourished by aqueous humour.

The retina and colour vision. The retina is the nervous layer of the eyeball. It develops from a cup-shaped outgrowth from the forebrain vesicle; the optic 'nerve' is therefore part of the brain. The retina lines some four-fifths of the human eyeball; it consists of an outer pigmented and an inner nervous layer. Modified neurones called *rods* and *cones* lie against the pigmented layer; they are light sensitive, and the rods contain a special pigment called visual purple (rhodopsin). Processes from the receptors relay with those of a bipolar retinal layer; others from this layer reach neurones in a surface ganglionic layer. Nerve fibres from this layer collect from all over the retina at the optic disc to enter the optic nerve. This area is devoid of receptors and is called the 'blind spot'. The retina is thus inverted, owing to its embryological origin; light reaching the receptors has to traverse the retinal layers. Cones are more abundant in diurnal animals; rods are more plentiful in nocturnal ones. There are estimated to be some 7 million cones and 125 million rods in a human retina; but there are only about one million nerve fibres in the optic nerve. Many receptors, particularly at the periphery, share a common pathway to the brain.

A yellowish area near the posterior pole of the retina is called the *macula lutea*: it has a depressed central part, the *fovea centralis*. The latter contains only closely-packed cones. The macula and fovea are the areas of most distinct vision and also subserve functions in binocular and stereoscopic vision. They are only truly found in man, apes, and some monkeys.

It is said that a human eye can distinguish 160 different colours. Colour vision is found in higher bony fishes, turtles, lizards, birds, and in all Primates except nocturnal lemurs and Tarsius. It may be present in some snakes and marsupials and is slight and poorly developed in cats and dogs. Colour vision is usually attributed to the cones of the retina. Thomas Young (1773–1829) put forward a theory, subsequently developed by H. L. F. von Helmholtz (1821–94), that there were three primary receptors in the retina for red, green, and violet. Hering proposed a second theory which postulated the presence of six types of receptor. Experimental work confirms that there are several different types of receptor in a mammalian retina each with certain spectral responses. There is not yet, however, any cytological evidence of different types of cone.

Blood supply of the retina. The retina is avascular in lower vertebrates; only in mammals are there true retinal vessels. Blood supply may be derived from the choroid (certain rodents, ungulates, and bats) or from a pleated vascular membrane or *pecten* in the vitreous as found in birds. Retinal vessels may ramify close to the surface as in snakes, but in Primates they leave the optic disc from a central artery that traverses the substance of the optic nerve. Branches ramify over the retinal surface and penetrate its substance. There is much variation in the amount of retinal vascularization; man is classified with the Primates as *holangiotic* in that the entire retina is supplied with vessels. The inside of the eyeball can be examined with an ophthalmoscope. The back of a Primate eye looks red because of blood in the choroid. Presence of a tapetum alters the colour.

Visual pathways. The pathways followed by impulses leaving the retina are somewhat complex. The two optic nerves pass back to the base of the brain where they come together and cross at the optic *chiasma* (the Greek letter *Chi* is crossed-shaped) to form two optic *tracts*. All vertebrates have a chiasma; in sub-mammalian ones, including marsupials, each optic nerve crosses completely. In lower mammals a small proportion remains uncrossed; in man a third, those from the lateral part of the retina, do not cross. Half of the fibres from the macula cross. The greater majority of the fibres in the optic tract pass to the *lateral geniculate body*. This and the medial geniculate body are developmentally part of the thalamus (p. 184) and lie close to it. They are relay stations for sight and hearing. The well-developed Primate lateral geniculate body is laminated. Six layers receive fibres from sharply defined retinal areas; fibres from the fovea have wide representation in that they pass to three laminae. Some fibres (fewer in man than in most animals) pass from the optic tract to the nucleus of the oculomotor nerve. These connexions bring about reflex eye movements, movements of accommodation, and alter the degree of constriction of the pupil.

Fibres pass to the visual cortex in a conspicuous tract, the *optic radiation*. The visual cortex is mainly on the inner side of each occipital lobe of the brain. It is called the *striate* area (p. 187) and is large and finely convoluted in man with a stretched-out area of up to 4,000 sq. mm. It is the true visuo-sensory area, around it lie association areas called visuo-psychic and visual memory centres. Images from each eye are superimposed in the striate area and so allow binocular vision. Association and other fibres pass forwards to all parts of the cortex in a most complex and so far undetermined pattern. 'The development of macular vision confers upon man the ability to see the world and appreciate its meaning in a way that no other living creature is able to do. His new vision depends upon powers of visual perception as distinctive as the use of articulate speech to give expression to what he sees and thinks' (Professor Sir Grafton Elliot Smith).

Taste and Smell

Organs of taste are found in the mammalian tongue and in immediately adjacent parts of the mouth including the palate. Called taste-buds, they are made of modified epithelial cells arranged in flask-shaped groups in the covering epithelium. They are most numerous in the covering of those large vallate papillae that form a V-shaped row separating the front two-thirds from the back third of the tongue. Supporting cells envelop spindle-shaped gustatory cells that end in a fine hair near the surface pore of each taste-bud. Sensory nerve fibrils lie between the gustatory cells and leave to join certain branches of the seventh, ninth, and tenth cranial nerves. It is usually maintained that taste-buds can only appreciate sweet, bitter, salt, and acid. Certain enzymes present in gustatory cells are believed to play a part in taste appreciation. No evidence has been presented of four kinds of taste-bud. G. H. Bourne has suggested that taste appreciation results from stimulation of a specific geographical pattern of taste-buds perhaps having varying enzyme components. Association of taste with certain colours and other factors undoubtedly plays a part in its appreciation. In older people taste-buds are fewer and are found more at the sides of the tongue papillae. They prefer food more highly seasoned than children, who have more taste-buds, particularly on the surface of papillae. Gustatory impulses are conveyed up the brain stem in the *tractus solitarius*, but it is not known for certain to which part of the cortex they are relayed. Gustatory perception became dominated by olfactory sensation as soon as vertebrates became air-breathing.

The sense of smell is localized in vertebrates in olfactory epithelium covering turbinal bones in the upper part of the nasal cavities (p. 79). Man is called *microsmatic* because of the relatively small extent of his olfactory epithelium. Dogs and many other mammals are *macrosmatic* and can be said to live more by their keen, discriminatory sense of smell than by visual perception. Whales are commonly said to be devoid of a sense of smell and to be *anosmatic.* Olfactory sensitivity in macrosmatic mammals is remarkably high and they can detect quantities so minute that the substances cannot be detected by physical instruments. Much work needs to be done to elucidate the physico-chemical background to scent appreciation.

The yellowish mucous membrane in the olfactory region contains supporting and specialized olfactory cells. The latter are bipolar nerve cells with a peripheral process that runs between supporting cells to end in fine olfactory hairs on the surface epithelium. The central processes, or non-myelinated olfactory nerve fibres, collect into bundles, pierce the cribriform plate of the ethmoid bone and end in the two olfactory *bulbs.* These are small in man; in lower mammals they are large and have cavities communicating with the lateral ventricles. Neurones in the olfactory bulbs send fibres along the two olfactory *tracts* to the brain. Olfactory pathways are too complicated to describe here except to state that the majority finally reach the cortex in man at the uncus on the under part of the temporal lobe. In macrosmatic mammals the uncus forms part of a larger *piriform* lobe; in a human brain this is very much reduced. Macrosmatic mammals have a relatively large part of their olfactory tracts that passes to an olfactory *tubercle* at the base of the brain. This tubercle is generally absent in microsmatic man but may be seen as a small eminence in a region called the anterior perforated substance.

An accessory olfactory area is present in the lower, front part of the nasal cavities in many mammals. It is called the vomero-nasal organ; it was described by Ludwig Jacobson (1783–1843) who was at one time a physician to the French Army. It appears only during embryonic development in man and disappears almost completely by birth.

Auditory and Vestibular Perception

It is natural to think of hearing as the proper function of the ear, but equilibration was the basic ancestral function of an auditory organ. In most lower vertebrates paired internal ears consist of a series of sacs and canals (membranous labyrinth) filled with fluid endolymph and contained in an otic capsule of cartilage or bone. Certain areas (maculae) in the labyrinth contain specialized receptors with sensory hairs (neuromasts). Calcium carbonate is deposited in gelatinous material covering the tips of the hairs. The body so formed is called an *otolith;* it varies in shape from species to species. A mechanism is thus produced that can provide information of the degree of the tilt of head or animal in a gravitational field. A static balancing organ has been evolved.

Information about movements of the head is provided by another set of membranous (semicircular) ducts. Three develop on each side of the head. Two are vertically placed at right angles to one another, one is horizontal; thus one lies in each of the three spatial planes. Each canal has a dilated ampulla containing specialized hair cells on a raised *crista*. Movements of the head stimulate receptors by setting up vibrations in endolymph within the ducts. Much evidence suggests that this vestibular apparatus evolved partly from a primitive 'lateral' line system sensitive to vibration in water: mammals require an effective balancing mechanism. Nerve fibres travel along the vestibular division of the eighth cranial nerve to nuclei in the hind-brain. Extensive connexions occur with postural mechanisms and the flocculonodular lobes of the cerebellum (p. 183).

Amphibia, reptiles, birds, and mammals show progressive development of another appendage of the labyrinth called a *cochlea*. Finger-like, and called a lagena in its early evolutionary history, it becomes coiled and other parts are added. Fluid-filled (perilymphatic) spaces develop about the membranous labyrinth so that the mammalian cochlea is really three associated tubular structures. The central one is the cochlear duct (an extended, coiled lagena with endolymph inside) and has specialized receptors on a basilar membrane on its floor. They form the *organ of Corti* and will be described in the next chapter. The end of one of the outer two tubules (scalae) has a small ossicle, *stapes*, playing against it. In lower vertebrates one end of the stapes, or columella, receives vibrations from an eardrum and conveys them across a cavity (middle ear) to the end of the perilymph-filled scala. Thence they are conveyed to receptors on the basilar membrane. Mammals have not one, but three, ossicles in the middle ear. A chain of articulating bones is formed that amplifies (aperiodically) vibrations received at the eardrum. The two additional ossicles, malleus and incus, can be shown to have been derived during evolution from bones involved in jaw mechanisms of lower vertebrates. Evolution of mammals involved a change in the mechanism of jaw articulation; superfluous bones were freed to take on new form and function. The history of the ossicles indicates how homologous structures, originally parts of the skeleton of gill arches (p. 135), become modified to take part in jaw mechanisms and later change into hearing aids.

Hearing mechanisms in man do not, therefore, differ greatly from the common mammalian pattern. More details will be given in the next chapter; the great value of hearing to man is inherent in his means of communication.

Other Receptors

A number of types of sensory ending provide information about affairs within viscera and blood vessels. Not enough is known to be sure if man shows any structural or functional characteristics in these endings. They include more generalized endings in the gut and other viscera and certain more specialized ones in relation to the heart, large arteries, and veins. Baroreceptors detect changes in blood pressure; they are present in heart chambers, large veins near the heart, and in the *carotid sinus*. The latter is a dilated portion of the common and internal carotids. The vessel wall is more elastic at this point and is specially innervated by the glossopharyngeal nerve. Structures such as the *carotid body* and *aortic arch body* may function as chemoreceptors that detect changes in the composition of blood. It might well be expected that these structures would show modifications in deep-diving aquatic mammals and in those mammals that run particularly fast, but little is known about such matters. Recent research has shown that certain vessels are more extensively innervated with receptors than was hitherto believed.

FOR FURTHER READING

'Nerve endings in Mammalian Skin'. G. Weddell, E. Palmer, and W. Pallie. *Biol. Rev.* 30, 159, 1955

The Anatomy of the Eye and Orbit. E. Wolff. 3rd ed. H. K. Lewis, 1948
The Vertebrate Eye. G. L. Walls. Cranbrooke Inst. of Science, 1942
Visual Development. J. H. Prince. E. & S. Livingstone, 1949
See also next chapter.

CHAPTER 12

HIS MEANS OF COMMUNICATION

MAN has developed to a remarkable degree the ability to convey information to others of his species, and even to non-human animals. Articulate speech is indeed a human characteristic, and man can so modulate, emphasize, or accentuate syllables that subtleties of meaning and interpretation can be skilfully conveyed. Messages and information can also be transmitted in other ways, by grimace and gesture, by a wink and pressure of the hand; in each instance a certain detectable signal is received by the observer and interpreted, it is hoped, in a known context or within a framework of accepted associations. Much theoretical work has been done in recent years on the mathematical and practical engineering aspects of communication. The stimulus of war, the incentives of commerce and the academic world have all played a large part in developing what is known as 'Communication Theory'. It is perhaps a little surprising that biologists have not been quicker to grasp the implications of communication theory in its possible application to biological problems. The communication of messages, signals, or information is taking place continuously in biological systems and we must assume that it occurs in some form or other at every level of complexity. One can even argue that some kind of chemical signalling system exists within cells, between the cell membrane and the nucleus, or even probably within the nucleus. There is undeniable evidence that it exists in neurones (see p. 176), and there is ample evidence that the cells of endocrine organs signal to various organs and themselves receive orders (see Chapter 14). The whole of embryonic growth would appear to be similarly subject to control by some such system, although we unfortunately know little of the mechanisms (see Chapter 7). This chapter is concerned principally with *how*, anatomically, individual men and women communicate with each other, not so much with the many ways in which communication theory or stochastics could be applied to biological problems.

Structurally a communication system consists of a transmitter, a medium for conduction of each signal transmitted, and a receiver; there must necessarily be some way of preparing each message and giving it content and meaning, and equally the received message must be capable of interpretation and analysis. The theoretical arrangement can be represented diagrammatically as below.

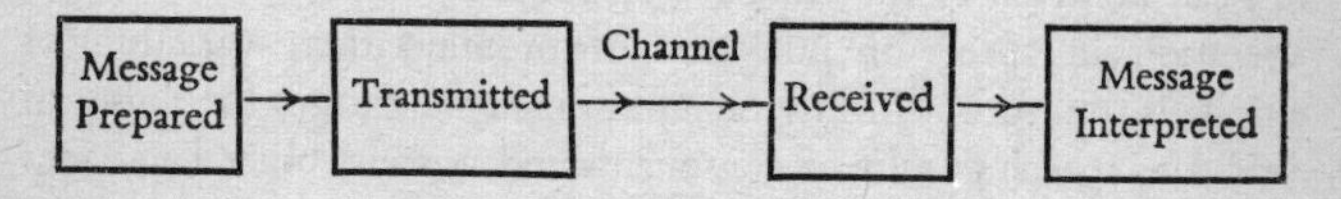

In the event of a man speaking, the message to be transmitted is prepared in the cerebral cortex, and in the previous chapter it has been shown that information necessary to formulate a message was acquired from an inherited component, from learning and from reception of some immediate signals.

The particular part of the cerebral cortex believed to be the site of initiation of the nervous impulses bringing about speech is called the motor speech area. It is found on the lower and posterior part of the frontal lobe, and includes the lower part of the inferior frontal gyrus and the lower part of the pre-central gyrus (see Fig. 18 and p. 187). Curiously, and so far without explanation, the motor speech centre is found on the left side of the brain in right-handed people. The area was first defined by the French surgical anatomist and anthropologist Pierre Paul Broca, who realized its importance when he noted in 1864 that damage to the area resulted in 'aphémie'. It was observations such as this that caused Broca to be a firm supporter and even proponent of the idea that particular functions were fairly closely localized in specific areas of the cortex. He produced a map to indicate the geographical distribution of the various areas, but as has been discussed on p. 187, neurologists are not nowadays inclined to be so specific in localizing function in the cerebral cortex. Yet the integrity of Broca's speech centre does appear to be essential for setting off the complex mechanisms resulting in spoken words, particularly in that the centre overlaps into the pre-central or motor area for muscles of the head and neck.

Phonetics

Articulate speech can only be produced by being able to make a selection of different noises, each unit of noise capable of being made in varying juxtaposition to other units, and thus into symbols, or words, or ideas. Emotional content, value, urgency, and other meaning can be given to the sequence of noises by spacing the symbols, alteration in speed or inflection of pronunciation, variation of emphasis, and so on. In English and in many languages the noises of articulate speech consist of consonants and vowels; other languages make more use of gutturals, of changes in tones (i.e. the five ways of enunciating 'chang' in Chinese) and of 'clicks' of the tongue as used by Zulus; but anatomically the same sets of structures are used. The name *phonetics* is given to that branch of study of language that is concerned with the way speech-sounds are elaborated by the organs of speech. It is also concerned with the manner in which speech-sounds are put in order or sequence, how they can be stressed or accentuated, how the voice can be altered in pitch, and naturally, how the speech-sounds affect the ear. Quite apart from the study of the anatomical production of speech, the science of phonetics has innumerable practical applications. It can give assistance in curing speech defects, aiding the deaf to speak, and helping to construct alphabets for the blind. It can help in teaching children to read and to understand their mother-tongue, and it is a boon to students of foreign languages and dialects, and those who study the meaning of words (philology). Its use in systems of shorthand, telegraphic communications, and other methods of signalling words will be obvious.

Speech therefore consists of a sequence of sounds, or particular types of air-vibration, produced by the organs of speech and capable of being heard by the ear. The organs of speech are the larynx and vocal cords, pharynx, tongue and palate, teeth, and lips. Other structures, such as the paranasal air sinuses, also play a part as resonators, but do not move actively. A current of air is caused to flow past the moving speech organs by a gradual emptying of the lungs during expiration; this is the usual method of generation of speech-sounds, although noises (of disapproval) can be made by drawing air in between lips and teeth. The passages enclosed by the speech-organs are capable of being much altered in shape as the air is exhaled, and so of producing sounds. If the air passage remains open then only 'breath' sounds are produced, but if the speech organs move in one of a variety of ways then a speech-sound is produced capable of being recognized by the hearer. The effect, that is the acoustic effect, of one speech-sound on the hearer is technically known as a *phone*. The production of a sequence of speech-sounds in the form of a speech-chain is therefore heard as a sequence of phones. It will be clear that there are two main classes of phones; consonants, produced by complete or partial closure of a part or parts of the air-passage, and vowels, to produce which air passes continuously and more freely through the air passage. Different kinds of consonants and vowels are therefore the result of the various ways in which the speech organs modify or halt the flow of exhaled air.

The Larynx

The most important of the speech organs is the larynx – the word is derived from the Greek *laryngias*, to scream; it is the structure that is primarily responsible for the voice. Although all land-living tetrapods with lungs have evolved a larynx of sorts, by no means all have a voice. The respiratory system of land-living tetrapods develops as a hollow outgrowth from the floor of the primitive pharynx behind the tongue region. The opening to the respiratory tube is called the *glottis* and there are muscles in its walls capable of closing it; in mammals a flap, containing cartilage, develops at the back of the tongue and can fold over the glottis in the form of the epiglottis. The muscular glottis and epiglottis can therefore close the opening to the respiratory system and prevent food or fluid from entering it. The larynx is an enlarged vestibule, surrounded by muscles and cartilage, placed around the glottis and leading into the trachea. In many amphibia and most reptiles the larynx and glottis are unsuitable for complex voice production, but most can produce a croak or hiss by expelling air violently through an almost closed glottis. A larynx is present in birds, but the voice is produced by a structure comparable to another larynx, present at a lower level on the trachea and called a syrinx. Frogs, toads, and nearly all mammals can use the larynx for vocal purposes, but only in man have two folds, 'false' and 'true' vocal folds, developed below the glottis with appropriate muscular control enabling refinements of phonation and articulate speech.

It might seem that there has been a deliberate construction of complexity in the larynx so that it could readily evolve into a voice-

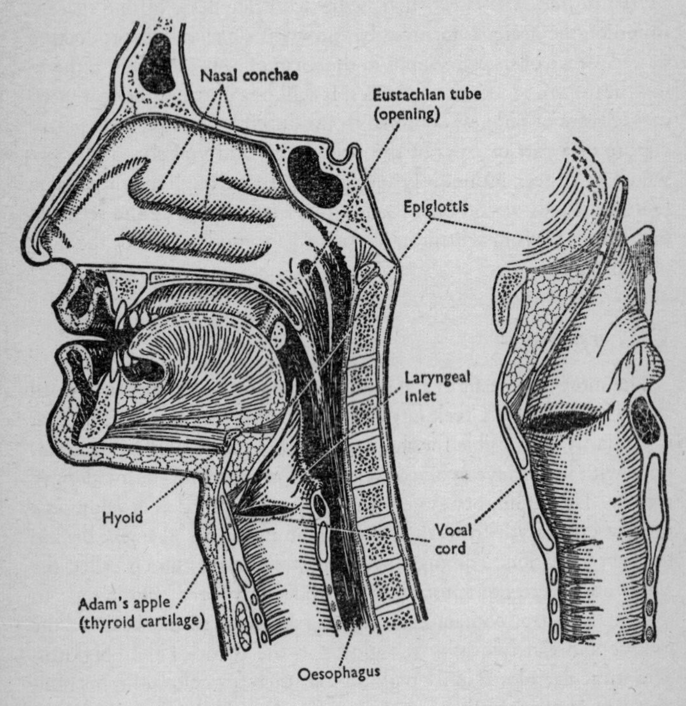

FIG. 24. Mid-line section of the nasal cavity, mouth, pharynx, and larynx to show position of larynx. Right: a section through the human larynx.

producing apparatus. Yet the larynx is not solely voice-producing in function. Its primary function is to provide rigidity in the opening of the air passage, and at the same time to prevent solids or liquids entering it by its muscular glottis. Extrinsic muscles are attached to it and the closely related hyoid bone from origins on the mandible, base of the skull and thoracic region. The larynx can thus be moved, and it is brought upwards and forwards during deglutition out of the pathway of swallowed foodstuffs. In some animals the muscular connexions of the larynx are strong enough to help fix the thoracic cage during tree-climbing. The larynx is not *solely* responsible for voice production. The sound it produces is feeble and hardly recognizable as the human voice until it has been amplified and modulated by the pharynx, mouth, nose, and other structures.

The human larynx is constructed of a framework of cartilages, of which the largest are the shield-shaped thyroid cartilage and ring-shaped cricoid cartilage. The thyroid cartilage is attached to the hyoid bone above by muscles and the thyro-hyoid membrane, and articulates by its lower horn to the cricoid cartilage, the latter being attached below to the trachea (Fig. 24).

The thyroid cartilage rocks backwards and forwards on the cricoid because of the way in which they are articulated. Perched on the upper surface of the back of the cricoid cartilage are two small, three-cornered arytenoid cartilages with which are associated a number of intricate little muscles. The true vocal cords stretch on each side from one of the processes of the three-corned arytenoid to the thyroid cartilage in front, and together with the adjacent sides of the processes of the arytenoid cartilages form the boundaries of the glottis. Both the vocal cords and the sides of the arytenoid processes are covered by mucous membrane which is tightly adherent to the vocal cords and thus gives it a pearly white colour in life. A number of small muscles are attached to the arytenoid cartilage and to the thyroid and cricoid cartilages in such a way that the arytenoids can be pulled towards each other, away from each other and also rotated. These movements will open or close the rima glottidis in the various ways. At the same time the tension of the vocal cords, and of the crico-vocal membrane that lies below it, can be altered by the tilting movement of the thyroid carilage on the cricoid.

Voice Production

Sound is produced by the larynx in the following way: air passes from the lungs during exhalation and reaches the vocal cords, causing them to separate. At once the intrinsic muscles, called the thyro-arytenoid and vocalis, contract and cause the vocal cords to approximate again. This process is repeated over and over again, setting up vibrations in the escaping air stream and so producing a tone. The pitch of the tone will vary according to the predetermined tension of the vocal cord; the tighter the cords, the higher the pitch. In attempting to produce pure tone, as in singing, the entire edge of each cord separates, but in making speech sounds only a part of the length of the apposed cords may separate. It is, in fact, impossible for the larynx to produce a pure tone, since a series of overtones are produced at the same time, and the tone that is finally heard results from the effect of resonators below and above the larynx.

The resonators comprise the thorax and the column of air in the bronchial tree and trachea, the pharynx, the nose, the mouth, and the paranasal sinuses. They are responsible for increasing the magnitude of the sound and altering the mixture of tone and overtones produced at the larynx. The importance of the resonators is clearly shown when a heavy cold blocks the nasal cavity and air sinuses, causing a characteristic change in the voice. Should the infection spread to the larynx, the voice will alter again and become hoarse, and if the vocal cords are so involved that they swell and cannot vibrate properly, the voice is reduced to a whisper or is completely 'lost'. A whisper can also be produced anatomically by keeping the glottis partly open all the time, partially closing the 'false' vocal or vestibular folds that lie just above the true vocal cords, and using the resonators in order to pick out and fuse the sounds so produced.

It is now possible to understand how the various consonants and vowels are produced. There are two main kinds of consonant: one is 'breathed' with the vocal cords abducted (f), the other is 'voiced' with the vocal cords producing sound (v). In producing a third kind, the glottal stop, the consonant is neither voiced nor breathed. Consonants can also be classified by considering the anatomy of where they are articulated, such as between the lips, between the teeth, or lips and teeth, between the tongue and hard or soft palate, in the pharynx, or at the glottis. The manner in which the consonant is produced provides another method of classification, whether rolled, plosive, or nasal, and so on. Vowels, on the other hand, are classified anatomically by reference to the position of the tongue, although the position of the lips is equally important.

Nervous control of speech is complex, and the central mechanisms taking place in the brain are by no means clearly understood. The utterance of words is the result of sending out a great many impulses along numerous nerves. Before a sound can even be made the speaker must be breathing; speech can only occur during the expiratory phase. Thus there is a preliminary demand for correlation with those levels of the spinal cord from which the phrenic and intercostal nerves arise. The laryngeal muscles responsible for adjustments of the vocal cords are supplied by the tenth cranial or vagus nerve through its recurrent laryngeal branch. The ninth cranial or glossopharyngeal controls movements of the pharynx and palate, while the twelfth cranial or hypoglossal nerve controls the tongue musculature. The position of the lips, and the grimaces or facial expressions often accompanying speech are due to the activities of the facial muscles, innervated by the seventh cranial or facial nerve. It is impossible to speak clearly without moving the jaws, the muscles doing so being supplied by the fifth cranial or trigeminal nerve through its mandibular branch. It being considered polite, and more effective, to look in the direction of the hearer, the eleventh cranial or accessory nerve and nerves from the cervical spinal cord will carry impulses to the trapezius, sternomastoid, and other muscles moving the head and neck.

Minor variations in the way the muscles are used and their actions correlated, variations in size of the rima glottidis, and the sometimes quite marked variations in size of the resonators cause us to have voices that are recognizably different. Similar variations in muscle action enable us to pronounce phones of languages other than our own. So subtle are the minor variations that the articulatory mechanism is capable of producing in the voice that the term *phoneme* has been introduced to include families of sounds. For example, in any language a consonant is pronounced in a slightly different way depending on the vowel that follows it.

Growth Changes

There are changes in character of the voice as an individual grows older. In children the vocal cords are shorter and more lightly built than in adults, although the larynx is relatively larger in calibre than the trachea. The resonators are also smaller in size, and some, such as the paranasal air sinuses, are hardly developed; thus the voices of children are characteristically high-pitched. At puberty the larynx enlarges rapidly, as also do the resonators; in the male changes in the voice are particularly marked owing to development of the front part of the thyroid cartilage (*pomum Adami* – Adam's apple) and the vocal cords become thicker and heavier. There is often some initial inability to compensate for this, and certain lack of muscular control, leading to 'breaking of the voice' in boys at puberty. In women, and in men castrated before puberty, the larynx does not enlarge so much in the antero-posterior direction, the cords stay light, and the voice remains high-pitched. It is interesting to note that the size of the larynx seems to have little relation with physique; a small, slight man may have a deep voice and conversely a giant of a man may have a thin, squeaky voice. The rima glottidis is between 22 and 24 mm. in length in men and 14 to 16 mm. in length in women.

Aphasia

It will now be obvious that the production of voice and of speech-sounds depends on the correct correlation of a large number of muscles (nearly 100 paired or unpaired) all of which must also be at the appropriate tension. It is hardly surprising that there are both organic and functional disorders of speech. Clearly it would be difficult to enunciate properly without teeth, or a tongue, or with a cleft palate; again, damage to the nerves supplying the various muscles will result in difficulty in moving the speech-organs. *Aphasia* is the name given to disease or damage of those centres in the brain that control the motor pathways effecting speech or which interpret speech on the sensory side. Functional disturbances of speech are stammering, in which speech is hesitant or repetitive, dyslalia, where articulation is defective, and lalling, when there is substitution of sounds.

An interesting observation has recently been made on children who stammer that may be of great interest. Should the child wear earphones through which a low continuous note is being transmitted, he will speak without stammering. As long as he cannot hear himself speaking incorrectly he does not stammer. This might suggest that the speech-sounds created as the result of cortical activity are heard by the speaker and correlated with what he is saying. A fault, caused perhaps by incomplete coordination, is heard and interferes with subsequent speech patterns in the cortex. The stammerer gets worse the more carefully he listens to what he is saying. In a similar category comes the person who, deaf from birth, cannot hear his own voice to check if what he is saying sounds like the phones produced by others. This leads to a consideration of the anatomy of hearing, of receiving and interpreting transmitted information.

Anatomy of Hearing

The human auditory mechanism has an external ear for collecting sound (see p. 80) with an external auditory tube or meatus at the inner end of which is a delicate tympanic membrane. The latter forms the outer wall of the air-containing middle ear cavity, in which are lodged the three small auditory ossicles. These convey vibrations of the tympanic membrane to the inner ear, the cochlea, or organ of hearing. The vestibular apparatus also forms part of the inner ear. It detects changes in movement such as rotation and inclination of the head, but it can also respond to very loud noises.

The evolutionary history of the auditory and vestibular apparatus is considered in Chapter 11; here the functional anatomy of the ear as it plays its part in communication will be discussed. The sound waves created by speech organs will reach the tympanic membrane and cause it to vibrate. The membrane is cone-shaped, with the apex or umbo directed inwards, and is set within the end of the almost circular bony tube made by the tympanic ring. The long process, or handle of the outermost of the three auditory ossicles, the malleus (hammer), is attached to the upper part of the tympanic membrane. The malleus articulates with the incus (anvil) and the latter with the innermost ossicle, the stapes (stirrup). The base of the stapes, called the footplate, is held by an annular ligament in an oval window on the inner wall of the middle ear. Immediately on the other side of the footplate of the stapes lies the fluid within the inner ear to which the ossicles convey vibration from the tympanic membrane.

Two muscles are also found attached to the ossicles within the middle ear. The tensor tympani is attached to the handle of the malleus and by its contraction preserves the cone shape of the tympanic membrane and keeps it gently taut. The tiny stapedius muscle is attached to the stapes and ensures that the ossicles articulate evenly; together with the tensor tympani the muscle has a 'damping' effect, protecting the auditory mechanisms from noise of too great an amplitude. Damage to the muscles, or deprivation of their nervous supply, allows 'chattering' to develop during movements of the ossicles and so gives rise to 'noises in the ears', or tinnitus. The action

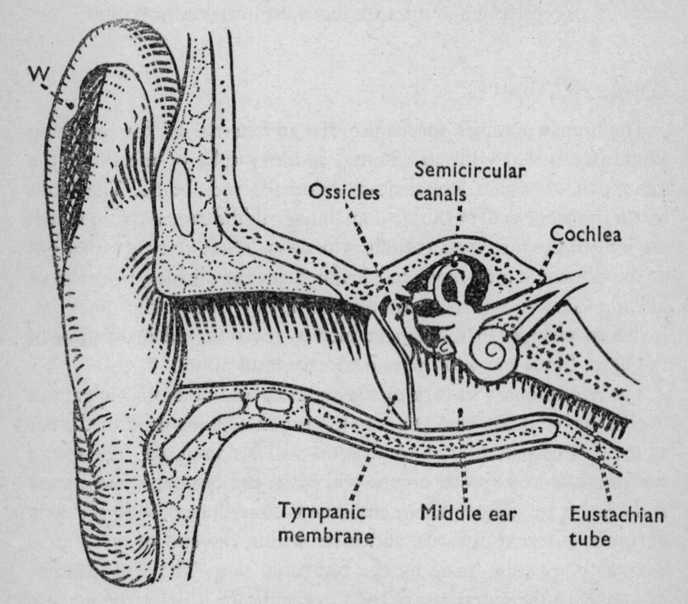

FIG. 25. Arrangement of the external, middle, and inner ear.
W: Woolner's (Darwin's) tubercle.

of the tensor tympani can cause some unevenness in movement of the ossicles. The muscle makes the tympanic membrane gently taut and causes it to move more easily in certain directions under certain pressure conditions. Thus, when two notes of different frequency are simultaneously being transmitted by the membrane and ossicles 'difference' and 'summation' tones are set up and may well be perceived by the hearer.

The three ossicles are not loose in the middle ear cavity, but are held together by elastic ligaments and covered by mucous membrane. They are also surrounded by air, that enters the middle ear cavity from the naso-pharynx through the pharyngotympanic tube (described in 1562 by Bartolomeo Eustachius). The middle ear must contain air for efficient functioning of the rapidly vibrating ossicles, and its pressure must equal that of the air outside. The pharyngotympanic tube is opened during swallowing, thus allowing equalization of the pressures on each side of the tympanic membrane. The tube consists of three parts, each part varying in the composition of its confines. The inner, membranous part, leaves the back of the naso-pharynx and presents a slit-like opening above the soft palate just behind the lowest of three scroll-like conchae found on the outer wall of the nasal cavity. The opening of the tube is kept closed, except during swallowing, owing to the action of certain pharyngeal muscles that partly arise from the second or cartilaginous part. The third part of the tube passes through the temporal bone to reach the middle air cavity.

The ossicles transmit the vibrations of the tympanic membrane to the oval window with great fidelity, apart from certain difficulties already mentioned, and also amplify the movements of the membrane about twenty times. The vibrations are transmitted to the fluid filling the inner ear, in particular to that part of it called the cochlea. The inner ear is found within the petrous temporal bone; it consists of a number of complicated fluid-filled membranous chambers and ducts, the membranous labyrinth, enclosed within the bony labyrinth. The fluid within the membranous labyrinth is known as endolymph and that which lies outside but within the walls of the bony labyrinth is called perilymph, but neither fluid has any anatomical relationship with that of the lymphatic system. The membranous labyrinth consists of the coiled duct of the cochlea, the saccule and the utricle (contained within the bony vestibule) and the three semicircular ducts (Fig. 25).

The duct of the cochlea is lodged within the two and a half coils of the bony cochlea and it contains the organ of hearing. The latter was first described in 1851 by the much travelled 'amateur' histologist, the Marquis Alfonso Corti (1822–88), and is often called the organ of Corti. The tunnel within the bony cochlea is larger than the duct of the cochlea; thus there is room for one canal above and another below the duct. The cochlea is in fact divided by two membranes, the basilar membrane forming the base of the duct of the cochlea and separating it from the scala tympani below, and the vestibular membrane separating it from the scala vestibuli above. The delicate organ of Corti lies on the basilar membrane (Fig. 26).

The oval footplate of the stapes fits into the oval window, making a water-tight seal with the scala vestibuli. Vibrations of the footplate are thus transmitted through the perilymph to the vestibular membrane, thence through the endolymph to the basilar membrane, finally into the scala tympani to cause a corresponding vibration at a membrane-covered round window opening onto the middle ear cavity.

The Organ of Hearing

The organ of Corti lies on the basilar membrane within the duct of the cochlea. It consists of a series of pillars, or stiffened rods, arranged sloping fashion over a tunnel with specialized 'hair cells' aligned on both sides. There are also supporting cells and other cells that 'weight' the basilar membrane. There are some 3,500 hair cells on the inner side of the tunnel of Corti and some 12,000 on the outer side. Electron microscopy has shown that the hairs of each hair cell are arranged in rows.

The hairs project upwards into a curious and almost structureless membrane, the tectorial membrane (Fig. 26), and as the basilar membrane vibrates the hairs are driven against the tectorial membrane and thus presumably stimulate the hair cell to initiate a nerve impulse. Early theories of acoustic physiology suggested that particular sounds were specifically transmitted in some distinctive manner by the various nerve fibres. It is now known, however, that each nerve fibre transmits discrete impulses of fairly fixed magnitude, but varying in the rate at which they follow one another. It has also been shown that the basilar membrane and organ of Corti have not a uniform structure throughout their two and a half turns about the central cone-shaped modiolus of the cochlea. The basilar membrane is shorter, more strongly attached at its edges and more lightly loaded with supporting and other cells at the end nearest the footplate of the stapes than at the apex or cupola of the cochlea. Several workers have suggested that there is a definite gradation in membrane length and tension, and in the mass of cells it bears at any point along its length, so that the organ could respond to different vibrations in different regions.

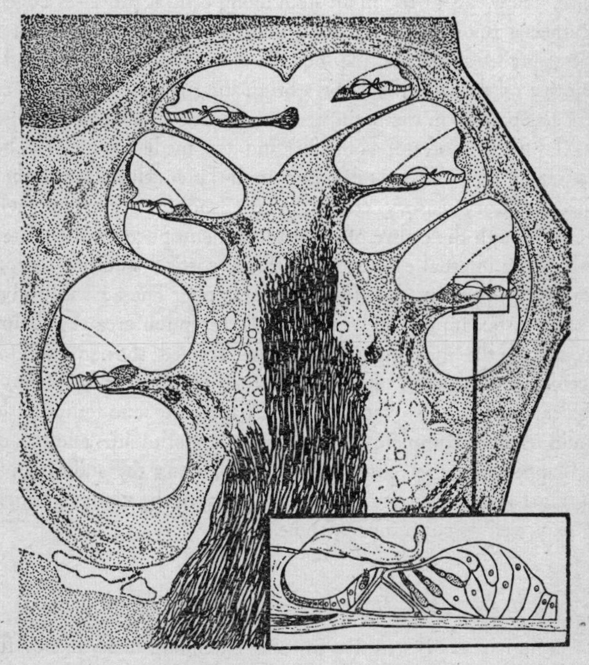

FIG. 26. Section through the cochlea (near the mid-line) showing its spiral arrangement (see Fig. 24) and the fibres of the eighth (auditory) cranial nerve leaving the organ of Corti (shown at higher magnification in the inset). See also Plate XX.

The hair cells are innervated by peripheral fibres originating from bipolar neurones in a spiral canal lying within the central modiolus of the bony cochlea. The fibres pass out to reach the inner and outer hair cells, eventually as naked axons, and according to electron microscope preparations, end by enclosing the base of a hair cell in an exceedingly thin, cup-like structure. It is said that more nerve fibres pass to hair cells of the first and second coils of the duct of the cochlea than to the apical.

Nerve impulses from the organ of Corti travel along the peripheral fibres of the cell bodies of the auditory division of the eighth cranial nerve. They pass to the brain stem along central processes collected together as the cochlear nerve in the internal auditory meatus. The central processes relay in the medulla at the cochlear nuclei, and the majority of the ascending fibres originating from these nuclei cross over and pass up in the brain stem as a bundle (the lateral lemniscus) to relay in the inferior colliculus and the medial geniculate body (see p. 202). Impulses are relayed from the latter cell station to the so-called auditory-sensory centre by the auditory radiation, which passes through the centre of the cerebral hemisphere in the posterior limb of the internal capsule to reach the cortical auditory reception area in the upper surface of the temporal lobe. There is said to be an area of cortex immediately around the reception area that helps in interpreting the 'meaning' of the stimuli received; the name auditory-psychic area is given to it. It is clear that not all the fibres from the cochlear nuclei cross over, otherwise damage to one temporal lobe would result in complete deafness on the opposite side, and this does not happen. Another complication in analysing the auditory pathways is that there is some evidence that part of the vestibular apparatus may well be concerned with hearing.

Hearing in Man and Animals

The human ear is sensitive to tones extending in frequency from 20 to 25,000 cycles per second, but the greatest sensitivity is from 1,000 to about 5,000 cycles per second at minimum audible sound pressure (0·0002 dyne per sq. cm.). If the intensity of a sound increases a point will eventually be reached when a painful sensation develops in the ear. This point, the pain threshold, is reached only when a sound pressure of about 1,000 dynes per sq. cm. develops. Thus it will be clear that the ear has considerable sensitivity and can cope with a very great range of intensity. The loudness of a sound is a quality judged by the hearer, i.e., it is subjective, and there can be considerable variation in the judgement of loudness among apparently normal individuals.

There is an extension upwards of the auditory range in at least two mammals. Dogs can hear higher frequencies than man, thus the well known whistles, apparently silent to man, can be heard by police dogs. Bats can hear frequencies up to 60,000 cycles a second and use the reflection of these short-wave sounds and the alteration of the timing of their return with flight to give them a sense of position at night. The ultra-sonic echo-sounding instruments used in determining the depth of the sea are believed to be heard by porpoises, possibly other whales, and also by seals, all apparently disliking the vibrations.

In birds, despite their powers of song, auditory perception has a limited range, and it is even less acute in reptiles and amphibia in which there is reduction in the size of the cochlea. Both cochlea and organ of Corti are lacking in fish, but despite this some fish, at least, can be taught to respond to a wide range of sound and even to discriminate pitch. It has been shown that the sensitive structures correspond anatomically with the utricle. Special auditory organs are found in insects, such as the tympanal organs in the abdomen of locusts, in which they principally subserve the function of finding the other sex.

The human ear is capable, to an extent varying in each individual, of analysing component sounds produced simultaneously. This ability to discriminate between notes is highly developed in some people, and the theoretical explanation has been, and still is, the subject of controversy. It is usually explained by assuming that the footplate of the stapes faithfully transmits the sound-vibrations to the oval window, and indeed its movements caused during the last movement of Beethoven's Ninth Symphony must be formidable. It is postulated, however, that not all the basilar membrane vibrates in unison, but that its movements are limited to certain definite regions varying in position with the pitch of the several tones falling on the ear. It is further suggested that the basilar membrane differs anatomically along its length so that its natural frequency at a particular point corresponds to that of a particular tone. In this way only those nerve fibres innervating that point are stimulated to convey impulses to the brain, and presumably, it is argued, to particular areas or even neurones of the cortex. This theory was propounded by the German physiologist and physicist H. L. F. von Helmholtz

(1821–94); it is known as the 'resonance' theory in physiological acoustics, and despite the belief of many workers that the behaviour of the basilar membrane is more complicated, the theory provides an elucidation of many of the observed facts.

Deafness

Anatomically two types of deafness can be recognized, one due to an obstruction or defect of sound conduction, the other due to a defect in the perception apparatus, 'nerve deafness'. Both types may occur together in one individual. Nerve deafness is not associated with 'nervousness', but implies that some damage has occurred to receptors in the organ of Corti, the auditory nerve or in the hearing centres of the brain. The bone surrounding the ear may become involved by a little understood affliction, otosclerosis, which can cause the footplate of the stapes to become fixed immovably in the oval window and so effectively prevent sound conduction.

FOR FURTHER READING

Hearing in Man and Animals. R. T. Beatty. Bell, London, 1932
Theories of Sensation. A. F. Rawdon-Smith. Cambridge University Press, 1938
Hearing and its Psychology. S. S. Stevens and H. Davis. Wiley, New York, 1938
The Mechanism of the Human Voice. R. Curry. Churchill, 1940
The Comparative Anatomy and Physiology of the Larynx. V. E. Negus. Heinemann, 1949

CHAPTER 13

HIS SKIN AND HAIR

SOME introductory remarks were made about the covering of man in Chapter 4, sufficient to emphasize its importance. When more than about three-quarters of the skin is lost not even the most modern methods of treatment can ensure survival. Not only does skin have a protective function, but its derivatives can actively secrete, it is very vascular and assists in temperature regulation, and it acts as a sensory organ.

It has been said that one of the most 'absurdly improbable' sights in nature is that of a man riding on a camel in blazing sun in the middle of the Sahara. It is absurd because one biological system or biomass is balanced on another and improbable because in such a place water conservation within cells is most difficult. The primary function of skin is to envelop and contain the components of the body, acting as a protective, relatively impermeable, covering. It prevents entrance of water and most other substances and controls their loss from the body. To do this the skin has to be many-layered, and the superficial layers have to undergo such drastic changes that they become hardened and die at the surface. The superficial dead cells are continually being rubbed off, particularly for instance after a bath, and have to be replaced from the deeper layers. Therefore the skin is not a static organ, but on the move all the time.

The surface of the skin is called the *epidermis* (*epi* Gk = upon *derma* Gk = skin) and is itself a many layered epithelium. Beneath it lies the *dermis* or *corium*, a layer of loose connective tissue containing elastic fibres. If a small piece of skin is nipped between the finger tips the epidermis is raised upwards owing to elasticity and looseness of the dermis. Below the dermis lies a fatty layer, the *panniculus adiposus*, varying in thickness in different parts of the body at different ages. The layer is thickest over buttocks, abdomen, and lumbar area; it is thinnest in scrotum and eyelids. Called blubber in aquatic mammals, its thickness conserves heat loss. Below the fatty layer is a sheet of voluntary muscle, the *panniculus carnosus*, vestigial in man, and not always completely continuous in those mammals that possess it. The layer is well developed in most Carnivora, allowing the skin to be 'rippled', and in horses and cattle, enabling them to flick flies off the skin. In man the layer has almost disappeared; its main remnant is a flat, thin muscle, the *platysma*, in the front of the neck below the chin. The muscle can sometimes be seen causing ridges in the skin when the chin is forcibly raised during violent exercise or acute agony. Lack of a panniculus carnosus is one reason why wound contraction is more disfiguring in man than in other mammals.

THE EPIDERMIS

The epidermis consists of a superficial dead layer, the *stratum corneum*, and a deep, living layer known after the 'founder of microscopical anatomy', Marcello Malpighi (1628–94). The stratum Malpighi possesses several other layers, the deepest being a single-cell-thick *stratum germinativum*, lying next to the dermis. More superficially is the *stratum spinosum* or prickle cell layer, of varying thickness and characterized by curious bridges passing from cell to cell. These intercellular bridges, and certain delicate striae (tonofibrils) that cross them, have been seen so constantly under the light microscope that they have been considered the reason why damage to one epidermal cell so rapidly affects neighbouring cells. Prickle cells grown individually in tissue culture seem to lose their bridges, and electron microscopists have been reticent in admitting presence of bridges. Careful preparations, by R. Porter in America, have shown that under the electron microscope prickle cells appear in contact with one another in very small regions, those of the bridges, and that fibrous tufts extend away from them into each cell with some keratinous fibrils sweeping across from one cell to the next. There does not, however, seem to be direct continuity of cytoplasm between cells, so that despite appearances under the light microscope we cannot yet firmly maintain that prickle cells form a continuous cellular system or syncytium.

Cells in the superficial part of the prickle cell layer become flattened and accumulate granules. These are often called keratohyalin granules in the belief that they are precursors of the horny material of the skin, keratin. The region is known as the *stratum granulosum*. Immediately outside is a layer in which the cell takes on a

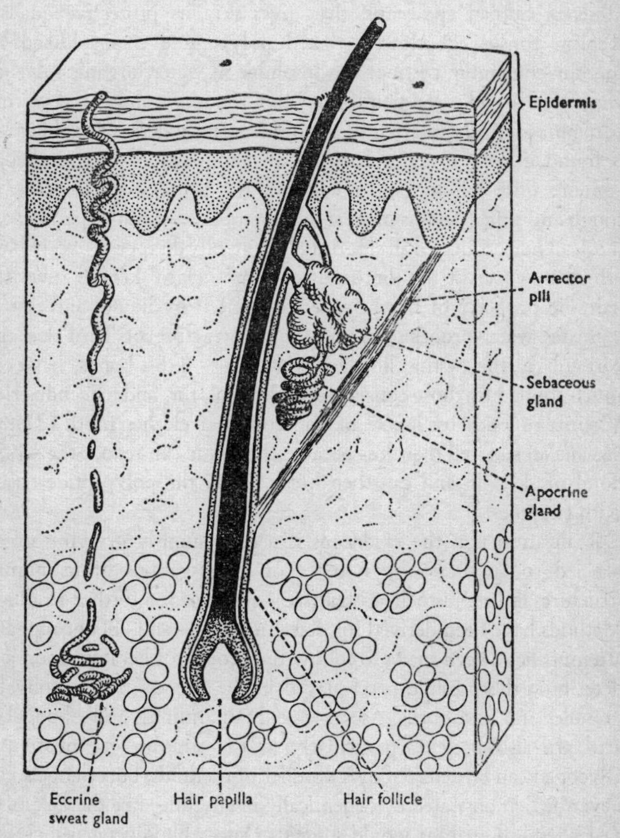

FIG. 27. Relationships of hair, sebaceous, apocrine, and eccrine glands. See also Fig. 22.

glassy or hyaline appearance, the *stratum lucidum*, so called because it is difficult to stain. The layer is only well developed in thicker skin of palm and sole. Thus it will be seen that there is a number of interesting changes in the minute anatomy of the layers of skin culminating strangely in death of the superficial ones. The latter form the stratum corneum of flattened scale-like dead cells containing the protein keratin. It is this substance, of which there are at least two kinds in human epidermis, that gives skin its protective quality. Keratin consists of closely packed polypeptide chains linked by sulphur-containing cystine; it is insoluble in water, organic solvents, weak alkalis, and is resistant to enzymes. Keratin found in the stratum corneum is usually referred to as 'soft' keratin, whereas 'hard' keratin is found in the cortex of hair and in nails. The former is pliable, contains little sulphur, and is continuously being shed; the latter is tough and stiff, contains more sulphur, and is much more permanent. If a dead body is buried all soft tissues eventually disappear, except hair, which may persist for thousands of years. 'Hard' keratin gives the hair the property of not being easily wetted by liquid, and thus it increases water-proofing of the pelage. Structure of 'hard' keratin, particularly the cystine linkages containing –S–S– bonds, has been much studied by those concerned with wool, fur, and hair industries. Victims of raids by larvae of the common clothes moth (*Tineola bisselliella*) suffered their loss because the larvae can reduce the –S–S– bond of keratin and can then break down the polypeptide chains with enzymes.

Realization that the epidermis is a continuously growing organ has led to an increasing number of investigations of its minute structure and its histochemistry (see references for further reading). Methods have been derived for detecting –S–S– and –SH groups and attempts have been made to follow the process of keratinization and determine the possible parts played in the process by keratohyalin granules and tonofibrils. Ascorbic acid (Vitamin C) and ribonucleic acid are also present, particularly in the stratum germinativum. Glycogen can be detected by a number of methods, but strangely can never be demonstrated cytochemically in anything like the quantities that chemical analysis would suggest. Detectable glycogen increases after irritation; merely peeling off of a piece of adhesive tape from skin results in glycogen appearing in basal cells of the epidermis some eight hours later. Even if the reason for this is not exactly known, it indicates the ability of skin to react rapidly even to mild insults. The epidermis contains numerous enzymes; phosphatases, esterases, dehydrogenase, and cytochrome oxidase have been demonstrated, but precise interpretation of their situation in various layers of the epidermis and their function at each site have still to be determined.

Skin Colour

The colour of human skin, that is its normal colour, is due to certain pigments of which the most important is a yellow-black substance called *melanin* (*melas* Gk = black). The other pigments are melanoid, allied to melanin, carotene in the stratum corneum and panniculus adiposus and reduced haemoglobin and oxyhaemoglobin in red corpuscles circulating in blood vessels in the dermis.

Melanin is present in 'white' skin in varying amounts in the basal cells of the stratum Malpighi; in skin of very dark Whites and of Negroes it is found in all layers of the epidermis and even in the stratum corneum. It is present as granules, capping the nucleus in white skin or evenly spread throughout the cell in dark skin. Melanin granules are also present in certain interesting cells called *melanoblasts* situated in basal layers of the epidermis. Melanoblasts possess dendrites and appear to form a distinct system; there is evidence that they are derived from neural crest cells (p. 178). They may be demonstrated by a selective method using dihydroxyphenylalanine (dopa) as a substrate; an enzyme, tyrosinase, present only in melanoblasts causes production of a dark pigment, dopa-melanin. It may therefore be postulated that melanoblast activity produces melanin, and that cells of the epidermis receive and store the pigment. It has been suggested from observations in the frog that melanoblasts inject melanin into neighbouring epidermal cells along their dendritic processes, but as yet such a phenomenon has not been observed in mammals. It is usually maintained that melanin granules are never actually inside epidermal cells, but are in reality only on the surface, being still attached to the tips of dendritic processes. The large number of dendrites that would be necessary to produce the pigmented appearance of a Negro's skin have, however, never been seen. Recently electron microscopic and other studies of human skin have provided evidence that melanin granules can in fact be found in epidermal cells. The number of melanoblasts per square millimetre in different parts of the body varies from 1,000 in skin from thigh and arm to up to 4,000 on face and neck. There is no significant difference in number or size of melanoblasts in similar sites in white and Negro skin, but in the latter melanoblasts are more active and produce much more pigment. Sun tanning causes increase in melanin production, but the real biological significance of pigmentation is to protect the eyes by the presence of pigment in the iris and retina.

Replacement

Continuous sloughing of superficial cells during normal life requires some process of active replacement. Cell division in the basal stratum germinativum brings about such replacement. Casual counts of the number of cell divisions, mitoses, in the epidermis, however, usually fails to reveal a quantity sufficient to bring about replacement at anything like the necessary rate. Mitoses have also been seen in layers superficial to the stratum germinativum. This has been explained by the fact that basal cells swell before they divide, and thus some basal cells are forced to a more superficial layer before division can occur. The failure to observe sufficient numbers of mitoses is due to at least two interesting factors that affect replacement rate. Mitoses occur more frequently at certain times of the day, and growth of the epidermis is cyclic, apparently linked with changes in the reproductive organs. Both these effects are better demonstrated in experimental animals such as rats and mice, but even so they are known to occur in man. Rats and mice rest during the day and more mitoses are found at noon than during the night. In man tissue is repaired at night when mitotic counts are higher in the epidermis than during the day. Fluctuation in thickness of the female epidermis in association with the reproductive cycle is due to a direct action of oestrogens on mitotic rate.

Thickness of epidermis in some animals may be related to cyclical hair growth. Hair follicles in mice pass through a growth cycle every twenty-one days and thickness of the epidermis varies with the phase of the hair cycle. The epidermis of the mouse is thin, much thinner than that of man, and seems to respond to certain stimuli more easily. There is no evidence that there is any correlation of thickness of epidermis in man with a cycle of hair growth.

The Dermis

The dermis is thickest on soles and palms in the human male, where it is several millimetres thick, although confluence with underlying tissues makes it difficult to measure. The dermis is the connective tissue layer upon which the epidermis grows. It nourishes the epidermis and may in some way control its growth and that of appendages. A superficial papillary layer of loosely arranged collagenous and elastic fibres fits into depressions or forms papillae on the undersurface of the epidermis and also surrounds hair follicles and other appendages. Capillaries extending to the base of epidermis and nerve fibres innervating the skin and its derivatives also lie in the papillary layer. Beneath the latter lies a thicker reticular layer that is dense and coarse: some of its fibres pass more deeply to join the framework of the fatty layer (panniculus adiposus). The layer also contains meshes of elastic fibres, and it is these, and the way that the other fibres of the reticular layer are arranged, that give the skin its elasticity and extensibility. Certain parts of the body possess muscle fibres in the dermis and their contraction can cause wrinkling of the skin. Such fibres are present about the nipple, and in the scrotum where collectively they are called the dartos muscle. The fibres of the dermis are more densely aggregated in the region of skin folds and creases and are often bound down tightly to any firm underlying structure. The dermis is particularly adherent to the cartilages of the nose and the ear and the subsequent lack of extensibility means that blocked, dilated, and infected glands are particularly painful in these regions, as also are chilblains of the pinna and 'cauliflower ears'.

Glands of the Skin

The glandular appendages of the epidermis are of three main types, eccrine and apocrine sweat glands, and sebaceous glands.

Eccrine sweat glands are those that excrete sweat as it is commonly understood. They are simple tubes that extend from their openings on the epidermis to deep into the dermis; the basal portion is much coiled, the remainder fairly straight. Their ducts open onto the surface of the epidermis on the ridges; their openings can be seen on the finger-tip ridges with a lens. There are over two million sweat glands in the skin of a man and they are found everywhere except on the lips, the glans of the penis and clitoris. They are most numerous on palm and sole, next on the forehead, back of the foot and hand, and least on the chest, thigh, and leg. The glands are all formed by birth, though they do not function as actively in childhood as at puberty and adolescence. There is apparently no racial difference in the number of glands, but Japanese are said to possess a greater number on the limbs than on the trunk. Eccrine sweat glands are most developed in the Primates, and of these only man and the chimpanzee have more sweat glands than apocrine. Mammals other than Primates only possess a few eccrine gland, and they are present on the paws.

Sweat glands function in response to heat and in response to psychic stimuli. In thermal sweating the glands on the forehead, neck, and trunk are first active, those of the cheek and limbs later, and the soles and feet least of all. In the psychic response glands on sole and palm are the first to be active. A bat or racquet does not slip in the hands of a professional, but when a 'rabbit' faces a fast bowler on a bumping pitch his palms may well be moist. These differences in sweating reaction are mediated through the nervous system, although the precise pathways from the cerebral cortex that are concerned in psychic sweating are not at all clear. It is known that there is a centre concerned with thermal sweating present in the hypothalmus (p. 184) and that the nerve supply to the sweat glands is from the sympathetic or thoraco-lumbar outflow. Over short periods of time up to 1,500 cc. of sweat may be lost in an hour, and although the loss of water can easily be made good, sodium chloride is also lost in sweat. There is experimental evidence of mechanisms to conserve sodium chloride lost by sweating (such as the action of the adrenal cortex) but there is always a risk in losing too much sodium chloride this way, and of suffering cramp such as that experienced by miners.

Apocrine sweat glands include a variety of organs found in certain regions of the skin of most mammals. It has been suggested that as mammals evolved there has been a gradual replacement of apocrine glands by eccrine, and a histologist, P. Schiefferdecker, has even suggested that the 'races' of man could be differentiated by an analysis of the number of their apocrine glands. Unfortunately there is little evidence to support his hypothesis: he took samples of skin from only a few regions of a few individuals and did not ascertain the degree of variation. Apocrine sweat glands display considerable differences in the various regions in which they are found in any particular mammal. They are found in man in the armpit (axilla), mons Veneris and mons Jovis, around the anus, labia of the female vulva, around and on the female nipple, scrotum, eyelids, and the external auditory meatus. The largest gland in relation to the skin, the mammary gland, is also an apocrine gland. Apocrine sweat glands are coiled glands, larger than eccrine, that usually open by a duct into a hair canal, but may open directly onto the surface of the skin.

Sweat from human apocrine glands is frequently coloured white, yellowish, or reddish and is milky. It contains proteins, sugars, ammonia, iron, and certain pigments, but it is only produced in small quantities and at intervals. It is odourless, but is almost immediately broken down by bacteria that are always present in considerable number (more in the unwashed) in those regions where apocrine glands are present. Products of bacterial degradation give rise to the characteristic odours of those regions. It is frequently maintained that bacterial action or oxidation on the skin surface also gives rise to the sometimes startling colour of apocrine sweat, but at least two pigments, a brown and a yellow, are present in the gland cells and may be precursors of the coloured substances. Secretion of true coloured sweat, *chromidrosis*, is a curious condition, little studied by modern methods. The sweat may be coloured yellow, red, greenish, blue, or black. Its sudden appearance may have given rise to the expression 'sweating blood'; although the latter is technically known as *haematidrosis* there is little definite evidence that blood ever normally escapes from intact sweat glands. Some mammals produce coloured sweat probably derived from apocrine glands; in the hippopotamus little red globules of sweat can be seen exuding from glands on the forehead; it is produced more profusely on excitement. Marine mammals are of interest in that adult whales are altogether devoid of sweat glands and seals have apocrine glands that produce curiously solid sweat rather like toothpaste in consistency. It probably helps in waterproofing the fur and may be the source of the characteristic smell left on the hands after handling seals and sealions.

Apocrine glands are inactive in childhood; thus children do not suffer from the social problem of body odour, at least from this source. The glands start to function at puberty, and although they show considerable individual variation in activity, sometimes in relation to differences of temperament, there is no certain evidence that they show cyclic changes or are influenced by menstruation or pregnancy. The glands involute after the menopause and in the senescent male.

Sebaceous glands are usually found in relation to hairs, opening into the upper part of each tube that ensheathes a hair. Many glands also open directly onto the surface of the skin, as on the nipple. Sebaceous glands are said to be present in all mammals, including whales, though apparently much restricted in the latter. There are about six or more times as many sebaceous ducts per square centimetre on face and scalp as there are in an equal area of other parts of the body (about 100 per square centimetre), except palm and sole where there are none. The glands are *holocrine* in their method of secretion, meaning that entire cells break away, die, and their contents become included in material secreted. They are active before birth and their secretions *in utero* form part of a cheesy material (*vernix caseosa*) that covers the skin of newborn children. Sebum is composed almost entirely of waxes, but differs markedly in its constituents in various mammals and apparently also in different parts of the skin of man. Human sebum contains squalene, an acyclic triterpene, its presence and manner of formation being unknown.

HAIR

Only mammals possess hair, but a few possess very little and most adult whales have none. Hairs grow out from the bases of invaginated tubes of epidermis; each tube is called a hair follicle and it stretches some way into the dermis. Each hair follicle is dilated at its base into a bulb which is hollowed out from below by a connective tissue plug known as a dermal papilla. This projects into the hair proper; both are ensheathed by layers of the hair follicle. These consist of an inner and an outer root sheath, the former being three layers thick, the middle one of which is known after T. H. Huxley (see p. 26) and which he described at the age of nineteen. The arrangement of these rather complicated layers is shown in the diagram on page 227 and it will be seen that the innermost layer of the inner root sheath envelops the hair and holds it in place. Only that part of a hair in relation to the dermal papilla, the hair root, is alive and shows cell division, growth and differentiation. The part of the hair beyond this basal region becomes keratinized and dies; in many ways hair can be considered a solid 'secretion' of the skin. Growth of hair, or its secretion, is cyclic and on most parts of the body short periods of active growth are followed by longer periods of rest; in the scalp the opposite occurs and growing periods are long. There is no evidence that cutting hair, shaving it, or wearing hats affects the rate of growth. Pulling and tugging at scalp hair, however, is said to increase activity of hair follicles.

Each follicle in human skin usually contains only one hair, but occasionally, particularly in the beard, a dermal papilla is duplicated. This may result in formation of conjoined hairs, two fused together, or two quite separate hairs may emerge from one opening. It is said that plucking beard hairs may damage dermal papillae and encourage multiple hair growth. Several hair follicles may share a common orifice on the surface of skin, a condition present in the chinchilla but not known in man. Such an arrangement improves the pelage and the commercial value of the fur. Hair follicles tend to be arranged in closely packed groups of two or three.

The function of hair is primarily protective. When it is present all over an animal it protects the skin from damage, allowing a seal to slide over rocks, a mole to burrow without lacerating its skin, and a monkey to slip through foliage. Each hair follicle has a sensory supply and any hair, in a broad sense, is a sensory receptor. Hair also protects in that a thick pelt preserves body heat and acts as an insulator owing to air trapped inside and between the hairs. Nearly every hair follicle is associated with a sebaceous gland opening into its upper part, and hair follicles in certain parts of the body also have apocrine sweat glands related to them. The waxy sebum also protects skin and hair. Hairs can be moved, but not voluntarily, by small bundles of smooth muscle extending from connective tissue of the skin to each hair follicle. Contraction of these muscle bundles causes erection of hair into a vertical position; the muscles are called *arrectores pilorum* because they make hairs 'stand on end'. Their contraction causes appearance of 'goose flesh' on exposure to cold or under emotional stress. They also raise the fur of animals during fright or excitement, increasing the apparent size of an animal or presenting spines or quills more directly towards an attacker. The muscles are innervated by the sympathetic division of the autonomic nervous system and although without much protective function in man (they are said to massage sebum from sebaceous glands) they are a useful attribute in fur-bearing mammals. Hair also plays a part in sexual attraction, the coat being frequently more brilliantly coloured or contrastingly patterned in males. Apocrine glands are sometimes more profuse in the male, and despite the fact that apocrine secretion is odourless it is often said to have sexual significance.

Certain hairs on the face of mammals are larger and have a more specialized and more profuse blood and nerve supply than body hairs. They are called whiskers, feelers, or vibrissae, and they are often sensitive pressure receptors. They enable cats to feel their way better in the dark and seals to swim underwater at night. Their nerve supply is frequently from the trigeminal or fifth cranial nerve, which also supplies the skin of the face, and so tactile hairs are extensions of the facial sensory apparatus. Eyebrow and moustache hairs of man are not specialized vibrissae; they differ in no way from scalp hairs.

TABLE IX

	No. of hair follicles per sq. cm.	*No. of sweat ducts per sq. cm.*
Forehead	770	360
Cheek ♂	770	320
Cheek ♀	730	250
Forearm	100	220
Thigh	55	125
Abdomen	40	210

Average number of hair follicles in adult skin (15–70 years of age) per square centimetre of skin of different regions: the total number of skin appendages on the head of a 24 year old individual is about 1,087,000. These figures were supplied by Dr G. Szabo.

Hair Distribution

The pattern of distribution of hair in man, and its apparent absence on the body, has often been quoted as one of his unique characteristics. The number of hair follicles per unit area of skin is, however, nearly as great as or greater than that in any other Primate, but not as great as in fur-bearing non-Primates. It is the degree of development of hair in various regions that differentiates man from other mammals.

TABLE X

NUMBER OF HAIRS PER SQUARE CENTIMETRE OF SKIN IN EQUIVALENTLY AGED FOETUSES

	Man	*Orang*	*Gibbon*	*Chimpanzee*	*Macaque*
Scalp	880	383	546	400	1240
Back	688	937	440	420	1406

From Danforth (1925)

Scalp hair, that of eyebrows, beard, moustache, 'side-boards', pubis, and axilla show special development in man, and in males long hair commonly develops thickly over the chest and in the mid-line of the abdomen. Elsewhere hair is of a fine vellus type; sometimes it is so fine that it is not thrust to the surface but remains coiled in the mouths of hair follicles. Hair is absent from sole and palm, from the wrinkled part of the eyelids and inner surface of the pinna of the ear, from the lower sides and back of the ankles, from the skin at the base of finger nails, and from the front of the wrist. It is also usually absent from the upper aspect of the base of the big toe in females, but there are usually some stoutish hairs present there in males. Stoutish hairs are found guarding many orifices of the body, nose, ear, anus, and outer surface of the labia, but not on the rosy skin of the lips. A little tuft of hairs grows from the tubercle (tragus) at the front of the ear; it is called the *barbula hirci* – little beard of the goat – and seems to fascinate some hairdressers, who insist on despoiling this pilary curiousity with their clippers.

Hairs are arranged over the human body in tracts, so that the hair radiates in a fairly definite pattern with certain striking peculiarities. Hairs on the chin, for example, grow downwards, towards the neck, whereas those of the front of the neck grow upwards towards the chin. Those on the forehead are directed downwards, as are those on the bridge of the nose; eyebrow hairs are directed laterally, but in a small area between the eyebrows the hairs are curiously directed upwards. Shaving one's face with strokes of the razor in definite directions each morning has no effect on the slope of hairs. The cleanest shave is obtained by passing the razor against the slope of each hair tract.

Hair Structure

Hairs of mammals are of many kinds, and their peculiarities are sometimes very striking. Quills and spines are modified *coarse* hairs, as are bristles, whiskers, and awns (sharp stiff hairs with a bendable softer base). The terms guard-hair and overhair are also used for coarser hairs of a fur or pelage. Short underhairs are *fine* hairs, also known as vellus or lanugo; in wool the fine hairs are long and curly. The porcupine appears to be one of the few animals that possess all the main types of hair.

A hair is covered on its outside by a cuticle of scales, arranged like tiles (imbricated) with the free overlapping edge of each scale directed tipwards. Scales are not pigmented, but may possess some waterproofing quality due to the presence of a fatty material. They exhibit a patterned arrangement, and since the shape of scales varies in different animals it is sometimes possible to determine the origin of hairs recovered, say, from turn-ups of trousers of suspected criminals. The best writers of detective stories will, however, be aware that hairs from one individual can vary considerably in cross-sectional shape and in scale pattern and that differences can be seen even along one hair. Scales also project at their free edges to varying degrees in different hairs; fine hairs have scales that project most. The projections fit into depressions in the inner root sheath and a hair is thus kept in place in its follicle. Well raised edges of scales of fine hairs also mean that individual hairs interlock closely, providing additional protection and improving the quality of material made from them. Human hair from scalp, axilla, and pubes is coarse; only that from face and limbs of women and from the body of foetuses and the newborn is of fine lanugo type.

Beneath the cuticle lies the cortex of a hair, comprising the greater part of it and made of dead, keratinized cells cemented together. The cortex of pigmented hair contains melanin granules and also numbers of small air-filled spaces. The latter are filled with fluid in that part of each hair that lies within the ensheathing hair follicle, but on emergence with growth, air replaces the fluid. Hair will therefore float for some time in water, as indicated by Millais in his picture of the drowned Ophelia. It also persists for great lengths of time even after burial, as certain murderers have found to their cost.

The centre of each hair is formed by a medulla consisting of loosely connected keratinized cells and quite large air spaces. The medulla varies greatly in size; it may be absent in the finest hairs or compose almost all of the hair, as in many rodents. Air spaces in the medulla are partly responsible for the 'sheen' of hair when light falls on it.

The degree of waviness of hair was mentioned on p. 54 as being one of the physical features upon which several attempts to classify mankind were based. Hair may be straight, wavy, or spirally coiled, yet the precise factors responsible for these differences are not known. Eccentric positioning of a hair in its follicles, asymmetric keratinization, differences in the keratin of cuticle and cortex have all been suggested as reasons for the production of waving. Bending or curving of the hair bulb has also been noted in scalp hair of Negroes, but it is not because of any spiralling or curvature along the length of hair follicles that waves are produced in hair. As has been stated earlier, hair is remarkably resistant, being insoluble in water, organic solvents, dilute acids, and alkalis, and resistant to digestion with the enzyme pepsin. Hair is thus not digested in the stomach and occasionally 'hair balls' are found inside that organ.

Growth of Hair

Mammals are born with their hair showing varying degrees of development; hair follicles only start to develop a few days before birth in rats and mice; other mammals, such as guinea-pigs, are born with a well-developed definitive pelage. Man falls into a third group in which hair follicles are developed well before birth and produce a primary hair or foetal lanugo that is obvious at birth and that persists for a few weeks before being mostly shed or moulted. The characteristic nodding of the head to and fro of a newborn child brings baldness to the back of the head, where it rubs against the pillow, after only a few days. The whole head is bald after three to four weeks and then hair follicles in the scalp start to produce secondary hair; it may be of quite a different colour. Each hair follicle may therefore give rise to different kinds of hair during its life, and this ability is demonstrated in places other than the scalp. Hairs on the face of males change in character at puberty from a vellus type to a coarse adult type and the follicles become larger. Hairs of the axilla and pubes of both sexes are similarly transformed. Should a man be castrated before puberty metamorphosis of hair follicles does not occur. A coarse hair follicle may also revert, as in many bald males, to produce a fine lanugo type of hair. Adrenal disease may cause lanugo hair to be replaced by coarse hair.

Patterns of hair growth vary widely in different mammals and in different regions of any one mammal; the rate of growth is equally variable. There may be seasonal shedding or seasonal fluctuation in the rate of growth; it takes longer to grow a beard on a polar expedition than at the equator. Hair follicles in human skin grow independently of their neighbours, each having its own cycle of rest and activity. Human hair grows between 0·2 and 0·4 mm. a day, but there is considerable variation; in rats and mice each hair follicle goes through a growing period of about three weeks, when a hair grows about 1·0 mm. a day. Hair plucked from a mouse is regrown therefore in about three weeks, but a hair plucked from a human scalp takes 5–6 months and from an eyebrow two months to regrow. Plucking may damage the basal part of the hair follicle and regrowth may then take even longer.

The type of hair growth, how much hair develops and how fast it grows in different regions of different mammals would seem primarily to be genetically determined, but there are numerous secondary factors influencing the pilary system. These include hormones, nutrition, age, external temperature, and other physical effects. Much experimental work has been carried out to test a hypothesis that no hair grows without there being a hormonal background to control the process. Such experiments are difficult to control adequately and it is essential to understand the normal hair cycle of the mammal used. It is no use claiming that a certain hormone inhibits hair growth when the hair of the animal under observation during experiment was in a period of rest. It is probable that there is little more to be learnt by experiments on hair and skin *in situ* in living animals, but that the best field for advance is in tissue culture experiments. Cortisone, from the adrenal cortex, the adreno-corticotrophic hormone (ACTH) from the anterior lobe of the pituitary, oestrogens and androgens are all implicated in control of hair growth. A daily dose of 5–10 mg. of cortisone inhibits all hair growth in all mammals, oestrogens induce the growth of fine, sparse hair and prolonged administration of androgens produces coarse hairs. Exactly how the effects of these hormones are interrelated in man is not known, nor is it known how they act on hair follicles. Cortisone has been used in attempts to stimulate hair growth in local and complete baldness in man, and in contrast to its effect on hair growth in rats, occasionally does so, though with only *temporary* results.

Hair growth is retarded when mammals are kept on a reduced diet, and lack of Vitamin A and of riboflavin in the diet also affect hair growth and structure. The metal zinc is a co-factor for several enzyme systems and its absence from the diet cause a rat's hair to fall out, though how is not known.

X-irradiation above a certain dose level damages hair follicles and hair falls out in about a week. Hair will regrow if irradiation has not been severe enough to damage dermal papillae. One therefore refers to an 'epilating' dose of X-rays, and in rats such a dose also affects melanoblasts, causing subsequent hairs to be white. Melanoblasts in human hairs are not disturbed, or not visibly, by an epilatory dose of X-rays.

Sensory innervation of skin is described in Chapter 11.

Skin and Disease

It would be extraordinarily fortunate if so complicated and active an organ as the skin were to escape from disease. The skin surface represents the frontier of the biological systems within the individual. Like all frontiers it will suffer insults from outside and reflect the state of affairs within. Skin disease is related to either organic and structural change or to disturbances of function; much overlap must inevitably occur. The skin is also exposed to parasitic diseases, either vegetable or animal in origin.

Man's apparent hairlessness may be said to expose his skin more freely to infection. He needs to be taught personal hygiene just as much as the cat that teaches its kittens to lick themselves clean. Yet more than in any animal, man's skin reflects his temperament; its disturbances of nervous, secretory, and vascular function can be dramatically expressive, either immediately or over a prolonged period. Often the disturbances are an expression of a failure of adaptation as between man and his physical or mental environment. Man's skin is indeed a mirror of his mood, his nature, his health, his sex, and his age.

FOR FURTHER READING

Physiology and Biochemistry of the Skin. S. Rothman. University of Chicago Press, Chicago, 1954

The Structure and Function of Skin. W. Montagna. Academic Press, New York, 1956

CHAPTER 14

HIS HORMONES AND DUCTLESS GLANDS

HORMONES are chemical substances or 'internal secretions' (Claude Bernard, 1855) produced by structures called endocrine glands. The word 'hormone', introduced by Starling (1905), is derived from a Greek word meaning 'to excite', but a hormone may have an inhibitory effect on the target organ that it influences. Endocrine differ from other glands in that they liberate secretions into the blood stream; they are thus intimately related to the vascular system, and, since they do not have ducts to convey their secretions, are often called 'ductless glands'. They are found in the head, neck, and trunk of the body; to some extent they exhibit specific functions and thus show varying degrees of cellular specialization that probably reflect the evolutionary stages in their differentiation. Their effects are frequently inter-related, that is, more than one hormone can affect the same target organ in different ways, and they are nearly all under the control of the pituitary or hypophysis, the master endocrine gland. It is difficult to devise a simple experiment on one part or one particular activity of the system so closely is it integrated as a whole. Furthermore, a very small quantity of some hormones can produce dramatic effects, and it is not uncommon for physiologically active amounts of a hormone to be measured in microgrammes ($1\mu g$ = 1/1000 milligramme). Most hormones are eventually either broken down in the body or excreted, some more rapidly than others. Endocrine glands therefore pour their secretions into the blood stream continuously to maintain their action, or intermittently when their effect is part of a rhythmical cycle of changes.

Study of the system quickly reveals intricate biochemical mechanisms, resulting in the production of hormones with very powerful biological effects. The latter are occasionally so dramatic, and so alter the appearance and activity of the target organ, that it is not surprising that excess or abnormal production of hormones was soon regarded as one cause of pathological changes in tissues, and also of cancer. This aspect of endocrinology is complicated and will not be discussed, but it is hoped that it will be the subject of another volume in this series.

The anatomist can seldom ignore or avoid considering the effects of hormones on structure. Virtually all dynamic biological processes are under endocrine control or influence and a species difference in structure of an organ may be accompanied by anatomical differences in ductless glands. For many years it was held that the nervous system was relatively immune from hormonal action; this view is now doubted.

Essentially the endocrine system is part of the internal communication or signalling system of a biological complex. The endocrine glands form a series of transmitters emitting chemical signals that are distributed relatively slowly throughout the body by the vascular system. One group of cells is capable, therefore, of giving off a signal in the form of a chemical substance than can act at a distance and influence activities of a second set of cells provided the latter are sensitive to the signal; such sensitivity is an attribute possessed by virtually all cells, although their response to each hormone will vary. In the nervous system chemical signalling has evolved into a highly successful, rapidly acting, and complex communication system. Communication in the endocrine system is less rapid, but the action of the chemical message can be sustained over a long period of time, and then can effectively alter the environment of the target cells. The quantity of the hormone arriving at the target is also capable of being increased or decreased, and thus presumably enhancing or reducing the effect. Man is largely unconscious of what is effected by his endocrine system, but in women menstruation is an obvious manifestation of endocrine activity.

By combination two or more endocrine glands can produce rhythmical or cyclical changes in the prevailing hormonal concentration, the type of hormone acting at the target area and in the response of the target organ. Thus, suppose an endocrine organ B to be under the control of endocrine organ A through mediation of hormone H1, and that B is thus caused to secrete a second hormone H2. Organ B will continue to produce H2 as long as it is stimulated by H1 from organ A. But let it be that a certain concentration of H2 can influence organ A and inhibit production of H1, and thus lead to a fall in production of H2. Thus the mechanism reaches a certain level of activity and then cuts itself off, rather like a thermostat controlling a heater. As soon as the concentration of H2 falls below the cut-out threshold, organ A produces hormone H1 again, and the process is repeated. A third organ C would experience these changes through its vascular supply in the form of successive waves of rising concentration of firstly H1 and then H2. If organ C, however, were sensitive only to the hormone H2, then its response will reflect only variations in the concentration of H2, and it will exhibit a cycle of periods of stimulation, regression, and rest. It could also happen that during the period of rest yet another endocrine organ, D, also perhaps under the control of A, might exert an effect on the organ C, and so produce quite different results. It will be remembered that a mechanism not unlike this is brings about the rhythmical series of changes that occur during the reproductive cycle.

Hormones of one type and another act dramatically at three different periods of an animal's life history – during embryogenesis and foetal life, during the period leading to maturation, and during the life of the fully mature animal. Several variables have to be considered during each period; they will involve the type and number of hormones concerned, activity of the endocrine glands producing them and integrative mechanisms of the system at large, the vascularity and sensitivity of target tissues, and possibly the genetic constitution of each particular species. Many years ago, when endocrinology was in its infancy, Sir Arthur Keith suggested that it might well be inherited instructions controlling the endocrine system that were responsible for morphological differences, particularly in the skeleton, that characterize the races of man. He was undoubtedly thinking of hormones of the type produced by adult endocrine organs, but recently evidence has been produced for the existence of foetal hormones, secreted by foetal endocrine glands, and the situation becomes more complex. Furthermore, it is not impossible that adult maternal hormones, or hormones of placental origin, can affect the foetus, and experimentally obtained alterations in the concentration of hormones circulating on the maternal side of the placenta can sometimes produce havoc in organogenesis.

Hormones are not only produced by organs with compact and

distinctive form and structure; they may be produced by cells incorporated in organs or structures that have functions other than endocrine. Islets of endocrine tissue are disseminated throughout the pancreas, and the latter has its exocrine functions controlled by secretions from cells in the duodenal lining. Several types of cell having endocrine functions are found distributed in placental tissue, though not apparently in all mammalian placentae. There is evidence that the uterus in a pregnant mare produces a substance that stimulates the ovaries.

Endocrine glands can be classified in a number of ways, according to their position in the body, their component tissues, their embryological origin, or by the chemical nature of their secretions. Each means of classification provides important information on structure and function and helps us understand abnormalities in the shape or situation of each gland. Occasionally certain glands may be out of place; embryology indicates where we should look for the ectopic organ.

The Pituitary

The pituitary gland or hypophysis cerebri is remarkably small considering its importance and is also of a complex embryological origin. Anatomically it enjoys a unique position in that it resides in its own fossa in the middle of the base of the skull. It lies in intimate relationship to the undersurface of the brain to which part of it is attached by a short stalk. It is closely related to the two internal carotid arteries, to a collection of venous sinuses, together known as the cavernous sinus, and to several cranial nerves as they pass through the sinus to the eye and face. It lies immediately above one of the paranasal air sinuses of the skull, the sphenoidal air sinus, and thus is close to the roof of the nasal cavity. It was this proximity to the nose that caused ancient anatomists to believe that the gland was responsible for production of nasal mucus; the word pituitary is derived from a Latin word *pituita* meaning slime.

The gland is approximately oval in shape, about half an inch long, and weighs a little over 0·5 g. The gland is clearly twofold when an antero-posterior cut is made and is described as having an anterior lobe (adenohypophysis) and a posterior lobe (neurohypophysis).

The two parts differ in their embryological origin; the anterior part develops as an upgrowth from the roof of the primitive pharynx of the embryo called Rathke's pouch (after M. H. Rathke, 1793–1860, a German anatomist) whereas the posterior lobe develops as a downgrowth from the floor of the third ventricle of the brain. The connecting stalk between the roof of the embryonic pharynx and the anterior lobe soon breaks down and seldom leaves any trace of its previous existence. That between the floor of the third ventricle and the posterior lobe persists, however, into adult life and contains an important tract of fibres that connects certain hypothalamic nuclei with the posterior lobe. The tract is believed to play an interesting part in transmitting a substance known as neuro-secretory material: the material is secreted by cells of the hypothalamic nuclei and is passed down the tract to the posterior lobe. It may be the precursor of a posterior lobe hormone – or even a hormone in reality.

The anterior lobe composes the major part of the bulk of the gland and it contains three distinct types of cell – poorly stained chromophobes, and two types of granular, strongly stained chromophils. Yet it produces more than three types of hormone and one must assume that one type of cell produces more than one hormone, unless one or two complex multiple hormones are first made, breaking down later into simpler substances. There has been much discussion during recent years as to how the pituitary is controlled. No adequate nerve supply has been demonstrated passing to anterior lobe cells although sympathetic fibres travel in the coats of larger arteries in the gland. Recently it has been shown that there is a portal system of small blood vessels passing from the hypothalamus down the pituitary stalk to the anterior lobe and that it would be possible for chemical instructions to be sent to that lobe from the brain. Grafts of anterior lobe tissue are, however, capable of surviving when transplanted to other sites in the same animal.

The anterior lobe produces a number of hormones, several of which act on other endocrine glands, and it is for this reason that the pituitary is often referred to as the master gland of the endocrine system. A few anterior lobe hormones have been identified and many of their properties are well known, but several other hormones are not clearly defined and their presence has only been established from the fact that they cause certain specific biological effects. Of the hormones that have been separated biochemically, and which are believed to originate from certain cell types in the pituitary, the growth promoting principle or somatrophic hormone (SH) is one that affects the growth of the skeleton. It is one of the factors influencing bone growth (see p. 286) and it is responsible to some extent for the characteristics of the skeleton which an individual possesses. Overproduction of the hormone during the period of development of the skeleton results in excessive size or gigantism, and underactivity during childhood results in diminished body growth or dwarfism. Should the anterior lobe secrete excess amounts of the somatrophic hormone during adolescence or after normal bone growth has ceased then the condition of acromegaly may occur. The word means 'big extremities' and there are changes in the bones of the hands and feet and in the jaws. The latter widen, thus the teeth become widely spread, and the lower jaw projects forward (prognathism). There are also changes in the soft tissues and the viscera; acromegalics are often extremely strong, but in later life the pituitary becomes exhausted and the once strong man becomes flabby and weak. Certain races, or racial subdivisions, occasionally display acromegalic features and one must assume that some inherited mechanism ensures slight over-activity of the anterior lobe. Many large, big-boned people display some minor evidence of acromegaly. The growth hormone is almost certainly produced by the eosinophil or acid-staining cells of the anterior lobe.

Three hormones concerned with reproduction are known to arise from the anterior lobe. They were mentioned in Chapter 5 and it is only necessary to name them here. They are firstly the follicle-stimulating hormone, FSH, that stimulates the growth and activity of ovarian follicles (after they have acquired an antrum) and also the testicular seminiferous tubules, secondly the lutealizing hormone, LH, that stimulates the formation of the corpus luteum and causes the testicular interstitial cells to produce androgens, and thirdly the lactogenic or luteotrophic hormone that stimulates milk secretion and causes the corpus luteum to secrete progesterone. The gonadotrophic hormones are probably secreted by the basophil or basic-staining cells of the anterior lobe.

The anterior lobe produces the adrenocorticotrophic hormone, ACTH, that stimulates the adrenal cortex (see later) and thus through the mediation of the hormones produced by the adrenal has additional control over metabolic processes. There is some evidence that it also produces hormones that have a direct effect on metabolism. One hormone is known that has an effect only on the thyroid gland. It is called the thyrotrophic hormone and has been isolated in a relatively pure state: removal of the pituitary causes rapid involution of the thyroid and a marked fall in the metabolic rate.

The structure of the posterior lobe is uniform throughout and consists of modified nervous connective tissue cells, neuroglial cells, called pituicytes. There are also many nerve fibres, derived from the tract (p. 247) from the hypothalamus. It is believed with some certainty that the chief hormone of the posterior lobe, the antidiuretic principle, is secreted in the hypothalamic nuclei, passed down the axons of the hypothalamo-hypophysial tract as neuro-secretory material, and stored or liberated in the posterior lobe. The posterior lobe principle acts on the cells of the renal tubules and promotes them to reabsorb a certain amount of the water originally filtered into the tubules through the glomeruli. Should the hypothalamus, its tract to the posterior lobe, or a greater part of the posterior lobe be damaged or rendered ineffective, then a condition called diabetes insipidus develops. Without the action of the posterior lobe principle 30% of the water is not reabsorbed by the renal tubules and urine is produced in excessive amounts by the kidney.

Certain other active substances can be extracted from the posterior lobe, a 'pressor principle' raises the blood pressure by causing smooth muscle arteries to contract, and an oxytocic factor causes the uterine muscle to contract (oxytocic means 'causing swift birth').

The Pineal

Another organ related to the third ventricle, to the back part of its roof, is the pineal, a small ovoid structure (0·2 g.) that has always been something of a puzzle, its purpose being by no means clarified when René Descartes (1596–1650) suggested it to be the seat of the soul. There is little evidence to suggest that it has endocrine functions, although its activity is said to be associated with development of sexual activity. Tumours of the pineal, or in its region, are occasionally in man associated with sexual precocity. The gland has a complex structure, its various parts being modified or suppressed in different vertebrates. One part of the complex, the parapineal, is differentiated as a photo-receptor in certain primitive vertebrates and in the interesting primitive reptile from New Zealand, the Tuatara (*Sphenodon*), the parapineal exists as a parietal eye, lying in the middle of the head beneath the skin. The human pineal is, however, derived from a different part of the complex and is in no way related to a parietal eye. In man the gland becomes calcified later in life and the deposits may often be detected in X-ray films of the skull of elderly people.

The Thyroid

A number of endocrine organs develop from the endodermal cells lining the inner aspects of the branchial arches (see p. 135) of the embryo: they are classified together as being branchiogenic in origin. The thyroid gland, found in the neck in front of the thyroid cartilage of the larynx and trachea, arises as a downgrowth from a midline pit on the floor of the primitive mouth cavity between the first and second arches, and there may also be a contribution to it from the fourth endodermal pouch. The evolutionary history of the thyroid is interesting: the gland is represented in primitive chordates by rows of mucus-secreting cells on the floor of the pharynx, called the endostyle. In somewhat more advanced chordates it becomes tubular and then loses its connexion with the pharynx altogether, only at this stage does it exhibit any endocrine activity.

The human thyroid consists of two large lobes connected by a thin isthmus that crosses the second to fourth rings of the trachea. It weighs between 20 and 30 g. and is heavier in women, particularly at menstruation, than in men; it is relatively large in children and smaller in the under-nourished. The gland is enclosed in an envelope of connective tissue, the lobes lying one on each side of the trachea, covered by the thin strap muscles of the neck and the sternomastoid muscle, and with the carotid arteries and internal jugular veins behind. The thyroid has a very rich blood supply from the two superior and two inferior thyroid arteries that arise from the external carotid and subclavian arteries respectively, and is probably the best vascularized gland in the body: in about an hour some nine pints of blood (equivalent to the total blood volume) percolate through its vascular bed.

The gland consists of a very great number of small spheroidal follicles or vesicles, about 0·1 to 0·5 mm. in diameter, each lined with a single layer of low cuboidal secretory cells and containing a jelly-like material called colloid. Each vesicle is surrounded by a rich network of capillaries. The cells of each vesicle secrete the hormone of the thyroid, in the past thought to be thyroxine, but now said to be tri-iodothyronine, a substance similar to thyroxine but with one less iodine atom. Iodine is present in greater amounts in the thyroid than in any other organ, and the thyroid 'takes up' iodine from the blood stream with great facility. The colloid acts as a reservoir and contains iodinated protein. Release of the active hormone is probably brought about by the breakdown of the large protein molecule by enzymes and the absorption of the smaller active thyroxine or tri-iodothyronine into the blood through the gland cells. The colloid is not, therefore, an inert storage depot, but its constituents are in a continual state of flux. The use of the radioactive isotope of iodine has helped considerably in investigating the secretory activity of the thyroid.

The thyroid hormone influences effectively the general metabolic activities of the body. Removal of the gland in the young, or its failure during childhood results in defective and inhibited growth and retardation of mental development: the condition is called cretinism. Similar failure of thyroid function in adults results in a lowered metabolism, changes in the skin, loss of hair, and accumulation of water in the tissues; such changes result in a state called myxoedema. Overactivity of the thyroid results in an increased metabolic rate, loss of weight, increased nervousness, and other changes that may eventually result in a toxic condition. All these disorders illustrate clearly that hormones may normally bring about only physiological responses, useful and even essential for efficient everyday life, but in certain circumstances they can be produced in too great or too small quantities and can then exert profound functional and even anatomical changes. Fortunately many of these abnormal changes are reversible with appropriate treatment.

Activity of the thyroid is closely linked with that of the anterior lobe of the pituitary; the thyrotrophic hormone from the latter influences activity of the gland. Other pituitary hormones, such as those promoting growth and gonadal activity, do not seem to be fully effective without collaboration of the thyroid hormone. Thyroid activity would appear to be so essential for normal body functions that it is not surprising to find that it is involved in many natural processes.

The Parathyroids

The four small parathyroid glands (they weigh up to 0·1 g. each; there are sometimes fewer and often more than four) are found on the back surface of the thyroid within its capsule or, in some mammals, within the gland substance. They develop from the third and fourth pharyngeal pouches (dorsal part) and thus technically each pair are referred to as parathyroids III and IV. Parathyroids III are often the larger and are lower in the neck than IV, probably due to the descent of fourth pouch derivatives being prevented by its involvement in thyroid development. The parathyroids were the last of the 'essential' glandular organs of the vertebrate body to be described (of all vertebrates parathyroid tissue has not been found in fishes); their discoverer was Ivar Sandstrom, when a medical student at Upsala in 1877.

Parathyroid tissue consists of three types of secretory cell, but they may well be different stages in the life-history of only one type of cell. The cells produce a hormone, a protein, that is essential to the life of the mammal in that it controls the metabolism of calcium and phosphorus. Removal of two of the glands has little effect, but total removal results in a fall of calcium ions in the blood to such an extent that respiratory and cardiac failure cause death in a few days owing to muscular tetany. The hormone therefore ensures the proper relation between the calcium in the blood and that in the skeleton and is a vital factor in bone development and growth. It can also affect the density of bone in later life and, since the bone calcium is 'turned over' at a rate of up to 20 per cent of the total calcium per month, overactivity of the organ soon results in decalcification and underactivity leads to deposition of calcium in extra amounts. Surgeons removing the thyroid therefore ensure that some parathyroid tissue is left behind. It has been maintained that the anterior lobe of the pituitary exerts some control over the parathyroid, at least in mature animals.

The Thymus

Another branchiogenic organ is the thymus, although it is not known if it secretes a hormone. The fact that its size and life history are closely related to body maturation and reproductive activity, and that it responds under experimental and other stimuli, all imply some endocrine function. The organ develops from the third pharyngeal pouch (ventral part) and at birth it is a flattened pinkish mass lying between the sternum and the great vessels and pericardium. It weighs about 13 g. at birth and enlarges steadily to about three times the weight at puberty, after which it gradually, but variably, involutes; even in quite elderly individuals the thymus may be quite large. Removal of the thymus does not seem to have serious results in mammals, and the problem of the functional significance of the gland remains unresolved.

The thymus consists of lobules of cells usually called thymocytes, that are really lymphocytes, epithelial reticular cells and curious corpuscles of concentrically arranged nucleated epithelial cells described first in 1846 by the English physician A. H. Hassall (1817–94). The epithelial elements are surely the source of any thymic hormone, but the presence of such a large mass of lymphoid tissue is difficult to explain. A thymus is present in all vertebrates, except certain primitive fishes, either in relation to the gills, the neck or within the thorax.

The abdomen contains endocrine glands in the form of certain islets of tissue in the pancreas, the adrenal glands and those parts of the ovary and testis that are capable of producing hormones.

The Pancreas

The pancreas (the word means 'all flesh') is a long, lobulated gland lying transversely on the back wall of the abdominal cavity; the greater part of it is behind the stomach at the level of the first and second lumbar vertebrae. It stretches from the duodenum on the right, into which its duct enters, to the spleen on the left; peritoneum is in contact only with its front surface. The gland develops as an outgrowth from the lower part of the primitive foregut and its exocrine function is to secrete the pancreatic juice with its enzymes trypsin, amylase, and lipase, along the duct that persists from that original foregut outgrowth. The pancreas also contains up to one and a half million islets of endocrine tissue, each islet consisting of about a hundred cells. The islets were first described in 1869 by the German pathologist Paul Langerhans (1847–88) and he called them 'clumps of epithelial-like protoplasmic cells'. They contain two main types of cell with characteristic granules in their cytoplasm.

The disease diabetes mellitus has been known since the time of Hippocrates, but the description mellitus arose from the observations of Thomas Willis (1775), who noticed the sweet, honey-like taste of the urine. Much later von Mering and Minkowski (1889) showed that if the pancreas is removed from a dog diabetes mellitus develops and death soon follows. It was suggested that the islets described by Langerhans produced a substance that normally prevented the development of the condition, and in 1921 the hormone insulin was extracted from them by F. Banting and C. Best. Insulin is a complex protein containing many amino acids and it is an essential regulator of carbohydrate metabolism. Lack of the hormone results in increase of the sugar concentration in the blood and its elimination by the kidneys into the urine. It is suggested that the hormone stimulates utilization of sugar by the tissues, regulates the release of sugar from the liver into the blood, and inhibits sugar formation from body protein. It is also clear that other hormones are involved in the process, particularly those of the anterior pituitary (the diabetogenic hormone is one; its experimental injection causes a diabetic state and destruction of one of the cell types in the islet tissue). One of the many interesting aspects of diabetes mellitus is that there is a family history in 25 per cent of patients. It is considered that its inheritance is due to a recessive gene (m) and that the development of the disease depends on the inheritance of the gene and the action of certain secondary factors.

The Adrenals

The adrenals (or suprarenals) are two endocrine organs lying one on the upper surface of each kidney, enclosed within the renal fascia and behind the peritoneum. The right gland is somewhat pyramidal; it lies against the inferior vena cava and is covered by the liver; the left gland is crescentic and is related to the tail of the pancreas and is covered by the stomach. Each gland weighs from 5 to 10 g. and possesses a cortical portion essential to life, and a medullary portion that is not. Most vertebrates possess the glands, but in fishes there is no distinct organ, but isolated clusters of cortical and medullary tissue are present beside the large blood vessels between the kidneys. The medullary tissue is considered as a derivative of the neural crest (see p. 178) and is part of the chromaffin system of 'paraganglia' found in relation to the peripheral sympathetic cells. The cortical tissue develops from localized thickenings of the coelomic epithelium close to the site of origin of the gonads. This close embryological origin of the adrenal cortex and the gonads has often been used to suggest that there is some cytological and functional relationship between them. Accessory cortical tissue is indeed often found in relation to the gonads.

The cortex of the adrenal consists of three zones, one within the next, composed of polyhedral cells arranged respectively in clusters, bundles and networks. The cells are rich in lipid, store vitamin C, and exhibit a number of histochemical properties that may well be associated with the activities of the cortex. The mere fact that the suprarenal is so well vascularized, being supplied by vessels from the aorta, the renal arteries and those supplying the diaphragm, indicates that the gland may well be of great importance. Many different substances have been extracted from the cortical tissue; the best known are the biologically active hydrocortisone and aldosterone. The former affects carbohydrate metabolism and the latter powerfully influences salt and water metabolism. Removal or destruction of the adrenal cortex, as occurs in the disease described by Thomas Addison (1793–1860) of Guy's Hospital in 1855, is fatal unless the cortical hormones are administered. The adrenal is also involved in enabling the body to withstand stress; insufficient cortical activity renders the body more sensitive to the damaging effects of exposure to cold and physical injury.

The adrenal medulla is of a darker brown than the cortex and forms about one-tenth of the mass of the gland. Its cells are large and granular and surrounded by numerous blood-filled sinusoids. A rich nerve supply passes to the medulla from the sympathetic division of the autonomic system; they are mainly pre-ganglionic fibres that arise from the lower thoracic and upper lumbar levels of the spinal cord. These nerves control the activity of the medulla and cause it to secrete adrenaline and noradrenaline: the process of secretion can be studied microscopically and it is practically the only endocrine gland in the body in which the discharge of its hormone can be observed. Injection of adrenaline experimentally produces effects similar to those obtained by stimulating the sympathetic nerves; there is a transient rise in blood pressure due to constriction of some, but not all, of the peripheral blood vessels, stimulation of the heart rate, an increase in the metabolic rate and a rise in the blood sugar level. It would therefore appear that the medulla of the adrenal can gear the body to react advantageously to any sudden demands or crises in the animal's life. There is also some evidence that the medullary hormones control the secretory activity of the cortex (see also ACTH).

The adrenals are remarkably large just before or at birth in many mammals owing to the presence of a characteristic foetal cortical zone deep to the definitive cortex. The zone is transitory and disappears by about the end of the first year after birth. It is well-marked in mice and is called the X-zone; it persists for some months in female mice, but disappears rapidly in males. Considerable interest has been aroused by this foetal zone as it raises the question whether the foetal adrenal is functional. Increasing evidence is being obtained of the abnormal effects of cortisone on foetal development; experimental injection of it and of ACTH into pregnant animals or directly into the foetus can interfere with normal development if given early in pregnancy. If given late it may have a detrimental effect on the teeth of the animal. Adrenaline, too, can damage foetuses, and if it is possible that the foetal endocrine glands function before birth it might well be dangerous to the foetus if they became over-active.

FOR FURTHER READING

Neural Control of the Pituitary Gland. G.W. Harris. Arnold, 1955
Recent Progress in Hormone Research. Ed. G. Pincus. Vols. I–XII, Academic Press, 1947–56

CHAPTER 15

HIS VANISHING TEETH

> Thy teeth are like a flock of sheep that are even shorn, which came up from the washing; whereof every one bear twins, and none is barren among them.
>
> SONG OF SOLOMON

TEETH, whether belonging to fish or beast, prehistoric or modern, set in rows in the jaw or rattling loose, are among the most fascinating structures that one can study. They are complicated structures, part soft tissue but mostly made of hard, mineralized material. They can virtually last for ever, can leave imprints of their shape and features in rock, and are not easily destroyed. They provide us with knowledge of prehistoric animals, sometimes being the only remaining trace, and they have frequently been the subject of scientific controversy, or even scientific 'jokes'. In 1922 the discovery was announced of a single water-worn, molar tooth from the Snake Creek of Nebraska. It was postulated that it was the tooth of a fossil Anthropoid of the Pliocene. The supposed owner was considered to be man-like in certain features and was given the name of *Hesperopithecus haroldcooki*. Illustrations were published of reconstructions of its complete form, male and female. All this from one tooth – and how sad – or amusing – when five years later this tooth was shown quite conclusively to have come from an early American peccary! Another, now notorious, scientific joke, more serious in that it seems to have involved a deliberate fraud, also centres around some supposedly prehistoric teeth – and other remnants. Portions of a brain case, part of a lower jaw with two molar teeth and a single canine tooth were found at Piltdown in Sussex between 1908 and 1913. Immense interest developed over these remains and although a number of anatomists expressed doubts and reserved their opinions, many regarded them as remains of possibly the most primitive type of man to have been discovered, and gave him the 'dawn-man' name of *Eoanthropus dawsoni*. The brilliant researches of the team that exposed the fake are a credit to the methods of modern techniques, and perhaps allow some invidious praise to descend on the head of the perpetrator. The removal of *Eoanthropus* has indeed 'cleared the air' of the problem of man's ancestry, and has removed a puzzle which involved, in the words of a national journal, the 'first man with false teeth' and at least was responsible for much unnecessary study.

It may seem somewhat conceited, after quoting these diagnostic failures, to maintain that 'the structure of the teeth gives a better clue to the affinities of a primate than either the brain, bony skeleton, muscular anatomy, or the structure and development of the placenta' (Broom).

Yet the study of teeth does indeed provide us with the most complete or continuous series of anatomical structures on which to base an examination of evolutionary trends and adaptations. A tooth, as an object, is at first curiously difficult to define, particularly if one had arrayed before one all the structures with tooth-like pretensions found in animals.

Definition of a Tooth

It is not just enough to state that teeth are mineralized dermal appendages, found in the margins of the jaws and used for eating. In many groups of animals teeth are found outside the mouth, such as in a saw-fish, or on the roof of the mouth, on the inside of the jaws, or in the throat. Strangest of all, teeth may occasionally be found in a rare tumour of the ovary. Teeth are not always equally mineralized, some animals having only horny protuberances whilst in others, such as the baleen whales, they are only found in foetuses and may never erupt. Teeth are used for many other purposes besides eating; they can be employed to kill in attack or defence, to carry things – including the young – or to act as another prehensile form of limb when all four legs are on the ground. In the form of tusks teeth are useful for digging up roots and can even be used for locomotion; a walrus pulls itself over ice by means of its long, massive tusks. In higher animals teeth can act in a sensory capacity to test toughness and consistency; give a strange object to a monkey and it will at once take a few exploratory bites at it. Articulate speech demands their presence; just try to say the word 'teeth' without any in the jaws. Teeth can be used for expression of emotion, exposing them to the accompaniment of a fierce snarl, or by a tender 'love-bite' to an ear.

Teeth cannot be used for all these various purposes unless held in position in the jaws. Some of the lowest types of animals lack teeth and even jaws (e.g. *Agnatha; a*—without, *gnathos*—a jaw). Jaws and teeth were first present in certain extinct fishes, the teeth being fused to the plates of bone on the jaws. Some fish, such as the hake, possess teeth that hinge backwards and as things enter the mouth they snap forward to bite. In mammals teeth are set in sockets and held in place with fibrous tissue. Such a peg and socket joint is called a *gomphosis*. Galen introduced the name, borrowing the word *gomphos* from the name for a peg used in ancient Greek shipbuilding.

Types of Teeth

As soon as teeth appeared, modifications and adaptations evolved in association with the function for which they were used. Carnivorous fish, such as sharks, evolved pointed, cutting teeth arranged in numerous rows. Those fish that live on hard molluscs that need crushing evolved flattened plates made of several teeth fused together. Thus on their earliest appearance teeth showed a diversity of form associated with differences in function, and although names for the various types are not really needed for teeth of fishes, they become necessary for mammalian teeth. In mammals teeth are reduced from the number found in fish and reptiles to a short series in each jaw, attached to the upper and lower margins of each half jaw. In a generalized mammal four types of tooth can be recognized from front to back:

(*a*) The *incisors* (*incidere* – to cut into) which are the sharp, chisel-like anterior teeth and can be used for nipping and cutting.

(*b*) The *canine* (*canis* – a dog), the single tooth in each half jaw behind, or lateral to the incisors. There is sometimes difficulty in deciding which is the canine, but it is definitely a long, stout tooth and is well marked in the Carnivora. It sometimes shows a sexual dimorphism, i.e. is larger in the male. The upper canines are called 'eye-teeth' and are the longer.

(*c*) The *premolars*, situated in front of the true molars and behind the canine, are defined as those teeth which, as they erupt, replace deciduous molars. They frequently display grinding surfaces, but in some animals premolars are not well developed.

(*d*) The *molars* (*molare* – to grind) of mammals usually have an expanded crown with a complicated pattern of little projections, or cusps, on the surface. The pattern of these cusps is characteristic for particular genera or even species, and there is a considerable literature concerned with the possible methods of evolution and development of the pattern. The premolars and molars are together known as the 'cheek' teeth, and they are often separated as the grinding series by a gap, called a *diastema*, from the anterior biting teeth.

The number and arrangement of teeth in a mammal can be expressed by means of a simple formula – on the understanding that one is looking at the upper and lower half jaws, starting with the incisor teeth on the left. Thus the primitive mammalian dentition can be expressed:

$$\frac{3.1.4.3.}{3.1.4.3.} = \frac{11}{11} = 22 = 44 \text{ teeth altogether.}$$

in that there are 3 incisors, 1 canine, 4 premolars and 3 molars in each half jaw.

The human *permanent* dentition can be expressed as $\frac{2.1.2.3.}{2.1.2.3.}$ showing, as mentioned on p. 77, that there has been a reduction in the human dentition by one incisor and two premolars from the primitive mammalian type.

We shall, of course, have to provide another dental formula to indicate the nature of the *deciduous* dentition, for although it is reduced in mammals, there always occurs the interesting and important phenomenon of tooth replacement.

Replacement of Teeth

Renewal or replacement of teeth is frequently found in lower animals, more often in those with simple, pointed teeth than in the types with the more massive grinding plates. Replacement of teeth may occur by an eversion, or rolling outwards of the teeth developing on the inside of the jaw. A second method is found in reptiles in which functional teeth alternate with young tooth germs in the series. The young tooth germs eventually grow up into functional teeth, and, as the first generation is lost, they in their turn are replaced from successive tooth germs at their base. In this way an almost continuous replacement is ensured; a dentition which displays a succession of generations is called *polyphyodont*. In mammals there are only two dentitions – thus the human dentition is *diphyodont* and even then the replacement is not complete. This may seem puzzling at first, as there are more permanent than deciduous teeth. The first dentition of the young child erupts as follows:

Deciduous incisors: 6–9 months.
1st deciduous molars: 12–14 months.
Deciduous canines: 16–18 months.
2nd deciduous molars: 2–2½ years.

and appears in order almost from front to back. Then, after a rest of three to four years, the series is continued by eruption behind the deciduous molars of the first permanent molars. As the series continues backwards with gradual eruption of successive permanent molars, replacement starts at the front, thus:

Replacement: Permanent incisors: 7–8 years.
Permanent premolars: 9–10 years.
Permanent canine: 10–11 years.

After this replacement the two other permanent molars erupt; this order of eruption is, incidentally, a specialized human feature.

Permanent 2nd molar: 10–13 years.
Permanent 3rd molar: 17–25 years.

Thus we could consider either that the deciduous dentition was incomplete to start with and that the second wave of erupting teeth was more generous – or that the three permanent molar teeth are not in fact part of the replacement series. They could be 'deciduous' teeth delayed in their appearance, and the replacement series is thus incomplete. Some anatomists consider that so-called permanent molars are so much more like deciduous molars than permanent premolars that they are indeed delayed members of the first dentition. This concept naturally delights those who argue that man retains or prolongs foetal characteristics into adult life. He would still be chewing with his first dentition long into the sixties – or so he hopes.

Replacement of vertebrate teeth is not only brought about by rolling outwards of successional teeth from within the mouth, by alternate replacement and by vertical replacement, but also in a horizontal manner. In the elephant there are six cheek teeth in each half jaw, but not all are present at once. There is a succession of teeth moving forwards along the jaw. As the first so-called deciduous teeth are lost from in front, the survivors move forwards and the permanent molars move into position from the back of the jaw until in old age there may only be one last permanent molar left. It is sometimes said that loss of this last molar results in the animal becoming a 'rogue elephant' owing to its exasperation at being unable to chew properly, or to the pain of the remaining upper (or lower) molar on one side biting against a raw, empty socket.

Other animals showing the horizontal type of replacement are kangaroos, manatees, and pigs, and to a limited degree it occurs in apes and man. When the two deciduous molars are lost not all the space left is filled by the two smaller replacing premolars; thus there follows a shift forwards of the first permanent molar in order to fill the gap. Should for any reason one of the premolars be lost or be removed, there follows a form of horizontal replacement by the molar teeth moving slowly forwards. It is as if the teeth in the human jaw were being persuaded to keep continually in contact and that this were brought about by forces shifting the teeth forwards from behind. It is the continuous working of the jaws, the manner in which the lower jaw is slung, and the pressure exerted by masticatory movements, that bring about the forward horizontal shift.

STRUCTURE OF MAN'S TEETH

A human tooth consists of a soft tissue core, the pulp cavity with its nerves and blood vessels, surrounded by thick layers of hard, mineralized material (see Fig. 28 for details of the arrangement of the dental tissues). The inner hard material is dentine, a substance not unlike bone in that it contains some 75 per cent of inorganic salts, mainly calcium phosphate. The outermost layer is the enamel, the hardest substance in the human body and the most difficult to destroy. The enamel does not cover the whole tooth, but only the crown, and it varies in thickness in different places. The root of the tooth is surrounded by the third hard tissue of the tooth – the cement. This substance is nearest to bone in its composition, and, in fact, it may be considered homologous with the so-called 'bone of attachment' which unites the teeth with the jaws in lower vertebrates. The composition of the various constituents of a tooth is tabulated below:

TABLE XI

CHEMICAL COMPOSITION OF TISSUES OF PERMANENT TEETH

	Enamel	*Dentine*	*Cement*
Inorganic	96–97 per cent (Various apatites–mainly hydroxy-apat. and some fluoroapatite)	70–75 per cent (Hydroxy-apatite) $10Ca_3 PO_4(OH)_2$	55–60 per cent (Apatite deposited about a collagenous matrix)
Organic	3–4 per cent (Mainly a protein with a resemblance to keratin)	25–30 per cent (Collagenous material)	40–45 per cent (A collagenous fibrillar network)
Calcium	35–36 per cent—	34–35 per cent—	35–36 per cent—
Phosphorus	17–18 per cent— of 100 g. Ash.	17–18 per cent— of 100 g. Ash.	17–18 per cent— of 100 g. Ash.

Enamel

Enamel is laid down by cells called ameloblasts present in the tooth germ (see Plate XXIII) and once it has been deposited it is there permanently. In an adult tooth it is dead tissue, and when damaged or chipped, as by opening metal hair-grips against the teeth or biting on screws or carpet tacks, the chipped edge will remain until the neighbouring enamel has been worn down to an equal depth. Enamel is made up of a very large number of prisms cemented together. The prisms pass at right angles to the surface of the dentine and extend with a somewhat wavy course to the tooth surface. The wavy arrangement of the prisms is probably responsible for certain optical phenomena in the form of lines or bands seen on a ground surface of enamel. The alterations in the rate of enamel formation, and the change in nutrition at birth, are responsible for other lines known as 'incremental' lines and the 'neonatal' line. A variation in the closeness with which the enamel prisms are packed and the thickness of the enamel produce differences in its colour. The thicker and denser the enamel the more blue or grey-blue it appears, whereas if it is thin and translucent the yellow dentine shows through from underneath.

Enamel differs in origin from other hard tissues in a tooth in that ameloblasts are derivatives of ectoderm of the dental lamina and can

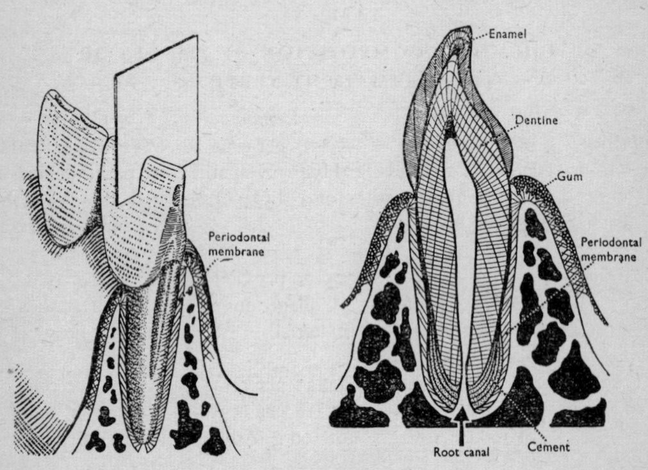

FIG. 28. Main components of a tooth, how it is held in place, and how the root canal leads to the pulp. Note facets of wear on incisors.

thus be considered as homologous with other localized skin derivatives. There are other differences, one being that, once formed, no further enamel can be made and it cannot be repaired or regrown. The cells forming enamel are thrust out from their protective covering in the jaw by growth of structures beneath, and having erupted into the mouth the formative area rapidly dies and is rubbed off. Thus the eruption of a tooth stops formation of further enamel except at its root.

Enamel is indeed dead and mainly inorganic, but curiously enough it is permeable to water, substances of low molecular weight and to some larger molecules such as dyes. Experiments with radioactive isotopes of certain substances have shown that some ions penetrate enamel with remarkable rapidity, perhaps passing through it by way of the keratin-like protein that cements enamel prisms together, or through minute cracks, fissures and fibrous lamellae. There is evidence of a change in permeability of enamel with ageing of interprismatic material, a process that may involve an increase in the degree of keratinization.

A particular type of enamel, known as tubular enamel, is found in nearly all Marsupialia, and it is also found in modified form in animals of great evolutionary antiquity. Minute tubules are continuous with dentinal tubules and extend to the tooth surface. Tubular enamel has been found in Insectivora, Rodentia, Lemurs, and Tarsius. There are tubules of a sort in human enamel, often referred to as enamel spindles, and it is possible that they increase permeability of teeth.

Dentine

Dentine is a yellowish material, not as hard as enamel and having a high degree of elasticity. It is made by cells called odontoblasts which form a layer on the inner surface of the dentine and thus surround the pulp cavity of the tooth. Recent research suggests that odontoblasts may have an interesting embryological history in that they may be derived from groups of cells extended from the neural tube and known as neural crest cells. The odontoblasts cause deposition of calcium salts onto a collagenous framework or matrix, but as dentine is laid down the odontoblasts leave behind them a long protoplasmic strand, called after Sir John Tomes (1815–95), the dentinal fibre of Tomes. (Sir John was the father of Charles Tomes (1846–1928) whose name is associated with the ameloblast processes. A textbook, *Dental Anatomy*, well known to generations of dental students, was written by the father and later edited by the son.) The protoplasmic processes persist and become elongated as dentine is laid down, and thus it is permeated throughout its substance by millions of narrow dentinal tubules (Leeuwenhoek (1678) counted 4,822,500 'pipes' in a human molar). The tubules radiate outwards from their origin at odontoblasts in the pulp cavity and pursue a sinuous course to the junction of dentine with enamel or cement. Dentine is laid down during tooth development in rhythmical phases of active deposition and rest. The increments give dentine a lined appearance on ground sections, and other lines are produced by disturbances in the deposition process; one such line, the neonatal line formed at birth, is particularly marked in dentine of deciduous teeth. Its detection in a ground section of an unerupted tooth from the jaw of a young dead child would be evidence that the child had lived at least for some months.

The tubular form of dentine (orthodentine) of human teeth represents an ancient type of tissue that is first found in fishes; it is widely distributed and is present in the vast majority of mammalian teeth. In some fishes and reptiles dentine is thrown into a series of folds (plicidentine) due to complicated arrangement of the pulp cavity, but basically it is tubular in composition. Dentine in other fishes is full of blood vessels that form a network of capillaries within it (vasodentine); rarely an occasional capillary becomes incorporated in developing human dentine.

Although the dentine required to make the form of a particular tooth has all been laid down by the time the tooth has fully erupted, it is possible for dentine to be laid down in later life as a repair tissue (secondary dentine). Odontoblast activity is perpetuated at the edge of dentine nearest the pulp cavity and in an old tooth secondary dentine is separated from that primarily responsible for tooth form by a dark line that is caused by change in direction of dentinal tubules. Deposition of secondary dentine is encouraged by any mild stimulus that affects odontoblasts; thinning of the surface coverings by attrition or caries could be such factors. Occasionally a dentist attempts to stimulate deposition of secondary dentine by placing a mild irritant at the bottom of a cavity that has extended close to the pulp. The degree of deposition of secondary dentine can be a guide, always bearing in mind the effect of factors mentioned above, to the age of a tooth. But, unfortunately, its examination involves preparation of sections of the whole tooth and thus destruction of its original form.

Before leaving the subject of dentine it may not be irrelevant to note that the elephant's tusk is the largest mass of dentine found in nature. It will be clear that it would be anatomically extremely difficult for an entire tusk to be made of, or even be covered by, enamel. There is a small tip of enamel on the end of each modified incisor, but this is usually soon worn or broken off. The tusk is thus made of fine-grained dentine, ivory, and is almost solid up to the short pulp cavity at the base of the tooth. The dentine is formed continuously throughout life and thus the tusk never ceases to erupt.

Cement and Periodontal Membrane

Cement is the tissue by which a human tooth is attached to the jaw. It surrounds the root of the tooth, except at the opening of the root canal, and extends upwards to the point of junction with enamel. The roots of human teeth are each set in individual sockets in the jaws. The bony socket is called an alveolus and it is lined by a vascular membrane, the alveolar periosteum or 'periodontal membrane'. Cement intervenes between dentine and the membrane-lined wall of the socket and the tooth is held firmly in place by fibres of connective tissue that pass from bone of the socket through the periodontal membrane and into the cement. Composition of cement is given on p. 263.

When the lining membrane of the socket becomes inflamed it swells and the tooth is forced upwards out of the socket. Its crown then projects above the level of its neighbours and in biting or chewing is struck first. Contents of the socket are subjected to pressure that is transmitted to sensory nerves in the periodontal membrane and gives rise to a painful sensation. The periodontal membrane is supplied by blood from apical vessels entering the root canal of the tooth, from vessels supplying bone round the socket, and from vessels passing down from the gums. When a tooth is extracted these vessels are ruptured and blood escapes. It soon clots in the socket and is replaced by granulation tissue, to be invaded later by bone. However, the site of the original socket remains for a long time and even when filled in by bone sometimes its outline can be detected on X-ray films.

The periodontal membrane is well supplied by nerves, branches from maxillary and mandibular divisions of the trigeminal or fifth cranial nerve. The sensation of pressure is particularly acute and the slightest degree of contact between teeth, or gentlest pressure exerted by something wedged between two teeth, can be appreciated. If a new filling in a tooth rises slightly above the level of the usual occlusion plane it is soon a source of acute discomfort.

The Pulp

The pulp of a tooth is the soft tissue found in the central cavity; it is present in the pulp chamber of the crown and in the root canals. The pulp is continuous with the soft tissue about the apex through the openings of the canal at the tip of each root. Through the opening, or openings, pass blood vessels, lymphatics, and nerve fibres that supply the tooth. The above structures lie in the loose connective tissue of the pulp and ramify through it towards the odontoblasts. The latter form a continuous lining to the pulp cavity and are kept alive by the pulp vessels and nerves. There is much debate as to the exact termination of the medullated nerve fibres; some maintain that the fibres end in the region of the odontoblasts in the form of a plexus of fine, unmyelinated fibres, whereas others produce evidence that the unmyelinated fibres proceed into the dentinal canals as long, fine, beaded fibres that extend in slender form as far as the enamel. The latter observations would certainly please those who find painful even the first grating of a dental drill in a shallow cavity.

A tooth deprived of its blood and nerve supply does not necessarily fall out, but may remain usefully in position for many years. Teeth knocked out by accident, by fists or cricket balls have been washed quickly, replaced, and with splinting or other treatment, have stayed in position for years. The tooth is not re-innervated and, as in the previous example, is a dead object. The root surface is invaded by bone from the jaw and the displaced tooth is held tightly enough to retain it. Recently efforts have been made, sometimes successful, to replace a lost permanent tooth in a young person by transplanting a young tooth germ from a more posterior position in the same jaw. Experiments have also been carried out in which tooth germs have been transplanted to other parts of the body of the same animal, or grown *in vitro* in tissue culture. In each case the explanted tooth germs began to develop into the type of teeth they were potentially due to form. Tooth germs cannot yet be transplanted with success from one individual to another.

DEVELOPMENT AND ERUPTION OF TEETH

The first signs of the development of teeth in man are seen about the seventh week of embryonic life, and are marked by proliferation of a continuous band of epithelium that projects from the surface into the tissues of the jaws. It is called the dental lamina and from it tooth germs will develop. Successive stages in development of tooth germs are shown in Fig. 29, and the relationship of the enamel organ to developing odontoblasts can be understood. The process of calcification in deciduous teeth starts about the fourth month of foetal life in the incisors and by the sixth month calcification has started in the second deciduous molar. The process of calcification of the crown of the incisors is completed about two months after birth and all the crowns of the deciduous teeth have calcified by the first year after birth. There are twenty deciduous teeth in man, and they provide a functional dentition up to the age of seven. Most mammals have a deciduous dentition, but in some one or both dentitions are suppressed. In guinea-pigs and seals the deciduous dentition may partially erupt while the foetus is *in utero*, and one can occasionally find calcified crowns of the first dentition on the gum, in the amniotic fluid or in a newborn animal's stomach.

From an evolutionary aspect the deciduous and permanent dentitions represent the sole surviving generations of teeth from the multiple generations (the polyphyodont condition) of lower animals. A series of successive generations of teeth obviously fulfils two important functions; first that of replacement, and second that of possibly being able to add to the number of teeth as the animal grows older and larger. Theoretically a dominant, cold-blooded marine animal, such as a shark, could live for a very great length of time and its method of continually replacing teeth must be to its advantage. In man the deciduous dentition has well been called the 'foundation' dentition in that it is an initial series of functional pioneer teeth preparing for the next generation. Modern dentistry is increasingly aware of the importance of attending to the proper functioning (chewing) and arrangement (spacing) of the first dentition. All deciduous teeth are well advanced in development by the time of birth and have been exposed to the same environment as that affecting the developing embryo and foetus. The importance of the placenta in transmitting nutritional materials has been emphasized earlier (p. 153) and it is probable that if deficiencies or excesses of certain substances passed to the foetus can do damage to other developing organs, the teeth will not necessarily escape. Tooth germs are actively growing

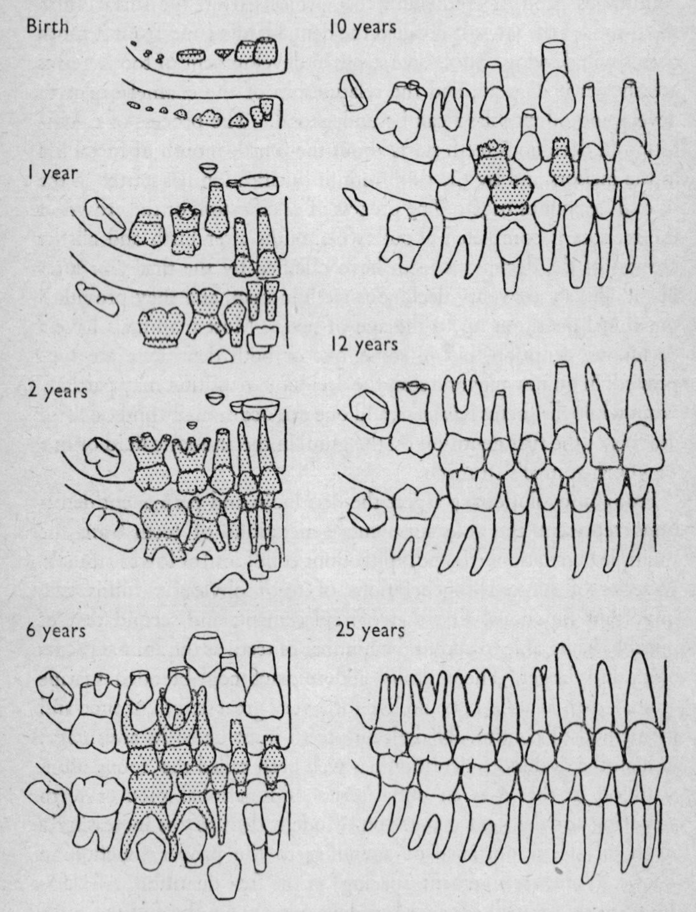

FIG. 29. Phases of human tooth eruption up to a complete secondary dentition. Teeth of the primary dentition are shown stippled.

cellular organs and would appear to be as susceptible to external influences as are developing eyes, ears, jaws and other organs.

Deciduous teeth display certain general differences from permanent teeth in that they are smaller, except for the molars, which are larger across the crown than the replacing permanent premolars. The crowns are all more bulbous, the neck is more constricted and the cusps more pointed on first eruption, as anyone can tell after being bitten by a two-year-old. The roots are shorter, yet the pulp cavities are relatively larger; root resorption commences some eighteen months before a tooth is shed. Deciduous teeth soon show evidence of attrition, which appears earlier and is relatively more pronounced than in the permanent teeth; an expression of the fact that the enamel is less hard.

In general the deciduous teeth of man are somewhat like those of the great apes. The chief differences are absence of a diastema between upper canine and lateral incisor, the smaller canines, and the details of the molar cusps. In fact in the ape deciduous dentition shows some characters of a primitive kind that have been lost in man. On the other hand, in man the order of eruption of deciduous teeth tends to follow that of Old World Monkeys with the canine erupting after the first molars and before the second. In apes the deciduous canine erupts last.

There is a difference in the order of eruption of human permanent teeth. In apes the second molars appear much earlier and interrupt replacement of the anterior deciduous teeth. In man the second molars appear *after* all deciduous teeth have been replaced. This specialized order of eruption in man is almost certainly associated with his longer, drawn-out period of childhood, during a good half of which the majority of the deciduous teeth remain functional. The delay in fusion of the ossification centres of the human skull until much later can be correlated with the later appearance of the second molar; it is said that the second molar does not start to erupt until certain ossification centres in the base of the skull have become firmly fused and that the third molar does not erupt until the whole bony base of the skull shows advanced fusion (the basi-occiput starts to fuse with the basisphenoid at seventeen).

Active eruption is defined as the actual movement of the tooth relative to the jaw, and the most important factor bringing it about is expansion of the pulp tissue at the base of the calcified crown. As the latter is pushed upwards the root starts to form downwards from its edges and the pulp tissue gradually becomes surrounded by dentine and cement. In front of the erupting tooth there is a loosening of the tissues until the residual epithelial covering of the enamel (Nasmyth's membrane) comes up into contact with the gum epithelium and fuses with it. Thus for the first appearance of the crown it has only to break through a bloodless epithelial layer and so eruption is not usually accompanied by bleeding. It is also thought that other factors may take part in eruption such as remodelling in the bone round the developing tooth, or active growth by the root itself, or even by opening up of tissue in front of the erupting tooth so that it is expelled rather in the way that a foreign body is expelled from tissue. However, eruption is an active process, with some force behind it, since if an erupting tooth hits the edge of another already erupted it will tilt on its axis and can cause pain.

Occlusion

The respective teeth of each opposing jaw usually erupt fairly close together in time so that, as they rise from the jaws, they come to bite against each other. When all deciduous, and later all permanent teeth have erupted and are in their final normal position, the jaws can be closed and held together in the resting position so that all the cusps, depressions, or fossae, and the cutting edges of the two dental arcades are brought into articulation. The way in which projecting cusps fit into the depressions on the teeth opposite is called the *occlusion pattern*, and there is a normal pattern for each dentition. In the more primitive human races the occlusion pattern usually develops with incisors biting together edge to edge. In modern races, particularly in the western hemisphere, the upper incisors occlude in front of the lower incisors, giving rise to an 'overbite'. In the cheek region the overbite decreases and the third molars occlude almost crown to crown with the upper third molar extending slightly over the back of the lower. The biting surfaces of the teeth, that is the plane of occlusion, are not always horizontal and in many people curves distinctly downwards in a convex sweep as seen from the lateral view (Fig. 1). The cause of this curvature is obscure; it has been ascribed to an adaptation to ensure a balanced articulation of the two jaws when eccentrically placed, or to the development of increased bone in the upper jaw in relation to biting stresses.

If teeth do not erupt normally, not necessarily at the wrong time, but in the wrong order or in the wrong place, varying types of malocclusion result. The orthodontist is concerned in correcting malocclusion by persuading teeth to move into correct occlusion by means of mechanical appliances. He does not undertake this purely for aesthetic reasons, but because malocclusion can sooner or later result in uneven biting, and later to changes in the temporo-mandibular joint which can be extremely painful and disabling. Why does malocclusion occur in the first place? Part of the answer is due to evolutionary forces that have set man up on his two legs. Man's jaws have receded, and although he has lost one incisor and two premolars from the generalized mammalian complement, it is as if he hadn't lost enough. Certain teeth are more liable to faulty eruption or overcrowding than others. The upper lateral incisors, the lower second premolars and the third molars are candidates for elimination. In the case of the first two it may be insufficient widening of the jaws at the age of six or seven which leads to faulty eruption. Most children of this age have a 'peeky' expression about the face; the brain has almost reached adult size and the brain-case is relatively large, but there are yet no reasonably well developed air-sinuses in the facial skeleton and the jaws seem small and inadequate to carry all the teeth that will shortly erupt. The arrival of the third molar occurs when the jaws are nearing the end of the stage of elongation, and in fact at the end of bone growth generally, and it is not surprising that about 15 per cent of the population show faulty eruption of the third molar. It is ironical to call them 'wisdom' teeth; *Homo sapientior* will be wiser not to have any – but then, of course, he will be having trouble with all his teeth, and not only those that summon the courage to erupt.

Caries

Modern man suffers an affliction that does not occur naturally in any other animal, except occasionally in horses, guinea-pigs, and monkeys in captivity – caries formation. This painful, unsightly, and exasperating condition does not occur in primitive races, nor is it frequent in hardy native populations. It may be said that animals do not live long enough to suffer caries, yet caries can occur in a child's deciduous dentition at the age of two to three. Anatomically there is little to offer as explanation apart from the remarks already made concerning overcrowding, malocclusion, and the fact that the arrangement of teeth in the jaw leaves numerous interstices and crevices for the accumulation of bacteria-ridden particles of food. It is not clear whether man would develop caries if his teeth were fewer and not so crowded, and the tongue and lips could sweep all round each tooth. Differences in hardness or composition of individual teeth and genetic factors also affect its incidence. The whole problem of caries formation is riddled with paradoxes. Even if carious teeth are encouraged by the type of food western man eats, even if the disease is entirely due to eating sweets between meals, what is it about the anatomy or structure of some individuals' teeth that enables them to break all the rules and keep a perfect dentition until death? The interprismatic substance cementing enamel prisms together may not have been properly keratinized, or may be more permeable to noxious substances. Some dietary failure or other insult during the early period of development may have weakened tooth hardiness. It is indeed a most fascinating problem and one which will probably only be solved by application of the methods of fundamental scientific research. Only too recently have such investigations been started.

Human Characteristics

It is possible to summarize the features of the adult jaws and the permanent teeth which are essentially human. The marked recession of the jaws, with the appearance of the flattened, more upright face, is associated with adoption of upright posture and with the setting of the enlarged brain-case in a better balanced position on the vertebral column. In its turn reduction of the jaws, and widening of the face, is associated with the rounded anterior part of the dental arcade and the shorter series of smaller teeth. It is as if the human jaws have been more elegantly constructed, not built on the strong, robust plan of the ape with its reinforcing simian shelf, but with all the features concerned with mastication far less marked. Thus the absence of ridges for attachment of masticatory muscles leaves the skull smooth and rounded.

The relatively small teeth, arranged in a parabolic curve in the lower jaw and an elliptical one in the upper, all show certain human refinements. The incisors are more chisel-edged and somewhat spade-like, but not so spatulate as those of the apes, and they stand almost vertically in the jaws, more so in the western European. The canines are reduced in length so that the tip of the crown hardly projects beyond the level of the incisors and pre-molars; nor are the canines in the male larger than in the female. The premolars in the upper jaw have one, or sometimes two roots; those in the lower are most frequently only single-rooted. All the premolars are remarkably alike and it is often difficult to identify them exactly. They possess two cusps, an inner lingual and an outer buccal, which in the lower first premolar are connected by a ridge. This is a primitive characteristic found in fossil apes. The three molars in man are not aligned in parallel rows on each side of the two jaws as in apes, the last molars are further apart than the first, and the last molars are also smaller than the anterior two. There are considerable differences in detail of the shape of the upper and lower molars, but, in general, the crowns are rhomboidal or cuboidal in shape, and the cusp arrangement (four on each upper and an additional fifth on each lower) shows modification of a fairly primitive pattern.

Evolution of Cusp Pattern

Numerous attempts have been made to explain the evolution of the cusp patterns of mammals, the best known being those associated with the names of E. D. Cope and H. F. Osborn – the so-called tritubercular theory – and with the Dutch anatomist L. Bolk – the Dimer theory. These theories have been used to suggest that mammalian molar teeth have a composite origin and that the cusps represent subdivisions of original fused components. They are ingenious exercises in morphology but they tend to disregard morphogenetic processes and have little sound embryological or palaeontological evidence. Until a satisfactory explanation is found of all the forces determining evolution of the numerous varieties of tooth form, these morphological theories will still have to be considered. Such theories will eventually become memorials to generations of anatomists who limited their observations to the final morphological form and did not examine genetic and environmental factors that influence the development of shape.

At least such theories show how little we know of factors determining and causing evolution of form. Examination of teeth can suggest much about the general anatomy of an animal, although it is perhaps being a little enthusiastic to reconstruct the whole animal from a few teeth; it can tell us much about its diet and habits, not how evolution is brought about. Despite the fact that dental relics span some 300 million years of time, and that adult teeth are accumulating at a formidable rate in numberless animal and human graveyards, it is at the other end of their life-span that our knowledge is so deficient.

FOR FURTHER READING

Introduction to Dental Anatomy. J. H. Scott and N. B. B. Symons. E. and S. Livingstone, 1952

Special or Dental Anatomy and Physiology and Dental Histology. T. W. Widdowson. Staples Press Ltd, 1946

The Aetiology of Irregularity and Malocclusion of the Teeth. J. C. Brash, H. T. R. McKeag, and J. H. Scott. Dental Board of the United Kingdom, 1956

CHAPTER 16

HIS LONG LIFE

'How old are you?' Edred asked . . . . .
' 'S old as my tongue an' a little older'n me teeth,' said the mole showing them.

E. NESBIT

MAN is the longest lived of all mammals, and yet he cannot resist the deteriorative process of senescence that eventually prevents him from withstanding the pressure of his environment. Comfort (1956) has defined senescence as an increasing likelihood of death with increasing age, and considers that it is not an 'inherent' property of multicellular animals, 'but one which they have on several occasions acquired as a potentiality, probably through the operation of evolutionary forces directed to other biological ends'.

The concept of death, the realization that his parents will grow old and die, is frightening to a young human child. This very realization is probably part of the child's own maturation. Ageing means deterioration, a deterioration that includes a variety of observable changes, and many that cannot yet be observed. They will eventually cause death with or without supervention of a truly pathological disease. It is not surprising that Medicine, having made such advances in cure and prevention of disease, is now examining with increasing vigour what is meant by senescence, what are its causes, and whether increased longevity is possible.

Longevity in Man and Animals

The greatest age reached by a man, reasonably authenticated (I. Fisher, 1923), is 120 years. The story is also told of Christen Jacobsen Drakenburg (*b.* 18 November 1626 – *d.* 9 October 1772) who lived under seven Danish kings during the 146 years of his life. After many adventures at sea and fifteen years in slavery at Tripoli he is said to have lived 'quite a respectable life after the age of 141'. In England an individual possessed a birth certificate showing him to be 109 years old, and another, by not having a birth certificate, was shown to be over 111 years old (Comfort, 1956). Certain geographical areas lay claim to having large numbers of old men; Bulgaria, the Caucasus, Russia (Abkhasia and Daghestan) being examples. These claims have not withstood critical investigation, and probably could not without special documentary evidence.

Man is almost certainly the longest lived mammal, living longer than the huge elephant and the smallest shrew, and probably longer, on the average, than the notoriously long-lived perch and carp. Authenticated maximum longevity records are dangerous figures to use as evidence of the distribution of ageing in animals. Francis Bacon remarked over 300 years ago: 'concerning the length and brevity of life in beasts, the knowledge which may be had is slender, the observation negligent, and tradition fabulous; in household beasts the idle life corrupts; in wild, the violence of the climate cuts them off'. Comfort (1956) discusses at length the difficulties of assessing longevity records, but at least in man they provide an indication of how long the hardier can survive given freedom from accident or attack by disease. A brief list of maximum longevity records for some common and domestic animals is given in Table XII, and Table XIII is a list of the average ages at death of the eminent in various fields of activity.

TABLE XII

MAXIMUM LONGEVITIES IN SOME ANIMALS

	Years		*Years*
Snail (*Helix*)	6–7	Rat (*Rattus*)	4–5
Ant (*Formica*)	7–15	Rabbit (*Oryctolagus*)	10–15
Queen Bee (*Apis*)	5	Dog (*Canis*)	15–18
Lobster (*Homarus*)	50	Cat (*Felis*)	20–30
Carp (*Cyprinus*)	40 +	Seal (*Phoca*)	15–20
Frog (*Rana*)	12 +	Blue Whale (*Sibbaldus*)	12–14
Tortoise (*Testudo*)	152 +	Pig (*Sus*)	12–20
Eagle Owl (*Bubo*)	68	Elephant (*Elephas*)	60–70
Goose (*Anser*)	35 +	Horse (*Equus*)	40 +
Pigeon (*Columba*)	30 +	Baboon (*Papio*)	27 +
Shrew (*Blarina*)	1½	Chimpanzee (*Pan*)	39
Bat (*Rhinolophus*)	7 +	Man (*Homo*)	109 (England)

Comfort, 1956

TABLE XIII

AVERAGE AGE AT DEATH OF THE EMINENT IN VARIOUS FIELDS OF ACTIVITY

Field of Activity	*Average Age at Death. Years*
Members of the President's Cabinet in the U.S.A.	71·39
Entomologists	70·99
Inventors	70·96
Historians	70·60
American College and University Presidents	70·11
Geologists	69·79
Chemists	69·24
Educational theorists	69·06
Educators, all kinds	68·98
Economists and political scientists	68·68
Contributors to medicine and public hygiene	68·57
Botanists	68·36
Philosophers	68·22
Historical novelists	67·89
State Governors (U.S.A.)	67·02
Authors of words to church hymn tunes	66·94
Mathematicians	66·62
Composers of grand opera	66·59
Composers of choral music	66·51
Composers of chamber music	66·26
Naval and military commanders (born from 1666 to 1839)	66·14
Authors of political poetry	64·47
Painters in oil	64·22
British authors and poets	63·91
Hereditary European sovereigns	49·14

Source: H. C. Lehman, 'The Longevity of the Eminent,' *Science*, vol. 98, p. 270, September 24, 1943.

PHASES OF GROWTH AND AGEING

A number of attempts have been made to divide man's life span into a succession of neatly compact growth phases. Each of these attempts has tried to analyse the successive phases by considering the changes in one or more tissues or structures in the body, usually the skeleton.

Unfortunately, not all such changes proceed simultaneously or at a similar rate, and they cannot be easily correlated. There is also variation due to the effects of the genetic constitution, due to hormones controlling growth and other processes, and due to nutritional and other environmental factors. Yet it is possible to make some general statements, related in the first place to the usual terms of everyday language; later these statements can be considered in more detail.

Our age is commonly estimated from the date of our birth, although it is said that the ancient Chinese added another year to allow for prenatal life. The first fourteen or so years cover *childhood* and lead to *puberty*, which does not occur on any particular day or week but develops over several years. The word puberty refers to the appearance of hair on the pubes – an area of skin over the pubic bones and just above the genital organs. There is an accumulation of fat beneath the skin of this region, which becomes more marked at puberty, and causes an elevation called the *mons Veneris* in the female and the *mons Jovis* in the male. It has been pointed out that the word puberty is not a good one, because hair is found normally, and often quite plentifully, in the pubic regions of young children. There is, however, frequently a change in its character at puberty, particularly in the male; the word is too much part of our language to alter now. Puberty is marked by numerous anatomical and behavioural changes, mostly related to the increased activity of the gonads.

The reproductive phenomena associated with puberty are described in Chapter 5. They are accompanied by marked enlargement of the ovaries, uterus, and mammary glands in girls, and in the testes and prostate in boys. The gonads have been slowly increasing in size some years before puberty, but the active growth of gland tissue in the female and in the prostate is particularly dramatic. Increase in growth occurs in the endocrine organs, but the thymus begins to retrogress.

In general the growth of boys and girls is equal until the 9th to 10th year when girls outstrip boys and exceed their height until the age of 14. Boys grow rapidly during their 12th and 13th years and re-establish equality by 14, after which boys steadily outstrip girls. By this age girls frequently show certain adult feminine features such as broadening of the hips, relative shortness of legs, and enlargement of the breasts. The most striking change at puberty is in the larynx of the male. The organ enlarges in both sexes under the influence of endocrine activity, but more in boys. In one year it doubles its size in the male and develops an angular form that is the basis of the Adam's apple. The vocal cords are increased in length, and, together with the other changes in size and shape, bring about the 'breaking' of a boy's voice. The larynx in girls only enlarges by a third at puberty, and retains its smooth form.

Apart from the fusion of the bony elements in the hip-bone, the ischium, ilium, and pubis, few ossificatory changes occur during puberty.

They occur rapidly, however, during the period of *adolescence* that lasts until about 18 to 20 in girls and until 20 to 23, or later, in boys. At the end of this period of consolidation of the skeleton both sexes will have reached adult height. Girls add only some two inches to their stature during adolescence, but boys increase in height by four to five inches. Changes occur in the hair, the beard and moustache appear in the male, but full efflorescence of beard and body hair is not exhibited until *early adult life*. During this period bone growth finally ceases and is marked by the skull, vertebral column, hip-bones, and clavicles reaching their final form. The young man of 25 to 27 is noticeably broader across the shoulders than the 'stripling' of 18 to 20 owing to growth of the clavicles.

It could be said that after becoming adult nature attempts, in various ways, to maintain the individual in the fullest effective condition, both anatomically and functionally. It is now, however, that the first apparent signs of ageing processes are seen; they exert their effects on nearly all the systems of the body, but not at an equivalent rate or to a similar degree. Some age changes affect certain systems more precisely and more dangerously than others. For as long as an individual can withstand the ravages of these various ageing processes, so long can he expect to live. In the majority of individuals nature can maintain the *status quo* for many years, and although the ageing processes are going on, they do not make their presence felt or apparent for some time. It is possible, of course, to assess ageing by investigating the various tissues, fluids, or organs in the body of individuals of different ages, or it is equally possible to assess the effects of ageing on the body as a whole. One can also examine the problem from a statistical point of view, that is to say, one can assess the expectation of life of any individual at a particular age, and attempt to investigate the influence of various factors known or suspected to affect senescence. We shall now select some of these aspects of ageing and comment briefly on them.

Age Changes in the Skeleton

The most reliable way of assessing the age of an individual from an anatomical point of view is by examination of the skeleton and the teeth. No other part of the body, however carefully examined, can give as much information. It will be seen later that the younger a person is, the easier it is to assess age accurately from the bones. Other tissues and organs in the body certainly show the effects of ageing, but not as constantly, from the point of view of the time of their appearance, as do those in bones. Let us suppose, therefore, that we are presented with a problem of deciding the age of an individual, and that there are available the particular bones that we shall need. It is not necessary always to have the dried bones; much useful information may be obtained from examination with X-rays. On occasions anatomists have been asked to confirm, if they can, the alleged ages of living refugees or children feared to be changelings. Radiological examination is then the only means of ageing the skeleton.

We should first wish to know if there were any major periods of time in the development and ageing of the skeleton into which we could place the unknown material with some confidence. The American anthropologist W. M. Krogman has shown that there are seven stages of major skeletal change during a man's life. Unfortunately they do not exactly follow the seven ages of man described by Shakespeare in *As You Like It*, mainly because they are more accurately delineated during the early period of life.

Krogman's *Period I* in the life history of the human skeleton extends from birth to the age of 5. Earlier, that is before birth, ossification had begun in many bones. The process starts at about eight weeks after fertilization at *centres of ossification* in each bone. It takes place in two main ways; one type is called *intra-membranous* and the other *intra-cartilaginous* ossification. Intra-membranous ossification is found mainly in the bones that are to form the vault of the

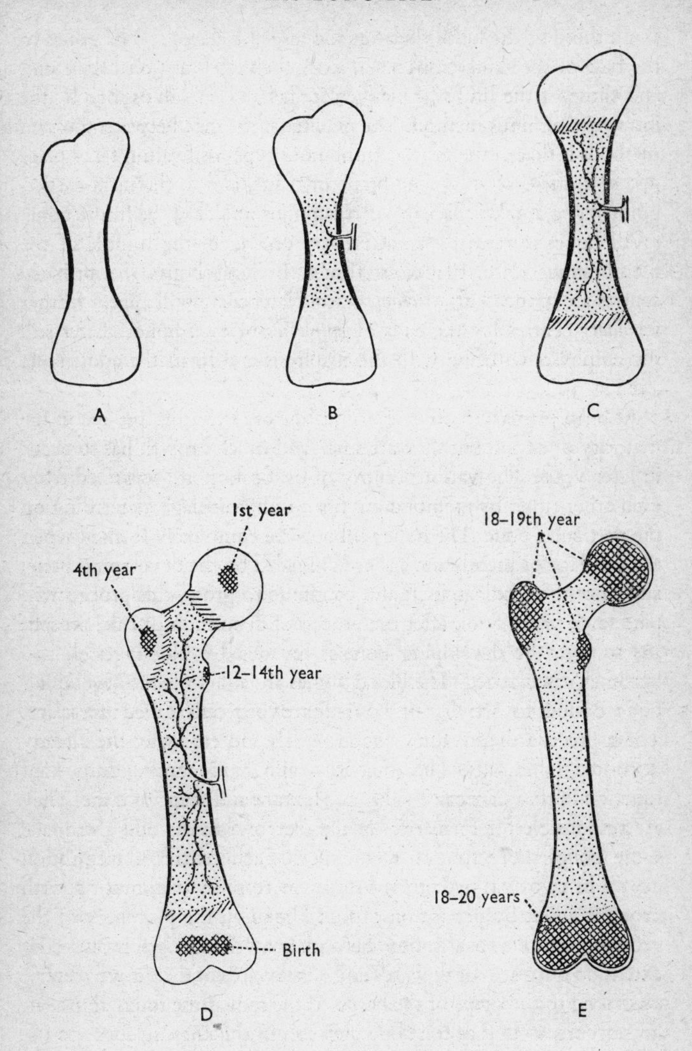

FIG. 30. Stages in bone growth: A: 7th week of intra-uterine life; B: 4th month of intra-uterine life; C: at birth; D: time of appearance of secondary (epiphysial) centres; E: times of fusion of epiphyses with shaft.

skull, those of the facial skeleton and also the clavicle. The bones of the base of the skull (basi-cranial axis), the vertebrae (axial skeleton), and those of the limbs (appendicular skeleton) are all ossified by the intra-cartilaginous method. The essential difference between the two methods is that in the intra-membranous type ossification takes place in a soft, mesenchymal membrane or tissue, and in the intra-cartilaginous type, it takes place in a cartilaginous model of the future bone.

All bones start to ossify at *primary* centres in the middle of the membranous or cartilaginous tissues. In long bones the primary centres are in the shafts or *diaphyses* and later there will appear further *secondary* centres for the ends or *epiphyses* of each bone. Later still the epiphyses will fuse with the diaphysis and form the adult bone (see Fig. 30).

At birth primary centres of ossification are therefore present in the majority of bones, but they are small and much growth has to occur in later years. The various centres of ossification are separated from each other either by membranous tissue or by cartilage, depending on the particular bone. The bone will only be completely formed when the cartilage or membrane has been invaded by the developing bone, and since the cartilage itself also continues to grow, this process will take some years. Soon after the process of deposition of calcium salts has started, the developing bone is invaded by blood vessels and becomes vascularized. The blood vessels are able to enter developing bone owing to activity of bone-destroying cells called *osteoclasts*. These precede the invading blood vessels and eat away the already deposited bone salts. The osteoclasts also have another important function in that they can modify the texture and shape of bone. They are responsible for formation of the marrow cavity, and also make some bones more spongy than others. Each centre of ossification grows in two ways; there is first an increase in thickness or girth brought about by deposition of more bone on the periphery of the growing centre of ossification. Second, growth in length is caused by extension outwards or upwards and downwards of the growth centre, according to the shape of the bone. At the same time internal modelling occurs, so that as the bone increases in thickness it does not become a solid rod with only a small central cavity. The osteoclasts are at work removing the bone lining from the marrow cavity so that the latter increases in size as the bone increases in thickness.

During the five years of Period I the remainder (except one) of the primary centres of ossification, and also the majority of the *secondary* centres appear. As might be expected, the actual time of appearance of each centre varies; the variation depends on such factors as sex and nutrition. In general, centres of ossification appear earlier in females; possibly this is partly genetically determined, but may also be due to action of female sex hormones. The centres appear earlier in individuals who receive better nutrition. The centres can be discerned radiologically when they have grown to a moderate size, and Plate XXIV shows the appearances in the upper shoulder region of a child aged three years. For some time a plate of cartilage remains between each epiphysis and diaphysis. This can be seen on an X-ray film as a narrow, dark line. It is called the epiphyseal plate, and as long as it is present the bone can continue to grow in length.

One additional primary centre and a few secondary ones appear during Krogman's *Period II*, which extends from the age of 5 to the age of 12, but the main changes are in alterations and growth in the ossificatory centres that appeared either before birth or in Period I. The last primary centre to appear is that for a little bone in the wrist called the pisiform.

The *third period* lasts from the age of 12 until that of 20, and extends from puberty until late in adolescence. During the first few years there is continuation of growth and change in size of the main and secondary ossification centres; towards the end of the period a new and important series of events takes place. This involves disappearance of the epiphyseal plates and fusion or coalescence of the primary and secondary ossification centres. This event results in the completion of the process of growth in length and thickness. The increase in thickness of the bone is brought about by the activity of cells in a layer immediately underneath the fibrous boundary of the bone, the periosteum. The osteogenic potentiality of this layer, however, is never completely lost, for if the bone is fractured even after the end of this *Period III*, the sub-periosteal tissue can lay down new bone to repair the fracture. Some generalizations can be made about the process of union between epiphysis and diaphysis. It occurs earlier in girls, and thus girls reach their adult height at an earlier age than boys. Those epiphyses that were the first to appear are the last to fuse with the diaphysis; this means that in a number of bones one end goes on growing after the other end has stopped, if only for a period of some months. Just as there were various factors affecting the time of appearance of any ossification centre, so there are also similar and other factors affecting the time of fusion. Not only do such characters as sex and nutrition affect time of union, but also deficiency of certain vitamins (D), and lack of certain hormones from pituitary and parathyroid.

The *fourth period* of bone growth is a short one and lasts only from the age of 20 to 24, and is really a continuation of the third period, but it is separated for specific reasons. By the age of 20 union of most of the epiphyses of the body has occurred, but one or two interesting ones have not yet finally fused. These are in the clavicle, the base of the skull, the pelvis, and the vertebral column. A secondary centre of ossification, very variable in its appearance, is present on the inner or medial end of the clavicle. It usually appears about the 21st year of age and closes a year or two later; but it can appear as early as 16 and fuse as late as the age of 28. It is the activity of this centre on the inner end of the clavicle that broadens the shoulders of a young man after the age of 18. Bony replacement of cartilage in the base of the skull starts about the 17th year of age in both sexes, and is completed by about the 22nd year in girls and the 24th year or later in boys. It is usually said that ossification of the base of the skull is not completed until the third molar tooth (wisdom tooth) has erupted. This is not quite true, but at least it helps to indicate that the base of the skull is one of the last parts of the skeleton to complete ossification; in fact bony changes continue in the skull until quite late in life. In the pelvis there is a marked burst of growth in the region of the pubic symphysis. This is responsible for bringing about enlargement of the bony configuration of the pelvis that is particularly marked in the female. In man the epiphyses of the vertebral bodies take the form of a series of flattened rings covering the upper and lower surface of each body. These ring-like epiphyses become linked with the body of the vertebra at the age of 25. Thus the vertebral column goes on growing much longer than the limbs.

Thus it can be said that by the end of Krogman's *Period IV* of bone growth, all the bones of the skeleton have reached their adult size and shape, and other characteristics. In all the cartilage bones the cartilage will have been replaced by bone, except at the articulating surfaces, and in membrane bones the only fibrous tissue not impregnated with calcium salts is that lying between the individual bones in the regions called *sutures*. The encapsulated joints between cartilage bones are known as *synovial* joints, except in certain specific places; whereas membrane bones articulate rather like the pieces of a bony jig-saw held together by fibrous tissue. In membrane bones the surfaces that fit together are usually serrated or have a toothed edge, and thus we talk about a dentate suture.

It is at the site of the sutures of the skull that the main changes take place during *Period V*, which is considered to extend from the age of 24 to about that of 36. At the beginning of this period the main sutures of the vault of the skull start to close on their inner aspect; bone invades the fibrous tissue across the suture line until eventually it is completely obliterated. Suture closure proceeds vigorously for the next five to six years, and the two parietal bones are often fused in the region of the sagittal suture by the age of 30. There is even greater variation in time of closure of various sutures than in other ossificatory events. Hardly any two skulls show similar characteristics in timing or order of closure of sutures, and occasionally one side of the skull may show a more advanced degree of sutural closure than the other; the reasons for these differences are obscure. It now becomes progressively more difficult to decide the precise age of a particular bone; although there are changes in the texture of bones and even in their feel (for example, the surface of the skull tends to become more granular in its surface texture than the smooth ivory texture of the young adolescent).

The *sixth period* shows further progress in fusion of cranial sutures. It extends from about the age of 36 to that of 50, and can be considered to mark the early part of middle-age. It is towards the end of this period that a new type of change makes its appearance in bones. It must be considered degenerative or even pathological in nature, and it starts to make its presence felt in the synovial joints. Certain changes occur on the articular surfaces of many bones and include lipping or extension of excess bone over the edge of the articular surface. Lipping may result in limitation of movement at the joint during life; there is also loss of cartilage on the articular surface, and thus a narrowing of the distance separating the bony elements. Areas of rarefication of bone can be seen by X-ray examination, particularly near the articular surfaces: these areas result from localized withdrawal of calcium salts. The original process of ossification involved deposition in various ways of lime salts (mainly calcium phosphate) on the organic fibrous matrix already present by cells called osteoblasts. The organic component of bone plays an important part in giving to it certain of its characteristics; a dried adult bone contains some 25–30 per cent of organic materials. A living bone is not only a hard structure, but is also tough and elastic, owing to presence of the organic component. Combination of organic part and inorganic salts makes bone unique in that its resistance to compression and extension is nearly equal. As an individual ages his bones become increasingly brittle and liable to fracture because of loss of elasticity of the diminishing organic components; later calcium withdrawal occurs (*halisteresis*). This has been called an expression of the failure of adequate nutrition that supervenes as a mark of infirmity in the aged skeleton. It is even more difficult to assess the age of a particular bone during the final *Period VII*, that extends from the age of 50 to the time of death. One particular skeleton just looks older than another. Sutural closure continues at a varying rate; there are more marked joint changes and the rarefication of bone becomes more pronounced. The deposition of calcium salts appears in some places where it is not normally found, such as in the cartilages of the larynx. All the bones become more brittle, the breast-bone, or sternum, becomes less pliable, and calcification also takes place in the cartilages at the anterior extremity of the ribs.

Whatever the influences which determine 'the formal pattern of bone architecture the pattern itself is an age character developing in childhood and youth, maintained during mature life and lost as age advances or infirmity intervenes' (W. M. Cobb, 1952).

Age Changes in Soft Tissues

All tissues and organs can display deteriorative or senescent changes, and although many of them are well known and have become incorporated into colloquial language, few are well understood. Sooner or later we observe a grey hair on our heads, usually first on the temple. This region got its name from the way greying of temporal hair indicates ravages of time. Hair goes grey as the result of an imperfection that develops in the enzyme system (tyrosine-tyrosinase) in melanocytes. For some reason melanocytes are eventually destroyed and hairs acquire a yellowish-white appearance because of the air they contain. The onset of greyness is uneven in distribution on the scalp and varies considerably in the age at which it occurs. It is also curious that hair of axilla and pubes shows far less or even no greying even when scalp hair and that of the moustache is quite white. It is often maintained that scalp hair thickens as age advances, but careful measurement shows that the diameter of a hair shaft does not increase after the age of 15. Baldness is often associated with advancing age, but there are so many types of baldness (alopecia) and so many factors influencing it that no clear relationship can be expected.

Changes also occur in skin, the main one being a loss of elasticity so that it becomes loose and wrinkled. Attempts have been made to assess ageing by estimation of the degree of loss of elasticity, but it is too variable to be correlated with any general senescent mechanisms. Skin creases become more marked and new ones appear as age increases, partly because of loss of elasticity and partly because of continual creasing in a particular region. Furrows develop on the forehead, at the outer angle of the eye (crow's feet) and round the mouth. They also increase in number and depth on the neck, and in women who have children characteristic striae are present on abdominal skin. Creases become so marked, particularly on the face, that at the line of a crease the epidermis becomes tightly attached to firm underlying connective tissue and the crease becomes permanent. The skin appears drier, more parchment-like, and wizened in old age. These changes used to be ascribed to the general dehydration that was said to occur in ageing cells, but recent work suggests that there is an increase in cellular and extracellular fluid in senile tissues. It has been maintained, but not proved, that there is a gradual decline in activity of sebaceous and sweat glands as age advances, but it cannot definitely be correlated with loss of reproductive power. Lack of 'oily' material secreted onto skin by these glands could be responsible for a change in texture and even for alteration in colour. Skin often appears thinner in the aged, because of lack of elasticity, difference in texture, and possibly of a slowing rate of replacement.

Decline in reproductive capacity due to senescence of gonads has been considered a criterion of incipient ageing since time immemorial. It is also one of considerable biological and evolutionary importance. It manifests itself first in a fall of litter size in those mammals that are polytocous, but in the human female there is the complete and relatively sudden onset of the menopause (p. 102) followed by a long post-reproductive period. It has been frequently suggested, and there is a little evidence for it, that the ovary ceases to function since it runs out of oocytes. Recent evidence suggests that the menopause precedes final follicular exhaustion, and that it is due to failure of ovarian response to pituitary hormones that immediately precipitates the menopause. There is ample evidence to show that there is no fall in output of pituitary gonadotrophin at the time of or even after the menopause, and thus it is the ovary that should probably be examined for ageing changes. Ovaries of elderly women are often surprisingly deficient in glandular elements of granulosa and theca families; perhaps it is these cells that succumb to senescence.

Neither removal of gonads, nor the time at which the menopause occurs, have, however, any definite effect on expectation of life. Cessation of activity of gonads is not, therefore, a cause of senescence. If after cessation of ovarian activity substitution is obtained by grafting, or by injection of ovarian hormones, changes occur that are as near to a 'rejuvenation' as any other known substance can produce. There is, however, no increase in longevity, and the main response is re-appearance of changes in certain organs, skin, and vaginal epithelium, that had accompanied normal reproductive activity.

What evidence there is suggests that there are no striking changes in the blood as people grow older, but disease of arteries kills more adults in our society than any other. The changes in arteries occur mainly in the middle (tunica media) of three tunics that compose a vessel wall, though the inner lining (tunica intima) may also be involved. The dangerous trio of atherosclerosis, arteriosclerosis and medial calcification, their relation to increased blood pressure and to the kidneys is discussed in Dr Clark Kennedy's Pelican volume, *Human Disease*. Study of vascular degeneration brings clearly into relief the problem of dissociating senescent mechanisms from truly pathological processes of disease. There are diseases of heart and vessels that often begin in early life and are still present in old age, there are diseases of the vascular system that are predominently found in the elderly, and there is the process of senescence as it involves the system simply as tissue ageing. It is on this third aspect that we have so little information. So frequently is a vascular catastrophe the end of life in the species that man cannot but wonder if there is any inherent weakness in the system. It seems that, just as his skin reflects his temperament (p. 242), so is Man's vascular system the slave of his mood, but that with age the ability of vessels to wax and wane in calibre is lost owing to degeneration. We also know that the heart and great vessels have a blood supply of their own. The heart has its coronary system, the great vessels have *vasa vasorum* in their walls; thus their efficiency is at the mercy of their own vascularity.

Senescent changes in the nervous system are as difficult to dissociate from those of disease as in the vascular system. It is known that significant alteration, or loss, of neurones is the most frequently observed age change. There are also characteristic changes in the intercellular matrix and the glia. Certain neuroblasts degenerate after only a short life during apparently normal and orderly differentiation. Some neuronal loss therefore appears to be part of the general design; there may be a genetic weakness in that loss is not held in abeyance until old age and may result in early dementia. In other individuals the brain functions clearly and lucidly long after the skeleton shows advanced changes. Genetic, vascular, metabolic, and toxic factors may all logically be assumed to play their role in cerebral ageing.

It is natural that the pituitary should be the gland chosen to 'explain' the onset of senescent changes, not only because of its homeostatic control of several other endocrine organs, but also because of its mediation of the onset of puberty. It is the latter that in many ways marks the turn of the tide; if puberty could be postponed indefinitely would the expected life-span be infinite? Several workers have been tempted to suggest that decline in production of the growth hormone from the anterior pituitary is involved in senescence.

An interesting paradox appears to exist; animals injected with anterior pituitary hormones late on in their normal life-span showed enlargement of certain organs as opposed to the expected decrease in size with age. Yet none of the animals so treated lived significantly longer and injection of pituitary hormones did not apparently inhibit or reverse fundamental ageing processes in cells. On the other hand the expected life-span can be significantly lengthened in animals if hormone injections are given early in life to retard onset of puberty.

Age Changes in Cells

Increasing attention has been paid in recent years to the question whether there are any detectable age changes in individual cells. It is necessary to consider if there are any fundamental differences in the life histories of various types of cell, and it is clear on only a superficial consideration that there are.

Certain types of cell are undergoing active division throughout their owner's existence. These are cells of the basal layer of the epidermis (see p. 230), precursors of blood cells and germ cells of the testis (see p. 115). Such a cell exists between one cell division (mitosis) and the next; they can be called '*inter-mitotics*'. Their existence is so short that hardly any evidence of ageing changes has been demonstrated in them. Inter-mitotic cells are precursors of the second great group; each cell of this type is formed as the result of division and steadily differentiates into a more specialized cell. Spermatogonia, for example, give rise to spermatocytes, basal cells of skin produce prickle cells that differentiate into keratin containing cells of the stratum corneum, and red cell precursors (megaloblasts) gradually acquire more of the respiratory pigment, haemoglobin, as they mature into definitive red cells (erythrocytes). Cells that arise from inter-mitotics can be called *differentiating mitotics;* their life-span is effectively limited.

A third type is known as *reverting post-mitotics*. These develop as the result of a series of divisions in the embryo and in childhood until they form an adult organ such as the liver. Their usual fate is to show age changes and eventually die; in the event of injury, however, and even in relatively aged animals, they 'revert' in that they can each undergo a new series of divisions giving rise to primitive cells that differentiate into functional cells of similar type.

The fourth group, the *fixed post-mitotics*, do not possess the attribute of reversion and rejuvenescence; they are highly differentiated when finally defined and are incapable of further division. Examples of this group of cells are the adult red cells of the blood, voluntary muscle cells and neurones.

One interesting suggestion emerges from such a classification, and that is that a cell that undergoes or has the potential to undergo division does not, at any rate for some long time, show such marked changes of senescence as others not so endowed. Cell division, therefore, seems to have a rejuvenating effect, and it has been suggested that it is the capability of certain cells to synthesize such substances as deoxyribonucleic acid in more than adequate amounts that endows cells with ability to divide.

There are certain changes that occur in many types of cells that appear to indicate senescence. They involve fragmentation, vesiculation or reduction in number of the mitochondria, accumulation within the cell of phospholipids, particularly in neurones, and fragmentation of the Golgi apparatus. Changes in nuclei also occur, involving extensions as vesicles of nuclear contents into the cytoplasm, and changes in their staining reaction until they become condensed and densely stained (pyknosis). There is an increase in calcium content of many tissues as they age, but it is not clear exactly where the extra calcium is situated. An increase in iron has been found, not due to the normal breakdown of red cells and liberation of the iron containing pigment haemoglobin. Ageing cells also accumulate certain pigments, but little is known about them and they are known rather loosely as 'senility pigments'; one, at least, is yellow, is called ceroid, and is found in walls of degenerating arteries.

The part played by enzyme systems in the ageing of cells is still obscure, although there is some evidence that as cells age the hydrolytic enzymes they contain increase rather than decrease in absolute quantity. It may be that there is some diversion of enzyme systems in ageing cells to perform functions not equally necessary in younger ones. Recently an intriguing suggestion has been made that cells may contain small bodies known as 'lysosomes' that have a number of hydrolytic enzymes within them. If activity of these enzymes were not restricted or inhibited they could rapidly destroy the cell; it is postulated that this is what happens when a cell dies and undergoes autolysis. This leaves us with the possibility that each cell holds its fate at bay by ability to restrict or inhibit the suicidal tendencies of the lysosomes. It has been suggested that it is activity of the lysosomes that is responsible for the steady decrease in the number of neurones in the ageing brain.

There have been suggestions that an insufficient supply of vitamins may play a part in initiating or speeding up age changes. Vitamin C deficiency in particular has been shown to be involved in some way in cellular ageing changes. It is unlikely, however, that diet alone could make man live for a period of time that might be a multiple of his three-score years and ten. There is some evidence, though not fully evaluated, that excesses of certain quite simple food substances, such as amino acids, fats, and carbohydrates reduce expectation of life in an animal and perhaps in man.

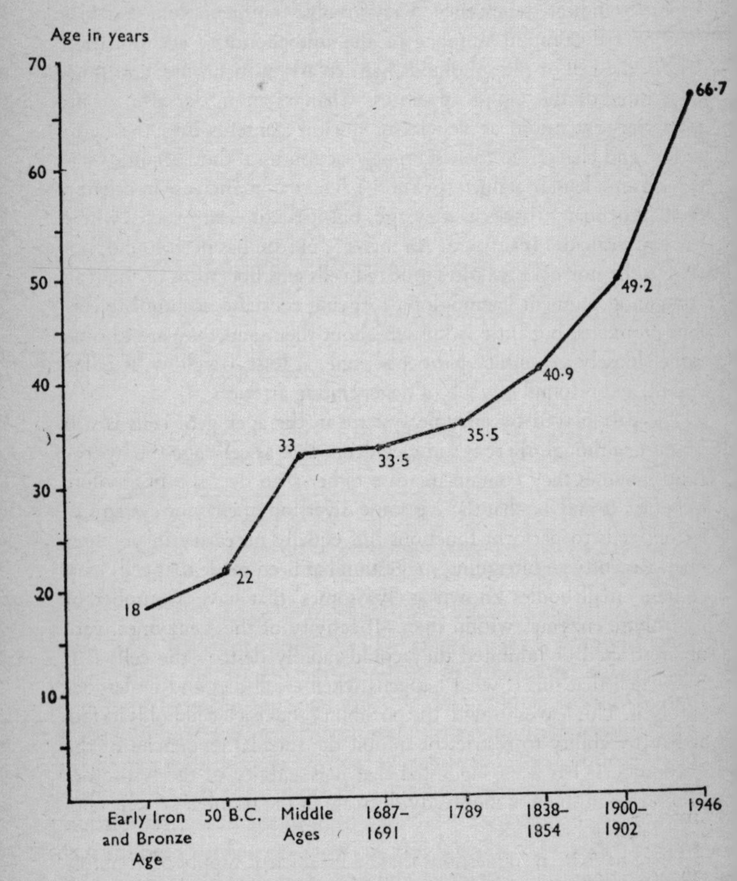

FIG. 31. Average length of life from Ancient to Modern times (from Dublin, Lotka and Spiegelman, 1949. Ronald Press Co., New York).

His Expectation of Life

Estimation of man's expectation of life from life tables is of the greatest value to the actuary, to those who 'insure' against dying too soon (life assurance) and to those who 'insure' against living too long (endowment assurance). We have already given one definition of senescence in that it implies an increasing liability to succumb to the external environment. That the risks and chances of succumbing to disease could be quantitatively expressed was first demonstrated by

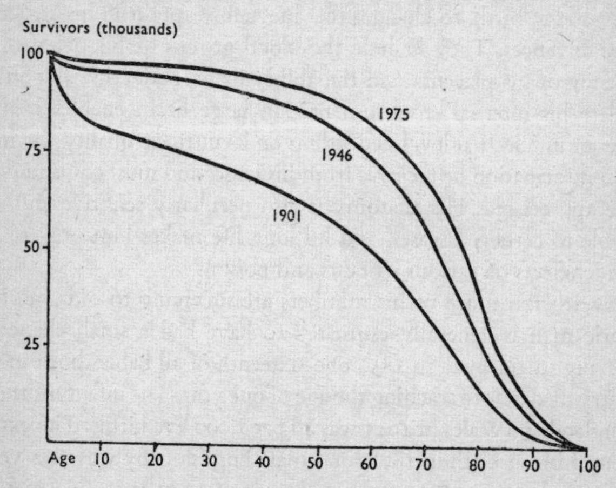

FIG. 32. Giraphs to show the number of survivors out of 100,000 male live brths (white) in the U.S.A. in 1901, 1946, and as estimated for 1975.

John Graunt and later by Sir William Petty (1623–87). The latter realized the importance of studies of the population, incidence of various diseases, fertility and mortality rates, and he urged creation of a government institution for collecting such statistics. Statistical study of populations, called *demography*, received much stimulus from the work of a Prussian clergyman J. P. Süssmilch (1707–82). He really intended to demonstrate a Divine design in the numerical relationships of vital statistics, but at least his work stressed the need for such investigations, and that large numbers must be examined. In 1801 there was introduced the census system in England, and it distinctly improved the value of such calculations. The subsequent work of Quetelet, Galton, and Karl Pearson showed how physical and intellectual characteristics of any man could be numerically compared to those of the 'average man' by application of probability theory.

It may be wondered how anatomical characteristics of man may be concerned with demography. Yet in one way or another the peculiarities or generalities of his structure outlined in each chapter are involved in providing vital statistics. Biological factors influencing mortality and longevity range from risks to embryo, foetus, and child before and at birth, to changes that inevitably appear in his structure as age advances. They include the blood groups of his parents, the efficiency of his placenta and the ability of his endocrine systems to regulate his internal environment. His large brain enables him to attain an intellectual level depending on its intrinsic quality; he must act on information he receives from his senses and must communicate to be appreciated. His anatomy is also peculiarly sensitive and susceptible to certain diseases, and his long life makes him prey to the chronic effects of various irritants and poisons.

Nevertheless more of his numbers are surviving to old age. Prehistoric man is generally estimated to have had a small chance of surviving to 40. Even in 1850 one-sixteenth of all babies born in this country died before reaching the age of one year. The infant mortality in England and Wales in 1945 was 46 per 1,000 live births. The expectation of life at birth in 1871 for a male English baby was 41·4 years, in 1950 it was 66·5. On reaching the age of 10 in 1911 an American woman could expect to live another 50·7 years; if she reached 10 in 1947 she could look forward to an expected life of another 62·3 years. These figures, of course, represent what happened on the average, what will happen to a particular individual must depend on a bookfull of variable factors, on all that is comprised in his constitution, on his reaction to environment; on the nature and nurture of his peculiarities and on the fact that he is both anatomical and philosophical man.

Theories of Ageing

There have been, not surprisingly, many theories of ageing and they have been critically discussed by Comfort (1956). Senescence has been regarded as an inherent property of multicellular animals, a product of natural selection, arising by chance and perpetuated as a beneficial attribute. It has been considered as the deteriorative effect of the rate of living, or the result of toxic or pathological processes, or the outcome of changes in the tissue fluids, or the terminal of a declining rate of cellular growth and replacement. More specifically it has been postulated that each cell must eventually die when certain enzyme systems or other cellular components are used up or could only be replaced by a cell division that does not occur. Living tissues progressively lose the power to replace themselves at the rate at which they were formed. This steady dissipation of 'growth energy', known as Minot's Law, has been considered as 'development, looked at from the other end of life' (Medawar). Senescence may be a measure of declining selection-pressure, the living system having persisted after its 'biological programme had been exhausted'.

There is some evidence that longevity in man is inherited, though complicating factors, such as heritable liabilities to certain diseases, show that we know more at the moment about the inheritance of short-livedness. It used to be said that it was advisable to choose long-lived ancestors if a man wanted a better chance of longevity, but it is not quite clear how much this is counteracted by the increased expectation of life that has occurred during the last fifty years. There is little point in arguing about inheritance of general health or bodily vigour when so little is known about the nature of senescence or how it might be modified by man's increasing adaptation to his environment.

The male is, in general, shorter lived than the female, and in man the male is more vulnerable even from the time of fertilization of the ovum, after implantation (p. 120) and in childhood, times when it is hardly possible to claim greater occupational hazards. The age of the mother, but not that of the father may influence adversely the longevity of the young in some animals, but little information is available for man. It is not known if it is advantageous to be the last child of a large family, or if to be such would be offset were the child a girl. Advocates of sexual continence or abstention have little scientific support for claiming a longevity greater than those trained in sexual athleticism. It appears that regular mating by the male increases rather than decreases longevity, and there is little reason to believe that a large number of normal pregnancies shortens the expected life span of the human female.

There are a few rare instances in man of an increase in the rate of senescence, of children or adults ageing prematurely. The name *progeria* is given to the condition, and it has been generally ascribed to endocrine disturbance, particularly of the pituitary. The changes are, however, more generalized than can just be explained in terms of hormonal activities. Progeria may occur in infancy or in early middle age. The children cease to grow, changes occur in the skin so that they look like little old men and they seldom survive the third decade. Adults lose hair that has suddenly greyed, show ageing skin changes and deterioration of tissues and organs.

There is some indication from the results of experimental work with animals that it is possible by restriction of high calorie value diets to cause prolonged suspension of growth during immaturity without any apparent acceleration of ageing changes. There is a limit to this suspension of senescence, the limit being determined by the need to allow weight increase to avoid the animal dying. Little evidence is available, however, that would indicate that starving man during his childhood or adolescence can affect longevity. In any event the method seems a little heroic to obtain a doubtful increase in longevity. Various factors, such as malnutrition and certain diseases, can postpone the onset of puberty in man, but there is evidence that such deficiency only shortens life. Yet it has been seriously proposed by a number of workers that too rapid an increase in body growth during childhood may result in a shortened life-span. Whether this can be associated with over-feeding during childhood, and whether shortening of longevity is mediated by some kind of pituitary exhaustion has not been substantiated.

It is inevitable that the conclusion of a chapter on ageing should reflect briefly on the wider implications of increased expectation of life in the human species. It must be made clear that Medicine has not yet increased the human specific longevity, but it has reduced the number of people that die before reaching the age allowable to the species. The efforts of medical treatment, preventative and curative, are therefore directed to seeing that everyone reaches his 'three score years and ten'; some people, but not necessarily an increasing number, will live longer. Thus it may be true to say that by his own efforts man is creating a situation in which there will be large numbers of people in each of the first seven decades, with a sudden drop in numbers in the eighth. It follows that there will inevitably be an increasing number of old people in a population of fixed number, and in an increasing population there must be an absolutely larger number of people in the seventh decade. Man has to face up to the fact that there will be an increasing number of old people in the world, and despite many savage remarks to the contrary, there is no valid biological or philosophical reason why this should be detrimental to the human species. It may well necessitate considerable social re-adjustment, but this is not the place to discuss the policy or politics that will arise from improved geriatric treatment.

Yes, it is useful to prolong human life.

I. METCHNIKOFF

FOR FURTHER READING

The Biology of Senescence. A. Comfort. Routledge and Kegan Paul, 1956

Cowdry's Problems of Ageing. Biological and Medical Aspects. Ed. A. I. Lansing 3rd Ed., 1952

Length of Life – A Study of the Life Table. L. I. Dublin, A. J. Lotka and M. Spiegelman. Ronald Press, New York, 1949

Hormones and the Ageing Process. N. W. Shock. Academic Press, 1957

Modern Trends in Geriatrics. Ed. W. Hobson. Butterworth, 1956

INDEX

Some other Pelican books
on biology, science, and natural
history are described on
the remaining pages

SOCIAL WELFARE AND THE CITIZEN

EDITED BY PETER ARCHER

A396

We live in the age of the Welfare State, when the community does what it can to assist its members while they are in need of help. But the difficulty is often that of finding out what provisions exist, and how to apply for them. The purpose of this book is to set out clearly the help which is available for those who require it, and the corresponding responsibilities of the public generally.

It has been written by a group of professional people, each of whom has had practical experience of the services which he or she explains. The subjects have been selected in the light of experience, as those on which members of the public most frequently require information, not always readily accessible. The topics covered include National Insurance, Income Tax, health provisions, family rights and welfare, education, tenants' rights, town planning, industrial relations, traffic regulations, national service, and provision for the aged and the handicapped.

The primary object has been to set out the facts, but the authors have also attempted, within the space available, to give a bird's eye view of social welfare in Great Britain. Sometimes they are controversial, and some attempt is made to point the way towards future developments.

There is an appendix setting out the addresses from which help and further information are obtainable.

THE HUMAN MACHINE

SIR ADOLPHE ABRAHAMS

A373

The book as a whole is based on analysis and description of the human body, and its structure and functions, in terms of inanimate machinery. It has been found possible to examine such details as the construction of the chassis of a motor car, the engine, the fuel, lubrication, ignition, heat regulation, and, apart from purely vital processes, to find reasonable analogies. Such topics as repairs and periodical overhauls in man and motor are compared. And the lessons learnt from the care a man pays to his motor car may encourage him to apply the same attention to his body that he is accustomed to treat with comparative neglect. Consideration of the principles of locomotion leads to the study of muscular exercise in general, its place in daily life, its physiology, its applications according to age, sex, physical capability, and inclination. The various interpretations of 'fitness' are examined, with the principles of athletic training, where the traditional fetishes are viewed in the light of modern scientific knowledge.

Such matters as athletic records and professionalism in sport, which nowadays receive widespread interest and encourage critical scrutiny and debate, are also included.

HUMAN PHYSIOLOGY

KENNETH WALKER

A 102

Most of us know too little of the way our bodies work, and are liable in that state of comparative ignorance to become the victims of groundless anxieties about ourselves. In this compact and authoritative survey Mr Kenneth Walker sets forth in plain language the most up-to-date knowledge on the functioning of the human body, and reminds us too how profoundly the mind influences the working of the body.

Starting from the cell, the basis of human as of all life, he describes the nature and work of the digestive, circulatory, excretory, locomotor, and nervous systems: the part that food plays in our lives; how we breathe; the functions of the special senses and the physiology of sensation; the chemistry of the body and the glandular system; and the processes of reproduction. A number of sketches in the text illustrate special points, and there are two plates.

'The layman wanting a simple, concise and trustworthy description of the working of the human body need not wish for a better guide than this.' – *The Times*

ANIMALS AND MEN

DAVID KATZ

A279

There are important similarities, as well as differences, in the ways in which animals and men behave. In this book the psychological continuity of the human and other animal species is emphasized, and many examples are given of the value of comparisons among them.

Difficulties, however, easily arise in interpreting animals' behaviour and there are some amusing illustrations of the mistakes that have been made. Reliable methods of investigation are discussed and it is shown how they have been used to find out how far animals are aware of the world around them, and how they respond in different situations. The methods have also been used to study instinctive and other inborn patterns of behaviour with which animals are equipped and the ways in which these come to be modified. Animals have often been found to surpass men in some of the things they can do; there are, for example, the mysterious powers of homing possessed by pigeons, dogs, and other birds and animals. Part of the book deals with the social psychology of animals. Many animals live together in groups. Simple but definite kinds of social organization exist – even in the hen run. The book ends with a discussion of the special ways in which man seems to be distinguished psychologically from other animal species.

MAN AND THE VERTEBRATES

A. S. ROMER

A303, A304

The purpose of this book is to give a comprehensive picture of the evolution of the human body. This cannot, of course, be done by considering man alone. It must include the history of the whole group of creatures known as the vertebrates, or backboned animals, to which man belongs. This involves not only the other warm-blooded hairy creatures to which man is closely allied, but such varied forms as birds, reptiles, frogs and salamanders, and fishes, for we cannot properly understand man, his body, or mind unless we understand his vertebrate ancestry. Starting with the earliest vertebrates, Volume 1 traces the main steps in the story of evolution from fish to man, and also deals with various groups of fishes, birds, reptiles, and mammals which are of interest but not closely related to human evolution.

Volume 2 deals with human origins and races. It includes a detailed account of the evolution and workings of the human body, and concludes with a discussion of embryology based on the development of man. Each volume has 64 pages of plates and many line drawings in the text.

ALCHEMY

E. J. HOLMYARD

A348

From the dawn of history the shining and untarnishable metal, gold, has exerted its fascination upon man. Very early the idea arose that other metals were either impure or unripe gold, and that therefore by suitable treatment they could be converted into the precious metal itself. Such a belief, the principal tenet of alchemy, led to vast programmes of experiment, from which, after the lapse of centuries, a scientific practical chemistry developed. But the fact that the belief in transmutation was almost universally accepted offered great opportunities to rogues and charlatans. Side by side with honest searchers, therefore, were clever scoundrels who fleeced prince, peer, and peasant by the skill with which they carried out tricks of sleight-of-hand and deluded their victims into thinking that there was an infallible method of acquiring unlimited wealth. Gold was attributed with marvellous therapeutic properties, and many of the alchemists attempted to prepare from it an elixir of life. Others found in alchemical theory a religious or mystical symbolism.

CHEMISTRY

KENNETH HUTTON

A353

Lots of people wonder 'what's this new stuff?' when they handle fibres, detergents, or other synthetics. Their interest in chemistry is apt to be stifled if the reply is 'sodium dichlorophenoxyacetate', and not sufficiently satisfied if they are airily told that it is made from coal, chalk, and salt. The author hopes to make both these answers intelligible and satisfying, and to provide enlightenment on a subject about which many people feel intelligent curiosity. He wishes to show the fascination and importance of chemistry, and to make it intelligible.

After an account of the most important of the chemical elements, such as oxygen, hydrogen, and carbon, chemical formulae and equations are explained in enough detail for the rest of the book to be understood. The various compounds are classified according to the ways in which they are useful to man: fuels and foods, clothes, fibres and plastics, anaesthetics, drugs, explosives, and the 'heavy chemicals', such as ammonia and sulphuric acid, which are used on a large scale in industry.

THE NORMAL CHILD

AND SOME OF HIS ABNORMALITIES

C. W. VALENTINE

A255

In recent years a great deal of nonsense has been written and spoken about 'Child Psychology'. In particular many things have been wrongly regarded as signs of abnormality by persons whose studies have been confined largely to problem children, and whose knowledge of normal children is very limited.

This book, by one of the leading authorities on the psychology of childhood, gives a clear introduction to the study of child psychology, stressing the great range of individual differences among mentally healthy children of normal intelligence. The account of the early years is freely illustrated by observations and experiments made daily by the author on his own five children and by the records and researches of many other well qualified psychologists.

No previous knowledge of psychology on the part of the reader is assumed.

'This is not only a fascinating introduction to child psychology but fulfils the secondary purpose of warning parents, teachers, and social workers of the wide range of individual differences found among normal children.' – *New Statesman*

MAN, MICROBE, AND MALADY

DR JOHN DREW

A73

Written by a bacteriologist for laymen, *Man, Microbe, and Malady* is an explanation of the principles that govern the origin and spread of many of the bacterial diseases to which man is subject in temperate climates. The science of bacteriology is developing so quickly to-day, and new knowledge about the biological activities of bacteria is being added so rapidly to our existing knowledge, that many books on bacteriology are out-of-date as regards many details almost as soon as they are published. This book is no exception to the general rule in that respect; but the principles controlling the interactions of Man and Bacteria have not changed appreciably during the five thousand or so years of recorded history, and probably will not undergo any fundamental change as long as Man and Bacteria co-exist upon this planet.

This book describes the various kinds of bacteria which are known to produce human disease, the conditions in which they normally live and multiply, the ways in which they invade the human body, and the means possessed by the human body to resist and repel their invasions. It explains the simple precautions that can be taken by individuals and by communities to combat infection.

ANIMALS PARASITIC IN MAN

GEOFFREY LAPAGE

A394

This book is not about bacteria or viruses, but about the animals that are parasites of man and cause, all over the world, serious diseases, such as malaria, sleeping sickness, the illnesses due to parasitic worms, and other troubles. Some of these parasites were plagues as long as ago 1600 B.C. They still inflict on man and other animals incalculable suffering, especially in tropical countries, and they hamper human industrial enterprises, reduce the world's food supplies, hinder or prevent the colonization of certain areas, and even prevent war.

The book explains how a parasite lives and it describes the life histories of animals that are parasites of man, how he becomes infected with them, and how his body fights back against the parasitic animals. It may therefore be useful to doctors and medical students and to others who try in various ways to promote the welfare of man. For the philosopher there is the fact that these parasitic animals, which cause so much suffering and kill so many human beings and other animals, are as beautifully and wonderfully adapted to their modes of life as are animals that live in other ways.